Systems for All

By the same authors:

Systems Models and Measures

Springer Verlag FACIT Series, 1994

ISBN 0-387-19753-2

Systems for Computer Systems Professionals

LSI 1996

ISBN 963-577-191-6

A First Systems Book for technology and management

Kaposi Associates 1997

ISBN 0-9529988-0-7§

Systems for All

Agnes Kaposi
Kaposi Associates, London

Margaret Myers
Richmond, The American International University in London

ICP Imperial College Press

Published by

Imperial College Press
57 Shelton Street
Covent Garden
London WC2H 9HE

Distributed by

World Scientific Publishing Co. Pte. Ltd.
P O Box 128, Farrer Road, Singapore 912805
USA office: Suite 1B, 1060 Main Street, River Edge, NJ 07661
UK office: 57 Shelton Street, Covent Garden, London WC2H 9HE

British Library Cataloguing-in-Publication Data
A catalogue record for this book is available from the British Library.

SYSTEMS FOR ALL

ISBN 1-86094-273-3
ISBN 1-86094-275-X (pbk)

Printed in Singapore by Uto-Print

Foreword

For many years the word 'system' has been plastered almost meaninglessly on to other words to make things sound more impressive. A systems programmer was thought to be more interesting than a programmer, a computer system was seen as being more intriguing than a computer and 'systems engineering' courses have been taught in various establishments bearing almost no resemblance to one another. Very few have done more to correct this misuse of language than Agnes Kaposi. As one of the UK's foremost engineers, Professor Kaposi has devoted much of her inventiveness to the creation of a rigorous discipline which allows engineers and managers to combat the ever increasing complexity of the activities under their control. In Kaposi and Myers' text, I am pleased to see a reflection of this long-standing effort. It is a reassuring thought that just as the world of engineering and management is beginning to become concerned that projects and processes are getting out of hand because of their complexity, here is a clearly written and authoritative text on what to do about it.

Igor Aleksander FREng
Professor of Neural Systems Engineering
Imperial College, London

Preface

The word 'system' is in constant use in business and science, public life and administration, professional practice, education and everyday life. The word can refer to objects great and small, live or inanimate; it might be applied to complex organizations, entities composed of many parts, items whose design calls for many different disciplines, and structures whose operation integrates a variety of different things. It seems that everyone is, or should be, concerned about systems!

This book addresses three kinds of readers: practising professionals (managers, engineers, scientists and administrators) whose job it is to develop, operate and manage complex systems; students (both undergraduate and postgraduate) whose courses demand an integrated study of several disciplines; members of the interested public who would wish to know what makes sophisticated systems tick, and why some important systems fail.

The book presents the 'Product/process (P/p) methodology': a coherent collection of generic but readily understandable concepts, rigorous but applicable methods, and principles of reasoning. The methodology assists in understanding *any* system, and helps in the formulation and effective solution of complex problems, regardless of the field in which they arise, and irrespective of the specialist disciplines needed for supplying the solution.

Problem solving demands effective communication among *all* concerned: customers and suppliers, professional problem solvers and financial controllers, managers, administrators, journalists and the general public. The P/p methodology enforces clear and unambiguous communication through precise and hierarchically organized definitions and the use of a graphical modelling language.

In the P/p methodology the principles of reasoning are rational, based on a systems philosophy, with firm foundations in engineering. However, recognizing that many aspects of problems and problem solving situations do not lend themselves to 'hard' scientific methods of representation and reasoning, the P/p methodology allows for 'soft' representations, and can even deal with ideas *prior* to their being expressed. It is a particular strength of the P/p methodology that its concepts and methods blend the 'hard' and 'soft' elements.

The P/p methodology adopts the simple notion of systems theory that all real world entities and phenomena may be modelled as systems, either black box or structured. The methodology discriminates between two sorts of systems: products (an instantaneous view) and processes (objects with non-zero duration). Both are represented as entities and relationships over them.

Rooted in engineering, the P/p methodology deals with facts, and – as far as possible – with decisions based on facts. For this, measurement is fundamental. Hard systems are measurable, soft systems are not. The P/p methodology unites the two by providing a path between them: identify a concept, define a concept, measure a concept. In this way characteristics of systems become attributes, and attributes become measurable.

Once a real life entity is modelled in terms of its well-defined measures, attributes may be compared and judgements made. Measures might arise from direct observation or intuition, they might represent facts or express value judgements, or else they might be derived theoretically from specialist contributions. The concepts, models and methods of the P/p methodology integrate all such contributions.

Understanding systems through their models and measures leads to the ability to control and improve them. Here we enter the field of general management and quality management. The structural models of the P/p methodology can represent the project plan as well as the operation of the problem solving activity in progress. Explicit, measurement-based plans aid the prevention of delays and difficulties, and the process models support early diagnosis of non-conformance. Process models also facilitate tracking any change in customer requirements, thus avoiding deviation between conformity and customer satisfaction.

The formal models and measures of the methodology allow for optimization of the performance of processes and continuous improvement of the quality of products and services. Thus, the use of the P/p methodology leads to enhanced maturity of organizations, integrating general management and quality management.

P/p methodology thus supports all levels of endeavour in a wide field of human activity and, when applied, should reduce risk and eliminate many sources of system error and failure.

The authors are grateful to John Kaposi whose support, helpful comments, constructive suggestions, patience and quality management greatly improved this text.

Contents

Part 1

Chapter 1 The 'systems crisis'

1.1 Systems spark a scientific revolution

The world is changing at an increasing rate. The technological advances of recent decades have enabled us to build powerful general purpose systems that can be adapted for a seemingly boundless variety of uses, and can be interlinked across the globe. The potential of the new technologies appears to be almost limitless, allowing complicated problems to be tackled and solutions of unprecedented complexity attempted.

Not all ambitious projects succeed. One by one, prestigious high-profile projects report embarrassing delays, many are subject to severe budget overruns, lead to disappointment, or even humiliating failure. Some of these projects affect more than their client and supplier: their impact extends to the whole community, including the taxpayer at a remote part of the country who may have had to contribute towards them from his/her taxes. Since technology appears to pose no obstacle, the fate of these projects is determined by the intellectual prowess and managerial acumen of the problem solver. Apparently, technological advance has outstripped our capability to understand its implications and manage its uses!

Management must always shoulder the blame, but lack of success often stems from the inherent complexity of the problem itself, and from the dearth of suitable methods of solution.

- Most of today's important problems are deeply embedded in their environment. When important projects fail, the inevitable post-mortems reveal that some projects were undertaken without proper appreciation of the task on hand, without isolating the problem and defining its boundaries, without identifying the key characteristics of the problem and specifying the desired solution, without drawing up an appropriate project plan.
- Even if project teams included all the right experts, communication within the team may not have been effective. Consequently cooperation suffered, designs became sketchy, deadlines slipped, costs escalated.
- When a complex system is finally built as a solution, often it proves to be capricious, unwieldy and all but unmanageable. When powerful but unpredictable systems are put into service, the manager is like the sorcerer's apprentice: in charge of powerful devices over which he/she has no control. Therefore, industrial plants, public utilities, essential services and major organizations are in potential jeopardy, and whole sectors of society are placed at unacceptable risk. Some project failures lead to major loss of resources, and some even to loss of life.

In recent decades it became customary to blame the ubiquitous computer. The 'software crisis' caused trepidation among computer users, and the alarm soon spread to the community. A few years ago the headline in a quality paper read: "Computer disasters have cost billions" [1]. More recently the software crisis has given way to a 'systems crisis': cause for even more general concern. Last year, a whole television series was devoted to major disasters in complex systems, and by no means were all attributable to the computer. The source of the trouble is a phenomenon identified in the famous book of T.S. Kuhn [2] as 'scientific crisis'. A scientific crisis exists when even the best professional practices persistently prove inadequate for solving some intrinsically important problems.

Kuhn shows that the way out of a scientific crisis is 'scientific revolution': a fundamentally new approach, calling for the definition of new concepts, and for the development of new methods and tools. In Kuhn's sense, such a comprehensive conceptual and methodological framework constitutes a *'paradigm'* [3]. At the heart of a paradigm is an overall concept accepted by most people in a community because of its effectiveness in solving important problems and explaining ideas or observations. A new scientific paradigm:

- provides scientific foundations for tackling problems that previously defied solution,
- is progressive: it provides a new, more powerful platform for problem solving, while also preserving accumulated knowledge and experience, and harnessing existing scientific disciplines.

The numerous and varied unsuccessful projects and unsolved problems have some important characteristics in common. They involve complicated adverse situations whose resolution calls for the coordinated effort of experts from different fields. The situations are multifaceted, and the solutions are made up of many intricately interrelated parts. The generic term for such an assembly is 'system'. The current day scientific crisis calls for a *systems paradigm.*

1.2 A 'systems paradigm'

As all scientific paradigms, a systems paradigm is not just a single concept but a comprehensive collection of mutually complementary ideas, some already well established, others still under development. One may list the key features:

- A systems paradigm must build on the *established disciplines* of science, computing, engineering and management.
- A systems paradigm must be widely *accessible*: comprehensible by any interested person, including members of the Board of the organizations involved with the project, senior management and technical staff, subcontractors and specialist experts, personnel, customers, the public, local politicians and members of Government. For this, the concepts of the paradigm must be clearly defined, the *definitions* must be consistent, and must form a coherent structure. It is helpful if the paradigm incorporates some kind of formal *notation* to aid comprehension and avoid ambiguity.
- The systems paradigm must utilize the advanced principles of *quality.* According to these, a project must not only satisfy the client – the paying

customer –, but must respect the environment and have regard for all interested parties as well as the needs of the wider community [4].

- Those responsible for the project are *accountable*. The systems paradigm must facilitate accountability: use appropriate *models* and *methods* for specification, unambiguous representation, design, implementation and project management. It must assist rigorous analysis and assure traceability, thus facilitating the delivery of a solution in due time and within budget. For this, the models must be *timed* and characterized by *measures* which can be checked objectively. The models must also aid the management of *risk*, the formulation of informed *decisions* and the articulation of *value judgements*.
- Problems might arise from any application domain and may demand any mixture of expertise. This means that the systems paradigm must be *general*: common to the largest possible class of problems great and small, based on the philosophy of systems theory, and must build on 'system' as a universal notion. By these means, the systems paradigm must provide a *'systems world outlook'*, embracing the 'hard' problems of classical science and engineering, the 'softer' problems of computing, communication and management, some of the associated 'soft' problems of cognition and comprehension, and any combination of these.

1.3 Who needs a systems paradigm?

A systems paradigm is to the advantage of all. To illustrate this, let us use a simple analogy.

> *Imagine that you live in Country A where all the doctors are highly skilled specialists. Should you have some ailment, it is up to you as the patient to decide which specialist to see. You have a persistent headache. Whom should you consult: the ophtalmologist? the ear-nose-and-throat specialist? the neurologist? the psychiatrist? At the end of a sequence of four consultations you will have spent a great deal of time and money, and may still have the headache. What to do now?*
>
> *In the neighbouring Country B, healthcare is organized around General Practitioners: family doctors trained to focus on the whole* person *rather than on specific organs of the body. GPs know the patient, are experts in identifying the likely seat of the trouble, can call upon a network of specialists, and are skilled to coordinate specialist contributions. While listening to the patient with the headache, the GP observes that the man has poor teeth and his neck has limited mobility. Most likely he suffers from arthritis of the spine, and may also have a latent abscess on one of his teeth. Since these are also possible causes of headache, the GP might direct the patient to a rheumatologist or a dentist, just as much as to an ophtalmologist, ear-nose-and-throat specialist, neurologist or psychiatrist. Should the ailment require the simultaneous attention of two or more specialists, care of the patient stays with the GP throughout.*

The healthcare system of Country B is clearly superior. It dispenses medicine cheaply and more reliably than that of Country A, and it may even save lives. This is no reflection on the expertise of the specialists of Country A: the specialists of the two countries may be equally skilled and well qualified. The contribution of the GP benefits all concerned. The patient gains a fast track to the remedy. The public gains a cheaper and better health service. There are fewer grounds for dissatisfaction, and the medical profession gains better appreciation.

The skills of the GP are not more valuable than those of the specialists: they are simply different in *kind*. Using Kuhn's terminology [[1]], we might say that the GP works in a different *paradigm* from that of the specialists, dispensing patient-centred rather than specialist medicine, being expert in developing the systems view rather than dealing with the problem detail by detail, and being skilled at interacting with the patient – the 'owner' of the problem – as well as with the full array of specialists – the ultimate custodians of the solution.

1.4 Role of the specialist and of the systems professional

After the polymaths of early science, in the nineteenth and twentieth centuries the professions of science and engineering evolved into distinct areas of *specialization*. Specialists are highly respected, each specialist having been educated and skilled to handle problems that lie within the accumulated wisdom of his/her particular field of expertise. Each discipline, and within this each specialist branch, has developed its own body of knowledge, theories, methods and codes of practice, its own tools, its language and symbolism, its own outlook, and its proud traditions. Applying the methods and tools of the discipline, the specialist handles the problems of a well defined field, and where the problem challenges accumulated wisdom, develops the specialist methodology, enhancing or perfecting the established framework of the discipline. Specialization in science and engineering has inspired research and fuelled progress. Only specialization could have given rise to today's powerful technologies.

As part of their code of practice, specialists adhere to strict professional ethics. Professionals are keenly aware of the difference between *expertise* and *awareness*, between *knowing* something and merely knowing *about* something. Scorning amateurism and unwilling to dabble in matters beyond their own field of expertise, where the problem is outside the established professional framework, the specialist declines to deal with it. Driven by regard to such professional ethics, the specialist focuses on the methods of *solution* offered by the discipline, rather than on the *problem*.

The adverse side of this commendably high-minded approach is that specialization carries its own limitations. By definition, the scope of each specialist field is strictly circumscribed, whereas practical problems are seldom well articulated, and rarely fall neatly into one or another field of specialization. A complex project engages professionals of different specialist disciplines who must *communicate* with their clients and with each other, and *cooperate* effectively in search of the solution. The systems crisis offers plenty of evidence that established educational curricula and professional development experience do not prepare specialist experts adequately for the challenges of interdisciplinary and multidisciplinary cooperation in complex projects [5]. Specialists engaged in complex projects need a fair measure of understanding of a *systems paradigm.*

The current state of development of science and engineering resembles the case of Country A of our healthcare analogy. The professions, among them the sciences, engineering, management and computing, are made up of highly trained, experienced and valued specialists. These include Information Technology experts, structural, electronic, mechanical, chemical, telecommunications engineers, material scientists, software engineers, quality consultants, financial analysts, industrial psychologists, bankers, lawyers, project management specialists, etc., – all devoting themselves to solving problems of significance. Nevertheless, the catalogue of disasters and failures is growing all the time. When specifying projects of importance, when managing the project – planning, organizing, implementing the solution and leading the project team –, where were the systems professionals: the General Practitioners of science and engineering? Which profession should have supplied the expert listener to the client's problem, the skilled person who should have developed a secure overview of the project, specified the tasks and coordinated the contributions of the various specialists, overseen progress, controlled installation, and assured safe adoption of the new system into service?

Employers are now aware of the need for *systems professionals.* Many jobs are advertised, seeking systems engineers, systems analysis, systems scientist, and the new quality standard advocates a 'system approach to management' [[4]]. However, at present, there is no 'systems profession': no professional institution, no dedicated courses of instruction. To fill the vacuum, a growing number of universities offer 'interdisciplinary' courses, consisting of a collection of loosely linked topics from two or more branches of engineering, computing and science. Where the need to interrelate the elements of the course is recognized, management topics are introduced, with the hope that these might provide the necessary 'integration' of the various specialist parts of the course. Some of these courses attract high calibre students: young people starting out in higher education, as well as practicing professionals whose work experience makes them realize the need of a new kind of outlook, knowledge and skill. The commitment and personal qualities of the students on these courses compensate, to some extent, for the deficiencies of the curriculum.

Consider the alternative: the pattern akin to Country B of our medical analogy, including in the picture the systems professional, the parallel in science and engineering of the GP in medicine. Just as the GP in the medical world does not invalidate the contribution of the specialist, the system professional would not replace experts in computing, engineering, management, or any other specialist area. Instead, the system professional would operate from a problem-centred 'systems discipline' which aids the formulation of the problem, and integrates existing domains of specialist knowledge in the interest of obtaining a high quality solution quickly and cost effectively. To gain insight into the needs of the client and of the wider community, the systems professional would liaise with the 'owner' of the problem and with experts of the *application domain* – the accountant, the social worker, the local government administrator, the industrialist, etc. The language of communication would be simple enough for all to understand, and yet precise enough to articulate demands unambiguously. Using the same language, the systems professional would then map the client's demands into specifications, and create a framework for the over-all solution, defining the contributions of specialist experts from the various fields of the *solution domain*, among them the specialists of computing, communications, engineering and management. The framework – comprehensible to the client, the specialists, and even to members of the interested public – would guide the management of the project: its planning, organization and control, the acquisition and development of human and material resources, the oversight of implementation, the management of risk, the assurance of quality.

Such is the approach needed for specifying, procuring, developing, operating and maintaining complex systems of assured quality. It is also the foundation of a *systems profession.*

1.5 Systems for all!

Systems matter not only to the problem solver and the specialist, but also to the whole constituency of any major project:

- the *client* who owns the problem, originates the project, provides the resources, will be the owner of the system, and hence stands to benefit from the success of the undertaking,
- the *systems professional* who cooperates with the client in defining the problem, is in charge of the over-all solution, and coordinates the contribution of the specialist experts,
- the *specialist experts* and *subcontractors* who cooperate in supplying the detailed skills and implement all components of the solution,
- the individuals engaged in the project: the *employees* of the customer who must use and operate the emerging results and whose working life will be changed, of the suppliers who participate in the project, and of the operators and maintainers who will look after the solution to assure its long life in useful service,
- the *'end users':* the people for whom the client's organization provides goods and services, whose indulgence might be requested while work is in progress to change over from the old to the new, and who must be convinced that the new is worthwhile,
- the *informed public:* people who seek insight into the world around them, are willing to invest effort to gain a measure of understanding of issues, and deliberately contribute to the formation of public opinion,
- the *public at large:* the man on the Clapham omnibus, people whose environment might change as a consequence of the new development, and who stand to benefit indirectly from the success of the projects, and whose taxes will be used ultimately to pay for failure or disaster,
- local or national *government* whose task is to guard the interests of the public and see to it that resources are effectively deployed,
- the *academics* in university departments who endeavour to educate the systems professional, and currently offer specialist or interdisciplinary education,
- the *students* on systems courses and on specialist courses.

The 'systems community' embraces the whole of this broad constituency. Only a few sectors of the systems community will need deep insight into systems and sophisticated systems skills, but each member would benefit from a fair degree of insight. Understanding systems is truly for all.

1.6 This book

This book sets itself the task to present a systems paradigm in a language that is precise and readily understandable, accurate enough to describe the problem and represent the solution to the various stakeholders in as much detail as they demand and are willing to absorb.

The book has a dual aim:

1. to inform the interested lay reader or members of a specialist profession, and
2. to contribute towards the formation of a 'systems profession'.

It presents a systems outlook, defines key concepts, and outlines the principles of characterizing systems. It introduces a language of expressing requirements and solutions, together with related collection of models, measures, methods and tools.

The key methods are Product/process (P/p) modelling and model-based measurement. P/p modelling affords the clear representation of any kind of entity as a system, be it simple or complex, man-made or natural, active or passive, hard or soft. It may be used for representing the problem, the solution, the organizations involved, or the *processes* of obtaining, managing and operating the solution. It can describe the system as a complete whole or as a structure of parts, and allows each part of a complex system to be characterized in any degree of detail, while keeping complexity under control.

At an *introductory level,* the language of P/p modelling is simple enough to be learned quite rapidly. Thereafter, anyone can use a P/p modelling to create a representation of a system, and anyone can read and interpret the representation created by others. Thus, the language of P/p modelling can be used throughout the constituency of a project, facilitating the expression of ideas and serving as the means of communication between all concerned.

The skills of P/p modelling can be refined into a *professional skill.* The systems professional can use P/p modelling and model based measurement in eliciting from the client the specification of the problem and the required solution, devising solution strategies, creating, analyzing and verifying over-all designs, guiding and managing system development, and interfacing between systems models and other, specialized methods and professional formalisms. P/p modelling also serves in assuring, controlling and enhancing quality throughout the project and in course of the utilization of the solution.

Structure of the book

The book is divided into three parts.

Part 1 is at an introductory level, requiring no preliminary preparation. It presents all the basic ideas and defines all key concepts of a systems approach [6].

Chapter 2 discusses the nature of *problems* and the processes of *communication.*

Chapter 3 explains the notion of 'definition', the importance and use of definitions from the viewpoint of problem solving, and the characteristics of definitions of good quality. It also defines other key *general concepts*, among them 'measurement', 'time', 'attribute', 'representation' and 'language'.

Chapter 4 offers a historical perspective of the systems approach, and goes on to define key *systems concepts*, among them 'system', 'referent', 'black box', 'structure', 'product', 'process' and 'systems methodology'. It also distinguishes various types of graphs, since graphs form the basis of the language of Product/process modelling.

Using these foundations, Chapter 5 introduces *Product/process modelling*: a generic, widely applicable method for representing problems, solutions and the processes leading from one to the other. Product/process models are simple in presentation, easy to use and understand, and their syntactical correctness is verifiable.

Chapter 6, the closing chapter of Part 1, uses Product/process modelling to review in detail the *problem solving process*, and discusses alternative problem solving strategies. It acts as a route map to problem solving: a process that is often confusing and ill delineated. This chapter defines 'specification', introduces a novel distinction between problem specification and requirement specification, and follows the evolution of the solution from the initial idea to the final validation of the implementation.

Part 2 is for the more advanced reader who has become acquainted with the contents of Part 1, perhaps with the view of becoming a systems professional. It offers deeper understanding of the concepts introduced in Part 1, expressing them formally, developing them further, and using the methods rigorously. In this part of the book, the presentation of ideas in natural language and in diagrams is complemented with mathematical symbolism. Mathematics can offer powerful assistance to the problem solver in expressing ideas precisely, and reasoning about them securely. The mathematics used is of a basic nature: sets, functions and relations are used, and should not prove an obstacle to the specialist professional or the intelligent layman.

Chapter 7 defines '*system*' as a mathematical entity, reinforcing the idea that 'system' is a universal notion, a representation of any entity in the real world. This definition gives the same format for representing a system as black box and as structure, and offers criteria for classifying systems. The chapter examines the role of the environment of the system and of the observer.

Chapter 8 is concerned with the fundamentals of *measurement.* It explains that a good measure need not be a number, and that, without a model defining their context, measures are meaningless. It reviews basic measurement scales, analyses the hierarchy of valid measurements, and shows the constraints which must be applied to 'utility' measures as the basis for forming and expressing value judgements and making informed decisions.

Chapter 9 explores the nature of the *black box representations.* It shows how to represent both individual items and classes of entities in the unambiguous framework of the generic system model detailed in chapter 7, and using the measures of chapter 8.

Chapter 10 applies the same argument to *structures* as chapter 9 did to black box representations. It explains the importance of structural representations, demonstrating that structures rely for their meaning on the black box representation of their basic components. This chapter also investigates the principle of constructivity: the need to define structures formally, such that one could derive the overall characteristics of the whole system from the characteristics of the components and the structural interrelationships between components.

One may regard the preceding chapters as an introduction to Chapter 11. Here we explain that any entity of the real world may be regarded as a *product* or a *process,* the two being distinguished by the attribute, of time duration. We then go on to define both products and processes as black boxes and as structures. The chapter also discusses all types of Product/process graphs, and introduces *gates*: essential modelling aids for structural representation.

Part 3 is entirely devoted to practical issues of general interest, giving comprehensive illustrations of P/p modelling and model based measurement at work.

Chapter 12 deals in depth with the topic of *process management,* adopting a generic approach that applies both to hard and to soft systems. Numerous examples allow the reader to examine applications in individual fields. Analytical rigour demands that, where possible, natural language statements are mirrored in mathematical language, but these latter are in no way essential to understanding the contents.

Chapter 13 introduces the topic of the *maturity* of organizations. This is of vital importance to managers, and provides a unique measurement tool to guide improvements in managerial practice, which can easily be mapped, into current quality assessment standards. The chapter goes on to discuss the development of quality management and the use of quality certification standards the context of organizational maturity.

Chapter 14 is an account of *contract management*, offering an overview, encouraging detailed examination of the subprocesses involved, and illustrating the allocation of responsibility and the factors which must be taken into account to achieve an outcome satisfactory to all parties.

Each chapter contains many examples, and Parts 1 and 2 include a collection of exercises.

The text is complemented by a *Glossary* which collects the definition of key terms, showing how they are based on everyday notions, and how they relate to each other.

1.7 Footnotes and References

1 Independent on Sunday, 3.12.95.

2 Kuhn, T S: "The structure of scientific revolutions". University of Chicago Press, 1970.

3

> paradigm
> a set of scientific and metaphysical beliefs that make up a framework within which scientific theories can be tested, evaluated, and if necessary revised
> Cambridge Dictionary of Philosophy, Ed. R Audi, Camb Univ Press, 1999

4 See e.g. the draft standard ISO/FDIS 9001:2000.

5 Interdisciplinary – involving two or more academic disciplines.
Multidisciplinary – of, or relating to, the study of one study involving several subject disciplines. Source: Collins English Dictionary, 1992

6 We quote from the SE Handbook, version 1, INCOSE 1998. The handbook refers specifically to systems engineers, but the ideas apply to all members of the systems constituency.

"It is essential to advancement of the field of systems engineering that common definitions and understandings be established regarding general methods and terminology. As more systems engineers accept and use a common terminology, we will experience improvements in communications, understanding, and ultimately, productivity."
"In many well-established industries there is historical precedent and good reason not to change terminology. This is certainly acceptable. What is not acceptable is an undefined or inconsistent system terminology. The good systems engineer will ensure that an acceptable terminology is established very early in the program and communicated to all."

Chapter 2 About problems and communication

The marketing director of one of the world's largest international corporations once declared at a public gathering: "In our organizations we have no *problems*, only *challenges*". No matter what term we use to designate it, the concept is the same. A problem – or a challenge if you prefer – is indicated when someone becomes aware that all is not well with the world. If this observant person is willing and able to act towards putting the matter right, he/she becomes the *problem owner*, and this marks the start of the problem solving process. When the solution calls for mounting a project with its own dedicated resources, the problem owner may have to become the *project champion,* the person who convinces those in control of finance and resources – the immediate supervisor, a member of the Board of Directors of the company, or some outside sponsor – that there is an adverse situation, and something is to be done about it.

Solving *any* problem takes courage and determination, and absorbs time and resources. Some problems are simple enough to be solved single-handedly by use of the problem owner's common sense and intuition. However, most problems need the deliberate effort of several people, the problem owner needing cooperation of others. Solving *complex* problems requires tenacity, discipline, resourcefulness, knowledge about the background and the application area, clear thinking, good articulation, creativity, a repertoire of sound methods, and, most of all, good communication skills and effective collaboration among those involved. When the problem is complex, the project champion will have to act as, or engage the services of, a professional *problem solver* who will be the supplier of the solution. To perform this task, the problem solver will employ his/her own skills, and will enlist helpers and specialist experts, forming the *problem solving team.* In most cases the problem solver identifies parts of the problem for subcontracting, and subcontractors might engage further subcontractors in turn. The solution of a complex problem will also affect those not directly involved; thus, when the problem is complex, the group of interested parties is large.

The problem solving process is greatly assisted if those concerned share understanding of key concepts, interact in an appropriate language, and use suitable communication media. This chapter outlines the nature of problems, their perception, conceptualization and articulation, representation, and communication in the preliminary phase of problem solving process.

2.1 What do we mean by 'problem'?

Problem as a question

'Problem' has been described as a difficult question without an answer, and 'problem solving' as the search for the answer. These definitions suit some circumstances, but if the question is not clearly formulated, how could one start looking for the answer?

Example 2.1

The company is not doing well. Turnover is 20% below expectations, this month's profits are half that of the same period last year, interim dividends have been cancelled, the share price has been declining steadily, Customer Services had to engage two extra people to cope with complaints, and last night the local paper announced that the competition is opening up a new outlet on our doorstep.

Example 2.2

The school is in deep difficulty. Examination results are way below the national average, truancy is rising, discipline is slack – last year 5 students had to be excluded –, and petty thieving has reached such levels that the police had to be called in twice during last term. Applications are down by 17%, morale is low, six members of staff have handed in their notice, and and six will leave at the end of the academic year.

Example 2.3

The underground network of a capital city is in the news yet again, and not for the right reasons. Trains are cancelled almost daily because of staff shortages, arrival time performance is 8% below target, on two lines delays have become the norm, and in the rush hour at least two (and sometimes five!) stations have to be closed regularly on weekdays because of dangerous overcrowding. A while ago it came to light that a fault on an escalator was common to a whole group of stations, and a large section of one of the major lines had to be closed for more than a week to repair escalators which threatened to collapse. Worst of all, service on one of the busiest lines is suspended altogether for the next 10 weeks to carry out several sorts of essential maintenance and repairs. The headlines read: "Chaos on the tube".

Example 2.4

Our corporation is no longer the undisputed world leader. We are still the largest and most profitable in the field, but newer, younger organizations are catching up fast. They are leaner than we are, and can respond more rapidly to changing market demands. They are more innovative, constantly take advantage of new technologies, and create new markets by launching a stream of attractive new products. Although they pay less well than we do, they still manage to siphon off some of our best staff.

Each of these examples embodies a problem, or even more than one, but what is the question to be answered? The definition of 'problem' as a question seems to overlook a critical part of the problem solving process: how to formulate the question itself? There is much truth in the cliché that "asking the right question is half way to finding the right answer".

Problem as a gap between goal and reality

'Problem' has also been described as *the difference between the present and the required state of an entity* – the company, the school, the underground system, or whatever. An example of such a deficit between goal and reality is the company failing to meet its planned profit targets, recruitment plans, or cost reduction goals. Such a problem may be cast in terms of four elements:

- the characteristics of the present state of the entity,
- the characteristics of its desired state – the specification of the solution,
- the target date by which the solution is to be achieved,
- the budget available for attaining the solution.

Example 2.5

Management of Barclays, the big High Street Bank, observed that "current systems and practices hamper our ability to serve the customers as we would like to". The reason was that the bank had two main data base systems. One of these was based centrally, carrying details of customers' balances and transactions, but otherwise showed no detail of the customer's business with the bank and did not contain a full account history. The second system was distributed among the 2000 branches of the bank, each branch holding details of its own customers. The management defined the problem: introduce a new customer system that holds all customer information in a centralized data base. A budget of £110 million was allocated, and the target date of completion was staggered, not all branches coming on stream at the same time. The project was large but relatively simple. The solution was achieved in time, within budget [1].

When a problem solving project had already failed, the options are to abandon the project altogether, or reaffirm commitment to the project and review its specification: attempt to attain the original goal, moderate expectations, or vary the aims in the light of experience. Of course, having failed at the first try, there is no guarantee that the project will succeed at the next attempt.

Example 2.6

By 1980's it was clear to the public, as well as to the directors and the operatives, that the manual control system of the London Ambulance service could not cope with the demand. The first attempt at computerization began in the early part of the last decade. That project had cost £7.5 million, but it was abandoned in 1990, because the computer system could not meet the specification.

Meantime demand on the service had increased, and traffic in the metropolis had worsened. Management confirmed commitment to computerization, and decided on developing a sophisticated, integrated Computer Aided Dispatch system which was to take calls, verify location and other incident details, determine which ambulance to send, communicate details to the chosen ambulance, and position suitable equipment and staff strategically to minimize waiting time. A target budget of £1.5 million was allocated, and January 1991 was set as deadline.

After numerous delays, the system went into service on 26 October 1992, but a week later it started to slow down gradually, and finally it locked up altogether. Promptly the Chief Executive resigned. A year later, having been denied an ambulance, a child of 12 died. Not until the end of 1997 had the problem been adequately resolve d[1].

Simple question, hard answer

In some cases the problem appears as a deceptively simple question, but the solution is fiendishly complicated. The most famous example of this is the four colour problem which could be understood by young schoolchildren, and yet the solution eluded the best mathematical minds for centuries [2]. This, and many other examples, illustrates that the complexity of the problem statement is not a reliable predictor of the complexity of the solution.

Explicit and implicit problems

In many cases the problem is manifest; in others, it is not specified explicitly, or else the specification takes the form of an object, an exemplar, a threat, or a potential for improvement.

Example 2.7

One of the major process plants of the British Steel Corporation had been in operation for decades. As the plant expanded over the years, and as new facilities were added bit by bit, the control system had developed incrementally, each new part being implemented in the technology of the day. As a result, the plant controller was a hotchpotch of thermionic valve circuits, electromechanical relays, magnetic devices, discrete solid state components, integrated circuits. The controller worked adequately, but spare parts were hard to find, repairs were time consuming, reliability became problematic, and finally management decided that the time had come to modernize. The problem could be stated quite simply: "build a programmable controller which performs the same function as the existing control system of the plant". The solution would have been easy to provide: all one needed was an explicit statement of the function of the existing controller. Identifying the control function and turning the 'simple' problem statement into an explicit specification was a hard enough task to form the basis of a PhD project [3].

Example 2.8

The company is profitable and its product lines are selling well, but an interesting new material has come to the market which holds great potential for reducing costs and enhancing performance. The Technical Director makes out a speculative case and convinces the Board to fund research and development. Leading experts in material science and applications are recruited, and a project is underway.

In all of the above cases the problem has some kind of manifestation, explicit or implicit. But what of the case when the 'problem' (or the challenge) is just a state of mind: hardly more than the problem owner's sense of unease about the situation, or his hunch that an opportunity exists?

In these cases problem solving starts when someone becomes aware that there is a chance of improving the state of the world, and, rather than ignoring the situation, elects to be the problem's 'owner'.

In the first instance, we define:

> **problem**
> an unsatisfactory situation
> Our working definition

> **project**
> planned, coordinated, controlled activity with its own budget and other resources, whose object is to solve the problem
> Our working definition, based on ISO/FDIS 9000:2000 [4]

and

> **interested party**
> person or group having an interest in the success of a project
> Our working definition, based on ISO/FDIS 9000:2000

2.2 Preliminary phase of the problem solving

Figure 2.1 displays a simple version of the preliminary phase of problem solving, from the appearance of unsatisfactory reality to the first communication between problem owner and his/her correspondent.

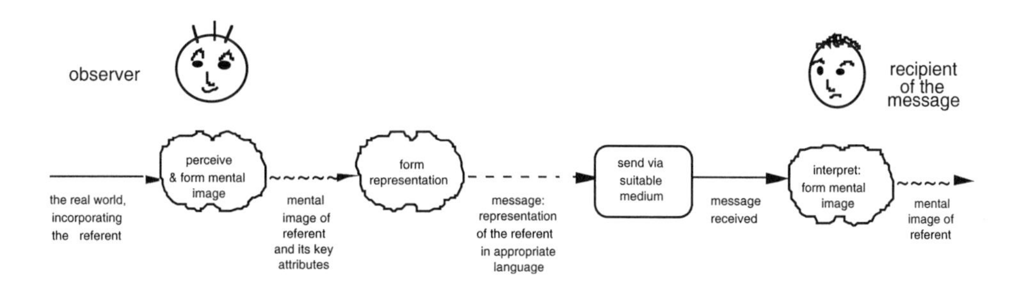

Figure 2.1: Preliminary phase of problem solving (symbols explained in the text and are defined in chapter 4)

In the figure, activities are represented as *processes*, shown by boxes, and passive entities at the input to and output from processes are represented as *products*, shown as arrows. The shape of the boxes and the patterns of the arrows have particular significance, indicating the *type* of product and process. We return to the concepts of product and process later, and shall explain these notation in full. Here we concentrate on some important aspect of the preliminary phase itself, and investigate each step of the process.

Forming a mental image of the problem

Initial vague unease stimulates purposeful observation. In due course, the problem owner focuses attention on some specific entity or aspect which is in particular need of improvement. The entity of interest may be the order book of the business, the computer facilities of the company, the educational services of the town, the state of health of a member of the family, the disturbance of domestic peace by the neighbour's cat, or whatever. In our discussions we shall call the real-life entity of interest the *referent.*

Perceiving that a problem exists is not the same as identifying *where* the problem lies, and defining *what* the problem is. Identifying and localizing the problem are important tasks in themselves, and their skilled execution is often the decisive factor in determining the outcome. The problem owner must:

- isolate the problem, focus on the referent, and establish the *boundary* between the referent and its environment,
- elucidate the concept of the referent, selecting and defining its key *attributes* – those features that characterize it, or may be of greatest need of improvement – thus forming its clear *mental image.*

Representing the problem

To act as project champion, the problem owner must *externalize* the mental image: represent the problem as a message in an appropriate *language*, suitable for his/her own further reference, and ready for being communicated to collaborators and other interested parties. The target of communication might be the person responsible for the problematical referent, the immediate superior of the project champion, an expert who may have the skills for solving the problem, the person who must be persuaded to set aside resources for the project, or all of these. The language of representation may be textual (a verbal description of the referent in the natural language), or else it may be a drawing, a mathematical formula, a diagram, a graph, a picture, or a combination of several forms of representation. The language must be fit for the purpose: familiar to all concerned, and suitable for expressing the message.

Quite often, the initial representation of the problem is crude, and the project champion realizes that further information is needed if the message is to be understood, and is to convince the recipient. The project champion obtains information that is more detailed and gradually refines the representation. The refinement may demand the use of a more expressive, more precise language than that of the original problem statement. It is helpful to bear in mind the obligation to choose an initial language of representation that is suitable for presenting the problem in subsequent stages of refinement, thus avoiding the need for the error-prone process of translation.

Communicating the problem

Once the problem owner/project champion is satisfied with the message, it can then be entrusted to a convenient *medium* for transmission to the intended recipients. The medium which carries the message may be handwriting on paper, telephone conversation, video presentation, word-processed document on a disc, image on a website, etc.

Interpreting the message

The next task in the problem solving process falls to the recipient: interpret the message, and form a mental image of the problematical referent. Most frequently this will call for further information, and a dialogue will be established between the problem owner as project champion and his/her correspondent: the problem solving expert, the decision maker, the custodian of the necessary resources, or the authority whose permission is necessary for the project to proceed.

The expected outcome of this extended initial stage of the problem solving process would have two components: forming a suitably refined *representation of* the problem, and making a *decision* whether or not to proceed to the solution process.

A comment on the preliminary phase

The process shown in figure 2.1 is a simplification: this kind of activity is seldom a straightforward sequence. In practice, the problem owner would have to retrace his/her steps several times, revise the mental image, modify the first appearance of the message, make further observations, collect more information, consult others involved, analyze the situation, clarify ideas, deepen the factual content, characterize the referent by measures of its key attributes, until a *preliminary problem specification* is established. Usually the preliminary problem specification will be further modified in consultation with the controller of resources, and clarified in cooperation with the problem solver.

2.3 Quality of the preliminary phase of the problem solving process

The preliminary phase of the problem solving process is successful if the mental image of the recipient is consistent with that of the observer, as well as with reality. Each step in this preliminary phase is critical, each step being a potential source of error and distortion which can be cumulative, leading to flawed representation, misunderstanding, or a complete breakdown of communication between the observer of reality and the recipient of the message.

To avoid this,

- the problem owner must act as *impartial observer*, alert and open minded when perceiving reality, clear thinking when forming the mental image, able to distinguish fact from comment, and accurate in reporting observations,
- the *representation* must be valid – consistent with reality – and of appropriate form and quality for the given purpose,
- the *language* must be suitable for expressing the message, and must be understandable to the recipient,
- the *medium* must be appropriate for carrying the message,

- the *recipient* must be ready to accept the transmission, and should have an open-minded attitude to form an unbiased mental image, and

- the *referent* itself must be clearly defined and sufficiently stable, such that, given the inevitable delay, the recipient's perception of it should be relevant and timely, rather than obsolete.

2.4 Summary

This chapter focuses on the start of the problem solving process. It describes how such a process might be initiated, explains the nature of problems, and outlines the wide community of people concerned with the process and solution of complex problems. It appraises the role of communication in the problem solving process, leading to the graphical representation of the preliminary phase of problem solving, and the discussion of factors affecting the quality of the process.

2.5 Exercises

Exercise 2.1

As transport manager for a large company manufacturing tractors, you are uneasy about the time it takes to deliver the goods once the order is completed. Articulate your concerns and prepare a report for the Board of Directors.

Identify a problem owner and suggest possible problem solvers.

Exercise 2.2

As a doctor, you are worried about a sudden large increase in the number of patients you are required to treat. Simulate your conversation with the Health Authority's representative, in course of which you both attempt to clarify the situation.

Who is the initial problem owner? Can the ownership be transferred? If so, suggest to whom.

Exercise 2.3(a)

A company experiences high employee turnover. Explain why this is a problem. Who would you expect to identify it, and who should initiate expressing, analyzing and solving it?

Exercise 2.3(b)

High employee turnover also arises in the local infant school: some staff changes occur at the end of each term, and some teachers even leave mid-term. How would the problem be manifested, who would you expect to identify it, who is the problem owner, and who should be the problem solver?

Exercise 2.4

Exercises 2.1, 2.2 and 2.3 outline problematical situations.

Identify a problem solver in each case. List at least three factors which appear to be under a problem solver's control, and at least three over which the problem solver can have no control. Make sure that allocation and distribution of resources are among the factors you have nominated.

Re-allocate the problem, nominating a different problem solvers. How would your list of factors change?

Exercise 2.5

Formulate the problem implicit in Examples 2.1 to 2.4.

2.6 Footnotes and References

1 Source: T Collins: "Crash – learning from the world's worst computer disasters". Simon and Schuster, 1997.

2 Definitive solution suppplied by K Appel, W Haken, 1976. Source of the information: R P Grimaldi: "Discrete and Combinatorial Mathematics". Addison Wesley, 1985.

3 R Chandra: "Design methodology for a microprocessor based process control system". PhD, CNAA (1980)

4 In ISO/FDIS 9000:2000 the definition of 'project' is:

"unique process consisting of a set of coordinated and controlled activities with start and finish dates, undertaken to achieve an objective conforming to specific requirements including the constraints of time, cost and resources."

CMM: SECMM-94-06-/CMU/SEI-96-HB-004 v1.1, March 1996 gives:
"the aggregate of effort and other resources focussed on developing and/or maintaining a specific product."

Chapter 3 General concepts

This chapter introduces some general concepts, mostly concentrating on ideas involved in the early part of the problem solving process. We shall choose our concepts deliberately and frugally, and define them with care: a science is only as good as it s definitions.

To define our concepts, we use as our sources general purpose dictionaries such as the Oxford Dictionary and Websters, specialist professional dictionaries, and the Vocabulary of the ISO 9000 international quality standard [1]. Only when none of these suffice do we resort to our own 'working definitions'.

3.1 Referent

In Chapter 2 we encountered the notion of *referent*, identifying it as the entity of interest. The term *entity* is a general notion, defined in an earlier version of the international quality standard as follows:

> **entity**
> that which can be individually defined or considered.
> NOTE An entity may be, for example an activity or a process,
> – a product
> – an organization, a system or a person, or
> – any combination thereof.
>
> ISO 8402:1994: Quality management and quality assurance – Vocabulary of the ISO 9000 Quality Standard

We adopt this definition, and use it to define:

> **referent**
> the entity of interest
>
> Our working definition

3.2 Boundary

When observing problematical reality, the first task is to isolate the referent. As part of the world of reality, the referent is surrounded by its *environment*, and is separated from it by a notional *boundary* that divides the world into two parts: the referent itself, and the rest. We define:

> **boundary**
> that which serves to indicate the limits of an entity
> Based on the Shorter Oxford Dictionary

All interactions between referent and environment take place across the boundary.

In many situations the notion of the referent is well established, and the boundary around the referent presents itself naturally. When the referent is the neighbour's noisy cat, the notion of 'cat' and the boundary – the hair-covered skin of the animal, its eyes, ears, etc. – are both well defined. However, in many cases, the boundary and the concept underlying the referent are unclear, and both must be defined deliberately for the problem to be understood and the problem solving project to have a chance of success.

In other situations in addition to the problematic entity, part of the environment may also be deficient. In such cases it is necessary to consider which parts of this environment we wish to modify, and include those parts inside the boundary.

Example 3.1

'Risk of infection' is a familiar enough notion, but the idea of 'risk' is not so straightforward. In case of an outbreak of infectious disease, it is hard to define the boundary between those members of the population who are at risk and those who are not at risk. The boundary may vary with the 'owner' of the problem (the Education Authority might decide to keep schools open, but some parents might decide to keep their children at home). Economic factors might play a part in determining the boundary (how much money can the local Health Authority dedicate to an immunization programme?). The boundary may be decided on several bases, such as geography (drawing a radius around the place where the outbreak was detected), age (the youngest and oldest sectors of the community), medical history (diabetics, people suffering of heart disease, people on immunosuppressive drugs), profession (doctors, teachers and others in contact with many people).

Example 3.2

Everyone might agree that 'computing capabilities' may be one of the key assets of a company in this day and age, but it is quite difficult to define what computing capabilities are, and where would one draw the boundary around them: tight around the hardware / software resources? More loosely, to include the peripherals and the network? And how about the human skills? And what of the telephone lines? Any other aspect of the infrastructure?

Vague definition of the boundary of the referent is a frequent source of confusion and misunderstanding. Consider that the problem owner seeks to draw the attention of his Managing Director to the order book that is becoming depleted fast. Confusion arises if the problem owner refers to the order book of the particular plant where he/she is employed, whereas the Managing Director looks at the order book of the company as a whole. The confusion need not involve both communicating parties: it may arise right at the beginning, in the mind of the project champion who concentrates on a certain aspect of a problematic situation, but changes his/her mind gradually in course of the process, without realizing it. This undesirable phenomenon is called the 'boundary drift', which is prevented, or at least arrested, by clear and explicit definition and judicious representation of the boundary.

Guarding against boundary drift does not mean that the boundary is rigid. There is often a case for revising the boundary in course of the problem solving process, in the light of increasing knowledge of the referent, the environment and the means of solution.

3.3 The 'meaning triangle'

Even if the boundary is well established, difficulties can arise if the concept behind the referent is poorly understood. Many problem solving projects start by observing a problematical entity, and leap directly to giving the project, or the desired version of the entity, a catchy name. The essential stage between the two – understanding and defining the concepts behind the problem and the solution – is missed altogether, and it is not surprising that such initiatives return no result.

Reality, concept, designation

The human urge to observe, classify, order and understand is very strong. It governs the process of learning, and motivates our earliest behaviour, explaining the popularity of childhood puzzle solving.

Observation starts with reality. The child first sees the ginger cat of the next door neighbour, then a little black-and-white kitten in the street, and soon generalizes the observations, forming the concept 'cat'. The young child may err along the way, mistaking a dog or a tiger for a cat, but soon the notion is clarified. Figure 3.1 offers an example for indicating the difference between reality, concept and designation, and outlines the relationship between them.

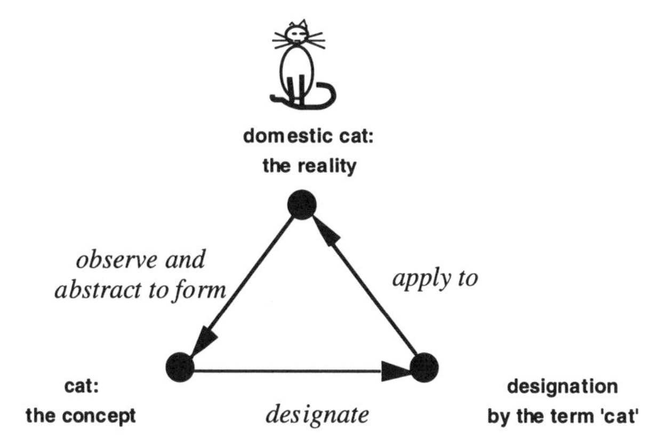

Figure 3.1: The 'meaning triangle' – forming and naming the concept 'cat' (nodes represent entities and arcs show connecting actions)

The cat next door is reality. Having observed many cats and abstracted the essential common elements from the observations to distil the concept, the observer recognizes next door's beast as belonging to the general class 'cat'. English speakers designate the concept with a word spelled 'c-a-t'. The concept is not dependent on language. The baby would rejoice at the sight of a cat long before knowing the word for 'cat', and the idea of 'cat' is shared between the Frenchman who calls it 'chat', the German who calls it 'Katz', and the Hungarian who calls it 'macska'.

- *Forming a clear concept* is essential: it could be fatal on safari to mistake a lion for a domestic cat.
- *Naming things aptly* is helpful, and the words we assign to a thing influences our attitude towards it (for example, calling GM foods 'Frankenstein foods', calling a type of software a 'virus').
- *Using designations consistently* is important: pointing to a cat and saying 'dog', or conversely, would be confusing, and so would it be to use the word 'dog' for designating the two different concepts.

This book endeavours to define concepts carefully, chooses designations deliberately, and takes care to use terminology consistently. This kind of discipline is necessary in dealing effectively with problems of complex reality.

3.4 Definitions

To form a mental image of observations, to express ideas clearly in a message, to communicate the message effectively to others, we must know what we mean. We adopt the notion of:

> **definition**
> the precise statement of the essential nature of a thing
> The Shorter Oxford Dictionary

Definitions and the meaning triangle

Recall the three nodes of the meaning triangle: reality, concept and designation. Definitions capture the concept behind the individual instance of reality: they put into words the key characteristics of the class of entities to which an individual referent belongs. The designatory term is merely shorthand: a key to the dictionary of definitions.

General uses of definitions

Defining terms clearly and using terminology consistently are prerequisites of effective human interaction. In science and technology, in business and commerce definition of terms is a professional obligation. Members of professions are accountable to their clients and to the community, and should use language for communication, not for building barriers. For ease of professional communication, simple sentence constructions and words in common use should be applied wherever possible. The meaning of words should accord with their *lexical definition,* given, for example, in the Shorter Oxford Dictionary.

Members of a profession are often forced to adopt the use of specific terms to designate precise concepts. The meaning of words that refer to well established specialist concepts will be given in the dictionary of each profession. For example, the words 'stress', 'creep', 'friction' may sound familiar to the lay person living in close proximity with a quarrelsome couple, but a dictionary of mechanical engineering will give these terms precise meaning, quite different from everyday use and devoid of emotional content. Similarly, the meaning of such words as 'noise', 'potential', 'interference', 'distortion' is defined for the everyday user in the Oxford Dictionary, but in electronics these words are reserved for special meaning, given in a specialist dictionary. Such a dictionary will also contain terms such as 'bandwith' [2], 'standing wave', 'magnetron', which are absent from the everyday language. Thus, for communication among experts of the same field, the general and specialist dictionaries combine to form the lexical basis. In case of conflict between the two, the specialist meaning takes precedence.

For communication between experts in different disciplines, or between an expert and a lay person, professional terms should be rephrased in words of the everyday language, if possible. When only specialist terminology can convey the precise meaning, the use of *known words with special meaning*, and the *meaning of new terms* must both be provided locally, such *stipulative definitions* being collected in a 'glossary'.

When managing people, when working as a member of an interdisciplinary team, or when communicating with the customer or the public, the professional must bear in mind that: –

- There is no excuse for using undefined jargon. Jargon may impress in the short term, but creates confusion in the long run. Quite often, the user of jargon even confuses himself/herself.
- There is no excuse for *vagueness:* there should be no 'borderline cases': instances when it is not clear whether or not the term can be applied. Definitions should not leave doubt about the meaning of the term and the scope of its applicability.
- Everyday terminology should be used wherever possible, keeping professional vocabulary to a minimum. However, the professional vocabulary must be rich enough to designate each distinct concept by a distinct term. *Ambiguity* arises when a term has multiple meaning: two or more concepts are denoted with the same term. This leaves the user uncertain which meaning applies.
- Definitions must be informative and objective, rather than emotional or judgmental. They should avoid influencing *attitudes* in a tendentious way. Manipulating people's attitudes by emotive terminology is unprofessional use of definitions. However, this does not mean that definitions cannot play a useful role in developing attitudes in a constructive manner. One of the most important tasks of teachers is to define and discuss ideas that develop pupils' attitudes towards each other and towards their environment. Similarly, it is the responsibility of every manager to motivate members of the team: identify and define ideas for stimulating people to be interested in

their job, be ready to cooperate with others, to act in accord with professional and general codes of conduct, be loyal to the firm.

In summary, definitions are used for several purposes, among them:

- to explain a concept,
- to increase vocabulary, designating a concept by a reserved word, or a new word,
- to eliminate vagueness, replacing an existing concept by a more precise one,
- to eliminate ambiguity,
- to influence attitudes.

Use of definitions in a systems methodology

As this book will explain, *measurement* is one of the cornerstones of a systems methodology. Entities of interest are characterized by measures of their attributes, and we use measures to formulate judgements and decisions about them. For its effectiveness, the systems methodology relies on measures of good quality, and the quality of the measures is conditioned by the quality of the definition of their attributes.

Quality of definitions

All definitions must satisfy established quality criteria which help us to ensure that definitions are *meaningful* and *informative*. According to these, a definition must:

- be *traceable* to a referent,
- be *direct*, using well understood concepts given in a general purpose dictionary, or *indirect*, constructed of terms *traceable* to general concepts,
- be *grounded*: free of undefined terms (if A is defined in terms of B and B is not defined at all then nothing is defined),
- use *unambiguous* language,
- be *free of jargon:* use terminology consistent with definitions of a general purpose or specialist professional dictionary (these are called 'lexical' definitions), or locally defined in a glossary (these are called 'stipulative' definitions),
- be *affirmative* rather than negative (don't say what it *isn't*, say what it *is*),
- *acyclic*: free of circularity and direct or indirect self-reference: it avoids defining something in terms of itself (if A is defined in terms of B, and B is defined in terms of A then nothing is defined).

Surprisingly, sometimes even the most authoritative lexical sources fail to meet these criteria. To be meticulous about the definition of key terms is not pedantry: the work invested in constructing good quality definitions is repaid several times over in course of the problem solving process, in forming clear ideas and maintaining good relations with colleagues and customers, and in dealing with the public.

Example 3.3, demonstrating vagueness, quoting from the Oxford Dictionary:

> *"**Caravan:** a house on wheels."*

> *This definition serves well enough when the meaning is clear from the context, but it is inadequate in professional practice. For taxation purposes should a caravan be regarded as a dwelling, or as a vehicle?*
>
> *To eliminate vagueness, the definition must be modified, distinguishing between anchored and permanently inhabited caravans (to be regarded as dwellings) from motorized caravans (to be regarded as vehicles).*

Example 3.4, demonstrating ambiguity, quoting from the Oxford Dictionary:

> *"**Sanction:** to authorize; to countenance;*
> *to enforce (a law) by attaching a penalty to transgression".*

In problem solving, one must be guided by general principles of quality and international quality standards. Many definitions of concern to the manager, technologist and systems professional are proposed in the ISO 9000 family of quality standards. International standards evolve continuously, each new version seeking to eliminate the weaknesses of its predecessor. Even so, the reader will come across several instances where the international quality standard fails to meet the general quality criteria for the definition of important concepts.

'Level' of a definition

For ease of reference, the key definitions of this book are collected into a Glossary which indicates the source of the definitions and their location in the text. The Glossary also shows the 'level' of each definition: the relationship of the definition to other definitions in the text. Definitions at Level 1 use only words with generally agreed meanings, definitions at Level 2 use general terms and terms at Level 1, the highest level term in a definition at Level 5 is Level 4, etc.

3.5 Attributes

Let us continue with the task of starting up the problem solving process. Having identified the referent, having set out its boundary and defined the underlying concept, the problem owner must *characterize* the referent.

We define:

> **attribute**
> a characteristic of the referent [3]
>
> Our working definition

Relying on notions about the quality of definitions, we stipulate:

> **well defined attribute**
> definition of an attribute that is meaningful, grounded and free of circularity
> Our working definition

Reality is boundlessly complicated, and each referent manifests an infinity of characteristics. Some of these identify them as members of a group, while others allow each individual to be distinguished from any of the others. Consider these examples:

"Ann's raincoat is *red*."

"XYZ Ltd is a *small* company."

"Your suitcase is *heavy*."

"My room is *12 foot long*."

In the first statement the referent is Ann's raincoat, the attribute is 'colour', and 'red' is the *value* qualifying the attribute of colour of the coat. Other coats and other objects would also possess the attribute of colour, and in those cases the value of colour may also be red, or else blue, green, maroon, etc.

In the second statement 'small' is the value qualifying the attribute 'size', other possible values being 'medium-size', 'large', 'extra large', etc.

In the third statement the attribute 'weight' has value 'heavy'.

In the last statement the quantitative value of '12 foot' designates the attribute 'length', other possible values being 13 foot, 15 foot, or whatever. The same information about length may be conveyed, for example, in metres, millimetres or nautical miles.

Expressed in words, attributes are *adjectives* (or *adjectival phrases*). We perceive a *class* of entities, such as companies, apples or steamboats, as having the attribute of 'size', and we qualify size by such words as 'large', 'small', 'medium'. Rather than using descriptive words, we frequently designate size by magnitudes such as the number of employees of the company, the displacement volume of the boat, or the number of grammes of weight of the apple. We also use the notion of value in relation to attributes such as 'colour', tying value to notions such as 'red' or 'blue', emphasizing that value need not be numerical.

Thus, we define:

> **value**
> the extent, amount or instance of a well defined attribute of an individual referent
> NOTE: value may be *qualitative* or *quantitative*
> Our working definition

Using the word in this wider sense, we distinguish between *qualitative* and *quantitative* values of attributes. If colour is one of the distinguishing attributes of a cashmere shawl, and if the departmental store stocks such shawls in every colour of the rainbow, then the colour attribute of an individual shawl can take up any qualitative value from (red, orange, yellow, green, blue, violet, indigo). If shawls come in two shapes to which the store refers as 'square' or 'long', then shape will be another qualitative attribute, each shawl taking a pair of values, such as (square, red), or (long, yellow). By contrast, retail price will be a quantitative attribute, with values given in £ Sterling to an accuracy of two decimal places.

Each attribute must represent a clearly understood concept, the meaning of which is shared by all those using it. We say that an object is red, taking for granted that all fully sighted people share the same idea of redness. The word 'red' is sufficient in the everyday context, but fashion houses or paint manufacturers, for example, will require further refinement of redness into scarlet, vermilion, carmine, cherry, magenta. Scientist may need to interpret 'red' even more precisely, associating it with a specific series of spectral lines expressed as wavelengths or frequencies. Observe that the qualitative or quantitative nature of value is not an inherent characteristic of the attribute; the attribute 'red' can be regarded as qualitative or quantitative, depending on the requirements of the given situation.

When an attribute may be critical, such as an object in transit being described as 'fragile' or – by default – 'not fragile', then tacit understanding of shared meaning among those concerned would not suffice: the attribute would need more precise definition. Similarly, a proper, quality assured definition is required when an unfamiliar attribute is being introduced into wide use, such as food being labelled as 'organic' or 'genetically modified', a watch being sold as 'waterproof', domestic machinery claimed to be 'user friendly', and some complex system being classed as 'safety critical'. Precise definition is also advisable when a familiar attribute arises in potentially hazardous situations, such as when one must be certain that a business partner is 'trustworthy', an employee is 'loyal to the company', or a politician has 'integrity'.

If a concept is being used to qualify another entity then it is an attribute. The same concept may be used independently when it is an entity with its own attributes. As an example, an address may be regarded as an attribute of 'employee', but to the postman or the rating officer 'address' is an entity with its own attributes of name of addressee, house number, street name, town, county, post code, country. Similarly, as we have seen, colour is one of the attributes of the referent 'coat', but for the paint manufacturer 'colour' can also be a referent in its own right, carrying its own attributes. This can lead to confusion, as definers of databases have discovered long ago. Bearing in mind the meaning triangle's distinction between reality, concept and designation, and identifying the referent and its attributes explicitly, helps avoiding such confusions. In a new field, new ideas are formed as important characteristics emerge. In time, these ideas are refined and an agreed definition of the attribute emerges.

Example 3.5

In software engineering – a profession with only a few decades of history – there is now reasonable consensus that 'functionality', 'portability' and 'maintainability' are among the key characteristics of software quality, and 'dependability' and 'security' are among the desirable attributes of safety critical software. Identifying and naming these characteristics is a useful step in the development of the discipline, but we have seen earlier in this chapter that definition of concept is far more important than denotation. To date, no adequate definition exists for any of these software quality 'attributes'.

Management science too is perceived as a relatively new field, and so is systems engineering, where concepts and methods are in development, and key attributes are in need of good quality definition.

3.6 Measures

Measures are fundamental to the development of science, technology and business. They are essential in everyday commerce, psychology, medicine, information technology, economics and politics. We offer here a simplified definition [4]:

measure
a value of a well defined attribute; if the value is quantitative, it is accompanied by the unit of measurement
Our simplified definition

Measurement is the means of establishing attribute values of entities, characterizing them and comparing them with each other. We need measurement to represent a referent factually, with confidence, precision and authority.

Measurement features at the beginning, at the end, and throughout the problem solving process. The problem and the customer's requirements must be specified in terms of attributes and their measures. Once the solution is produced, it must be validated against the specification, and quality assured against the requirements of the 'constituency' of the newly created system. Only by measurement can we prove conclusively that the contract has been fulfilled, the new system has been made operational within time and budget, and is consistent with all relevant standards, laws, safety requirements, environmental criteria.

Measurement presupposes that the referent has been identified, and the attribute of interest defined.

Measurement is comparison: there must be at least one other entity beside the referent. This may be another referent, or some predetermined standard used as 'yardstick' or 'benchmark'.

Example 3.6

We can sort the children in a class of 20 in ascending order of height by repeatedly comparing them pairwise. No yardstick is needed.

We can also give a comparative measure to indicate height by assigning to each child a number from 1 to 20: the larger the number, the taller the child. (Note that numbers can be assigned differently, the tallest child being given the number 1 and the smallest the number 20!)

For such comparative measurement we don't even need numbers: our alphabet is just as good a basis of the measure. Each child can be given one of the first 20 letters of the alphabet, 'a' being assigned to the smallest. Thereafter, the taller the child, the later his/her designatory letter in the alphabet.

Equally successful would be the use of any other established alphabet: the Greek, the Cyrillic, the Arabic, the Hebrew, provided that the intended users of the alphabetic measure are familiar with the letters in the selected alphabet, and with the order of the letters in that alphabet.

Example 3.7

Quite different is the case when there is only one child whose height is to be measured. Here we need a tape measure or yardstick as the basis for comparison, and the measure will be numerical: the corresponding reading on the yardstick, a multiple of 1 inch, or 1 cm, say.

Example 3.8

One of the most important uses of measurement occurs in quality assurance where the value of some key attribute of the referent is compared with the norm for conformance. This might be the case with loaves of bread whose minimum weight is specified on the label. Quite often, as in this case, the outcome is a two-valued measure: 'Pass' or 'Fail'.

The last of these examples is classification: an important use of measurement. The range of values of the key attribute may be as few as two ('Pass' and 'Fail' in the example), but it may be more (such as 'Pass', 'Fail for the given purpose but can be used in another application', 'Fail but can be repaired', 'Fail and reject altogether'). The set from which the attribute value is selected must be predefined and used as class labels, and the allocation of an item to a class must be based on objective evidence.

Example 3.9

The game of 'animal, vegetable, mineral' classifies entities into at least three categories. The mouse, the dinosaur and the population of the USA may not have much in common, but they all find themselves in the 'animal' class. The game of classification becomes more complicated if an entity may fall into several categories simultaneously. To accommodate this, the number of categories has to be increased, for example by adding a 'mixed' category.

As the examples show, good measures need not be numbers. Conversely, in many cases, numbers are used to qualify entities, but not all such numbers would necessarily be valid measures. This is exemplified by the allocation of numbers to poorly defined concepts such as interoperability, dependability and user-friendliness.

3.7 Time

Time is the common characteristic of all entities in the real world: all events occur at some time instant and all happenings unfold in time. We refer to:

> **time**
> a characteristic common to all entities in the real world, either as *position* ('real time'), or as *distance* (time duration)
> Our working definition

Measurement theory allows us to distinguish between the two kinds of time measures:

- the measure of *real time* (or *calendar time*): time measured on a scale of counting multiples of the revolution of the earth, and traditionally taking as zero midnight of the day of the birth of Jesus Christ, or
- the measure of *time period* (or *elapsed time*, or *duration*): time measured by a stopwatch as multiple (or submultiple) of the internationally agreed time unit of 1 second.

This leads to the distinction of two kinds of views of a real-life entity:

- If we are not interested in the way an entity changes, but wish to record its characteristics at a given *real time instant* then we regard it as *passive* entity, and take a snapshot of its attributes. The attribute measures, together with the 'signature' of the time instant when the record is taken, provide a coherent representation of the entity.
- All change takes time. To register change, we must observe our referent over a time period, viewing it as an *active* entity, and include among its attributes the time measure of its *duration*.

Activities act upon *inputs* that are passive entities, and at the end of their duration they deliver *outputs* which are also passive entities. Both inputs and outputs are passive entities. Figure 3.2 shows the simple activity of polishing a motorcar. The passive input entities are the polish and the car itself at the real time instant t_1, and the passive output is the shiny car at real time instant t_2 (together with any residual polish). The activity occupies the time period $\partial t = t_2 - t_1$.

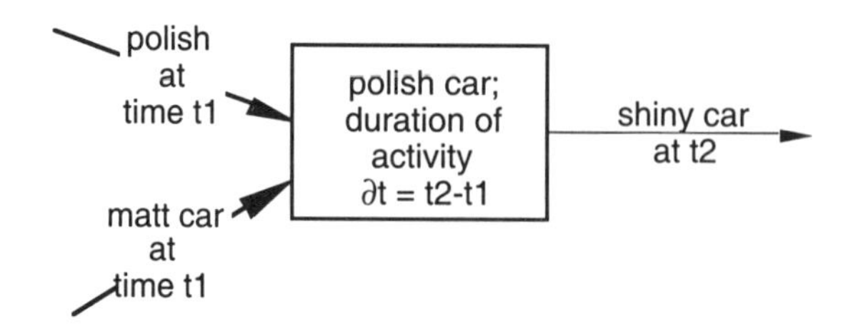

Figure 3.2: An activity with its passive input/output, showing time measures (passive entities shown as arcs, activity as node in rectangular box)

3.8 Representations

To identify the referent, to characterize it and record its characteristics for future reference, to communicate about it with others and facilitate discussion about its features, the referent must have some kind of *representation*. We define:

> **representation**
> expression of ideas about the referent
>
> Our working definition

Reality exists independently of representation, but a representation is meaningless without its referent. On the other hand, representations are essential, since we can only communicate about reality *through* its representations.

The representation can take many *forms*: names, verbal descriptions, photographs, scale models, catalogues of attributes, samples, computer simulations and the like.

Some forms of representation will suit a given situation better than others: representations can be helpful and revealing; they can also be ambiguous, obscure, incomprehensible, or deliberately misleading. In business transactions, the quality of representation is crucial. The systems professional must have skills and knowledge to choose the appropriate form of representation, and assure the quality of the representation: its fitness for the purpose of all intended users.

In a problem solving situation there are three kinds of referents: (i) the entity in its past or present state, (ii) the entity sometime in the future, and (iii) the entity as determined by the customer, or by the local, national and international rules and regulations which society imposes, to which the future referent must conform. Correspondingly, representations too are of three types: *descriptive, predictive* and *prescriptive.*

Descriptive representations

We define:

> **descriptive representation**
> representation the referent at some specific time of the present or the past
>
> Our working definition

Descriptive representations are factual, must be unambiguous, and must register both the observations and the time of the observations, called the *time signature* (or time stamp) of the representation.

Examples 3.10: Descriptive representation

Newspaper and television reports of current events, bearing today's date, intended for conveying information immediately. Archived copies are kept for future reference.

Photographs of objects, landscapes, people's record of their appearance at a given time, stored for future reference.

The name of a person is a label by which the individual is identified. This label can give rise to ambiguity since it is possible for more than one person in a community to bear a certain name. Where unique representation is essential, the name is complemented by other attributes of the individual, such as a distinguishing adjective (small John Smith, tall John Smith), the date of birth, or the passport number. For forensic purposes further distinguishing characteristics may be added, such as fingerprint, dental record, DNA signature.

Representation of the customer's deficient world at the start of the problem solving process. Attributes might include the balance sheet of the company, the share price and turnover, the rising or falling tendencies of share price and profits, the present product portfolio, client base and complement of staff skills, the gap between the state of relevant technologies and the company's equipment park and technological infrastructure, etc.

Predictive representations

We define:

predictive representation
representation of the referent at some specific time in the future, deduced from the descriptive representation with the aid of some theory, or else representation of a planned referent at a specific time when it is eventually realized

Our working definition

As all representations, the predictive representation takes the form of a collection of the relevant attributes of the referent together with the time signature of the predictive representation.

Although the predictive representation is futuristic, it is neither a guess nor a mere fantasy. It is an extrapolation from current knowledge on the basis of some kind of *theory*. The 'theory' may be scientifically well founded, or else it may be empirical, based on accumulated experience. It must allow deduction of the predictive representation of the referent from its descriptive representation, the dynamics governing the expected change, and the time distance between the time signature of the descriptive and prescriptive representation. In due course, when the predicted referent eventually materializes, the theory must be capable of confirmation or refutation by comparing the predicted representation with the descriptive representation of the extant referent.

Examples 3.11: Predictive representation

Ordering a suit from the tailor on the basis of measurements of the client's present size.

The customer may plan to maintain his/her measurements between the time of ordering and the time of collection. If such a change is likely, (diet, bingeing, pregnancy) then the customer must predict how the measurements will change over the supply period, using a 'theory' based on past experience.

Orders issued by a manufacturing company operating a 'just-in-time' policy. The production director issues the orders to suppliers on the basis of predictive representations of the demands of the production process.

Mathematical models of banks representing future market trends and predicted currency rates when deciding which currencies to hold.

The budget of long-term public projects, predicting total cost of the completed project at the time of commencement. The usual experience is that projects are delayed and budgets are exceeded, bearing witness to the weakness of the theory which is the basis of the predictive representation.

In the context of problem solving, the most important use of predictive representation is in the *specification* of the future system. The various kinds of specifications, discussed in the next chapter, form the basis of the contract between customer and supplier. They set out the criteria the future system must satisfy, represent the starting point of the problem solver's activity, and provide the formal record against which the attribute measures of the finished solution will be checked.

Prescriptive representations

The prescriptive representation of the referent may refer to an instant in the past, the present or the future. The purpose of the prescriptive representation is to command by law, convention or contract, or recommend, as a matter of common sense or professional wisdom, the properties of an acceptable referent. We define:

prescriptive representation
the required attribute values of a referent, or the bounds within which the attribute values must lie at a specified time instant, or over a specified time period

Our working definition

Prescriptive representations would be used to set standards for discriminating between referents as *valid* or *invalid for a purpose*, protecting society against undesirable or dangerous materials, objects, practices and ideologies. Sometimes the prescriptive representation identifies a specific *individual*, such as the payee of a cheque, or a *class* of individuals, such as chartered engineers and qualified medical practitioners. In many cases, the prescriptive representation sets acceptable *limits of tolerance* for attribute values within which an entity would be deemed valid.

Examples 3.12: Prescriptive representation

Thousands of years ago, a prescriptive specification of the behaviour for a civilized society was handed to mankind on tablets of stone.

Standards bodies, such as the International Standards Organization (ISO), give prescriptive representations of a technical nature, specifying limits for measurable characteristics of acceptable systems, components and materials.

Statutory bodies, such as the Health and Safety Executive, issue legally binding prescriptive representations of working conditions.

Professional organizations issue codes of conduct which are prescriptive representations of behaviour expected from the membership.

The specification of an artefact on order is a prescriptive representation of the object under the contract.

Quality of representations

GENERAL QUALITY CRITERIA

Representations document all phases of business transactions, and are the basis of communication between contracting parties. Thus, the quality of representations is a vital factor in assuring harmonious relations between customer and supplier, and between supplier and subcontractor, and is an important factor in determining the success of any business transaction. Among the features of good quality are that the representation is:

- *true* of the referent, matching it in some significant sense, distinguishing it from others, free of deliberate distortions of reality,
- *unambiguous*, characterizing the referent in terms of well defined attributes, leaving no doubt about meaning, and avoiding the possibility of misinterpretation,
- *valid*: consistent with observations,
- *concise*, preserving all features which are important for the given purpose, but suppressing characteristics which may also be valid, but would overcrowd the picture, and deflect attention from the essentials,
- *internally consistent*, free of contradictions,
- *usable* by all those for whom it is intended and all other interested parties.

QUALITY OF DESCRIPTIVE, PREDICTIVE AND PRESCRIPTIVE REPRESENTATIONS

The referents of *descriptive* representations *exist,* or existed some time in the past. The quality of the descriptive representation of extant real-life referents can be checked by direct observation, analysis, measurement, or by reference to records, or to a consensus of informed opinion.

Since the *predictive* representation is futuristic, its validity cannot be checked against reality at the time of its creation. Instead, the predictive representation must be *verified* on the basis of the *current* attribute measures of the present situation, and evidence of the *validity* of the scientific or empirical theory on which the prediction is based. In addition to facts and theories about the future, this predictive foundation may involve ascertaining the availability of resources required for the realization of the prediction.

Example 3.13

Predictive representations of navigation systems should be made on the basis of current technology, either extant or under development. Over-optimistic forecasts of what could be achieved, and failure to make the necessary skills and resources available, have led to many a failed system.

Prescriptive representations are the domain of statutory, standardization and certification bodies, lawyers, politicians, and safety experts. In addition to the general quality criteria of representativeness, absence of ambiguity and the like, prescriptive representations must have appropriate technical quality to protect the community against dangerous or shoddy practice. Inadequate technical quality – for example in preventing accidents or disasters – is usually recognized with hindsight, leading to the tightening of standards. Externally prescribed representa-tions are frequently complemented with appropriate internal house standards, and these are guarded by line management and the company's quality function.

Examples 3.14

The notorious tragedy at London's Kings Cross Underground station has led to a tightening of standards both in the construction of escalators to avoid the accumulation of combustible rubbish, and in the type of materials used to decorate public areas.

For many years the use of asbestos as an insulating material in the building trade was thought innocuous, but the material has subsequently been found highly injurious to health. Standards have been revised to ban future use and implement its replacement in existing buildings.

Guarding the referent in the interest of quality

The validity of the representation relies on the clear identification of the referent and the stability of its properties. If the identity of the referent is ambiguous, if the referent is substituted by another, or if its characteristics are liable to change while the representation is being formed, then the quality of the representation will suffer.

Examples 3.15: Some further examples

The descriptive representation of the weight recorded on an item on the supermarket shelf becomes invalid if the referent is unstable because the packing is poor, and some of the contents evaporate or spill.

The documentation of a software package becomes an invalid representation if, in course of maintenance, the software is modified without notice. Configuration management must ensure that the modification of the referent (the software) is carried through to the representation (the documentation).

3.9 Languages

Philosophers identify uses of language as to inform, to evoke and to influence. For the purposes of representation, professional ethics usually confine scientists, engineers and systems professionals to the *informative* use of language.

The dictionary defines:

> **language**
> words and methods of combining them for the expression of thought
>
> Based on the Shorter Oxford Dictionary

For professional purposes the notion of 'language' must not be constrained to natural languages such as English, Spanish or Chinese, but must extend to deliberately created artificial languages, including graphical, pictorial, mathematical /logical, physical and other means of expressing ideas. For this, we must interpret 'word' and 'method' in the definition broadly, to include various forms of compositions over many sorts of meaningful atomic elements of representation.

Example 3.16

The generally accepted notion of 'queue' is that it is a collection of items arranged in a line, awaiting their turn for service. Assume that the queue contains n items, and items may be of any kind: people waiting for the bus, objects on the production line, entries into a data base, or whatever. In addition to this English language description of 'queue', figure 3.3 shows the representation of a queue in four different languages.

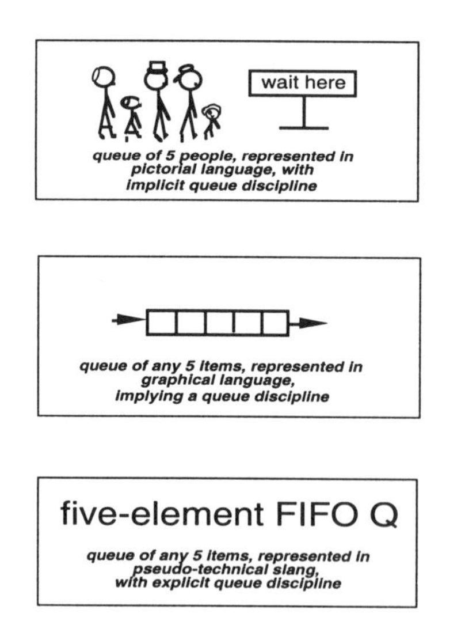

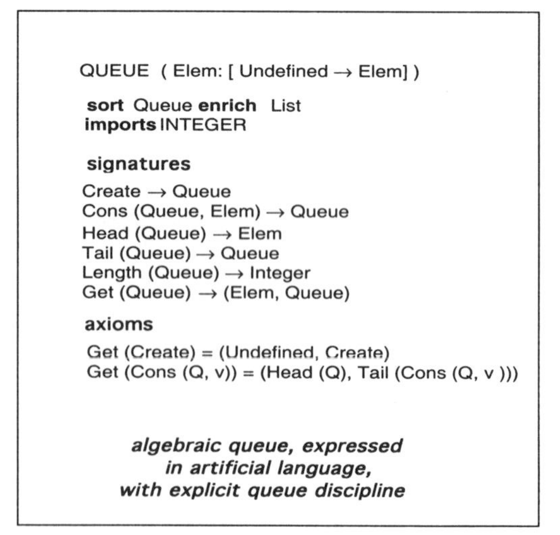

Figure 3.3: Representing a queue in various languages

Classifying languages

NATURAL LANGUAGES

Natural languages have evolved through the ages to meet the needs of social intercourse, to convey information, to express feelings, to provide entertainment. Natural languages develop continuously, in accord with the experience and expectations of the community who use the language (pragmatics). New words and expressions appear, old ones fade, yet others acquire new meanings. The rules governing the combination of words into sentences (syntax) are identified by common usage, and are descriptive rather than prescriptive (in spite of the efforts of grammarians). Natural languages are characterized by implicit *meaning* (semantics). Word or phrases map into the real world, the initiator of the message assuming that the recipient will understand the concepts. These languages offer opportunity for subtle emotive associations via figures of speech, similes, metaphors, plays on words, ambiguities and double meanings, resulting in expressive power beyond the literal meaning of their words, and leading to the rich fields of literature and poetry. The beauty of natural language is vested in ambiguity: allowing for different shades of meaning, according to associations in the minds of the initiators and recipients.

Example 3.17

O Rose, thou art sick!
The invisible worm,
That flies in the night,
In the howling storm,
Has found out thy bed
Of crimson joy;
And his dark secret love
Does thy life destroy.

William Blake

In business and science, the ambiguity of natural language is undesirable. Specialist professionals, such as lawyers, doctors and engineers, attempt to overcome ambiguity and misunderstanding by selecting subsets of the natural language for general use, and stipulating explicit definitions for key concepts [5]. In this way, professionals seek to ensure that the language of representation can unambiguously convey the meaning intended by the initiator of the message. The resulting *professional language* – a version of the natural language, using a subset of the vocabulary, but assigning more precise meaning to some words and extending the dictionary with specially created technical terms – often lacks beauty, and can be all but incomprehensible to the lay person.

Example 3.18

Extract from Land Compensation (Scotland) Act 1973: 39. (1), selected at random:

"Where a relevant authority within the meaning of section 36 above provide or secure the provision of accommodation for any person in pursuance of subsection (1) (a) or (c) of that section, then, if-

(a) the authority providing the accommodation ("the rehousing authority") not the same as the authority by whom the land in question is acquired or

are redeveloped ("the displacing authority"); and
(b) the displacing authority are not an authority having functions under Part VII of the Housing (Scotland) Act,
the displacing authority shall make to the rehousing authority periodical payments, or if the rehousing authority so require a lump sum payment, ..." etc.

ARTIFICIAL LANGUAGES

Natural and professional languages are the first choice of engineers, managers, lawyers and scientists in discussing any system, real or potential. As the scientific foundations of the discipline develop, as ideas become firmer and scope for misunderstanding and error increases, the professional will turn to more rigorous and exact forms of expression, and *artificial languages* are invented. They range in variety from informal graphical language of stylized sketches to the most formal (logic and mathematics). They are based on explicit definitions, rather than relying on implicit meaning. Their symbols and entities are assigned local meaning (stipulative semantics) at the point of usage. As Bunge [6] puts it:

> *"Like any other human creation, language can be studied both in itself (internal study) and as a social object (external study). The latter approach is the one adopted by the psychologist, the anthropologist, the sociologist and the historian interested in language as a cultural phenomenon. Such an approach ... has no particular relevance to our goal: we are not so much concerned with the uses of signs in real social life (PRAGMATICS, the union of the above mentioned empirical sciences) as with the structure of signs (the object of SYNTAX) and with their relations to ideas and things (the object of SEMANTICS). The reason for selecting syntax and semantics as the proper tools for investigating the scientific languages is this. We are ultimately interested in the ideas and procedures of science rather than in the historically conditioned ways in which such ideas and procedures are expressed by the various scientific communities ..."*

The characteristics of *formal* languages, such as mathematics and logic, are precise *definitions*, unambiguous *symbols* and *reasoning power*. Such languages are linguistic systems, which assemble words into sentences in accord with grammatical rules, and draw deductions from collections of sentences by use of a code of reasoning. The code provides means of deducing consequences from such collections of sentences, where the consequences are expressed as new sentences, which reveal new truths about the referent.

A more relaxed type of artificial language may be characterized as *semi-formal.* Such a language will have a precise syntax, but may not have a full compliment of definitions, and may have no rules of deduction. Examples are flowcharts, Data Flow Diagrams, the pictorial language of the highway code, all having their own symbols and rules for applying them, but no code for reasoning.

Regrettably there also exist *non-formal* artificial languages, ones which represent entities by undefined or partially defined symbols in disorderly or only partially ordered arrangements. Such languages are used, for example, in some branches of management, creating a false impression of sound scientific basis.

Media

The dictionary defines 'medium' as an intermediate agency: means, instrument, channel or intervening substance through which impressions are conveyed to the senses (based on the Shorter Oxford Dictionary). We adopt an alternative definition:

> **media**
> a generic term, mostly used to indicate means of transmission of information (or entertainment)
> based on the Fontana Dictionary of Modern Thought, 1988

The notion is not to be confused with language.

Examples 3.19: Different kinds of media:

for keeping notes and records in any language:
handwriting, printing or drawings on paper, carvings in stone, recording by magnetic, electronic or optical means, etc.,

for communicating personal messages in a natural language:
the spoken word at face-to-face meeting, through the telephone, by sealed letters, etc.,

for communicating to selected sectors:
copying written messages by post or email to all people on the circulation list, teleconferencing, private communication links, etc.,

for public communication:
public address at open meetings, publications in newspapers, television and broadcasts, pages in the world wide web, etc.

Since all professions need representations, they also need media, but the needs vary from profession to profession.

Examples 3.20: Media suitable for specific purposes

'memo' in use of business management,

televised or printed visual images,

short printed text and jingles in advertising,

telephone conversations and email in marketing and sales promotion,

electronic means of banking.

The suitability of some specific sorts of media for professional use is determined by factors such as retentiveness, lack of distortion, lack of inadvertent interference.

Graphs

Graphs are formal, artificial languages, useful in representing relationships. They deserve a separate section here because they provide particularly useful means of displaying the composition and operation of many different kinds of referents. Graphs have wide application in documents of business and commerce, industry and administration, science, computing and engineering. Used in a disciplined manner, graphs are powerful problem solving aids.

Graphs are abstract structures of points called *nodes* (or vertices) and lines called *branches* (or arcs, edges). A graph can be defined as:

> **graph**
> a finite set of nodes (or vertices), and a finite set of edges which connect pairs of nodes; the set of nodes must contain at least one element
> source e.g.: M Attenborough: "Engineering Mathematics', McGraw Hill, 1994

DIRECTED AND UNDIRECTED GRAPHS

Graphs are either *undirected* or *directed.* All arcs of directed graphs carry an arrow, as in figures 3.1, 3.2, 3.4. They display a collection of paths *from* one node *to* another. In this book we use directed graphs extensively, defining them as follows:

> **directed graph**
> a graph where all edges are replaced by arcs (edges carrying an arrow)
> source e.g.: M Attenborough: "Engineering Mathematics', McGraw Hill, 1994

Figures 3.5, 3.6 are examples of undirected graphs: nodes connected to each other.

Figure 3.7 is neither a directed nor an undirected graph: it is only a diagram:

> **diagram**
> a figure composed of lines, serving to illustrate a statement, or to aid in a demonstration
> The Shorter Oxford Dictionary

All graphs are diagrams, but not all diagrams are graphs.

CYCLIC AND ACYCLIC GRAPHS

Directed graphs can be further classified as *cyclic* or *acyclic.* An acyclic graph, such as in figure 3.2, has no route back to the same node, whereas in a cyclic graph such as that of figure 3.1 and 3.4, the flow may visit the same node several times.

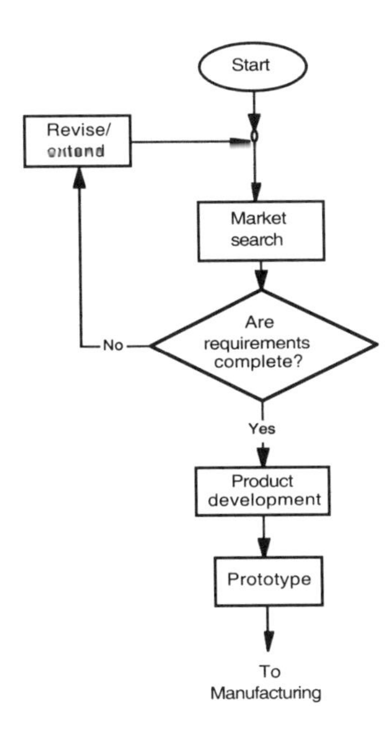

Figure 3.4: A directed graph – extract from the Quality Manual of a manufacturing company (key omitted)

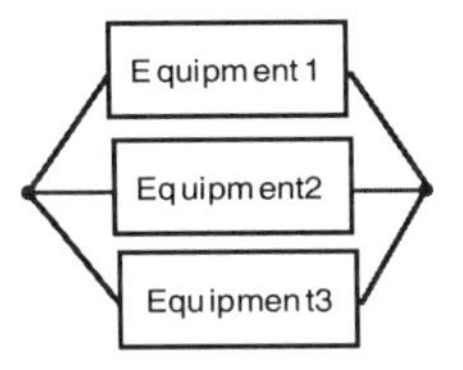

Figure 3.5: An undirected graph – triple-redundant equipment for enhancing reliability (key omitted)

THE MEANING OF GRAPHS

Graphs are mathematical objects: they obey only the theory of mathematics, having no inherent referents in the real world. It is up to the problem solver to *associate* graphs with a class of referent, declare explicitly *which* characteristics of the referent should the graph represent, and what *meaning* should be attributed to the nodes and arcs or edges of the graph.

- Graphs are versatile: they can be used to represent many different kinds of referents. It is the obligation of the creator of the graph to supply a *key* to the graph. The key should list each kind of symbol used, and should declare explicitly the meaning of each type of symbol; otherwise the message carried by the graph is incomprehensible to others.
- In a graph the same type of arc or nodal symbol may be used many times over. For clarity and ease of identification of the elements of the graph, each arc and each node must carry a unique *label.*

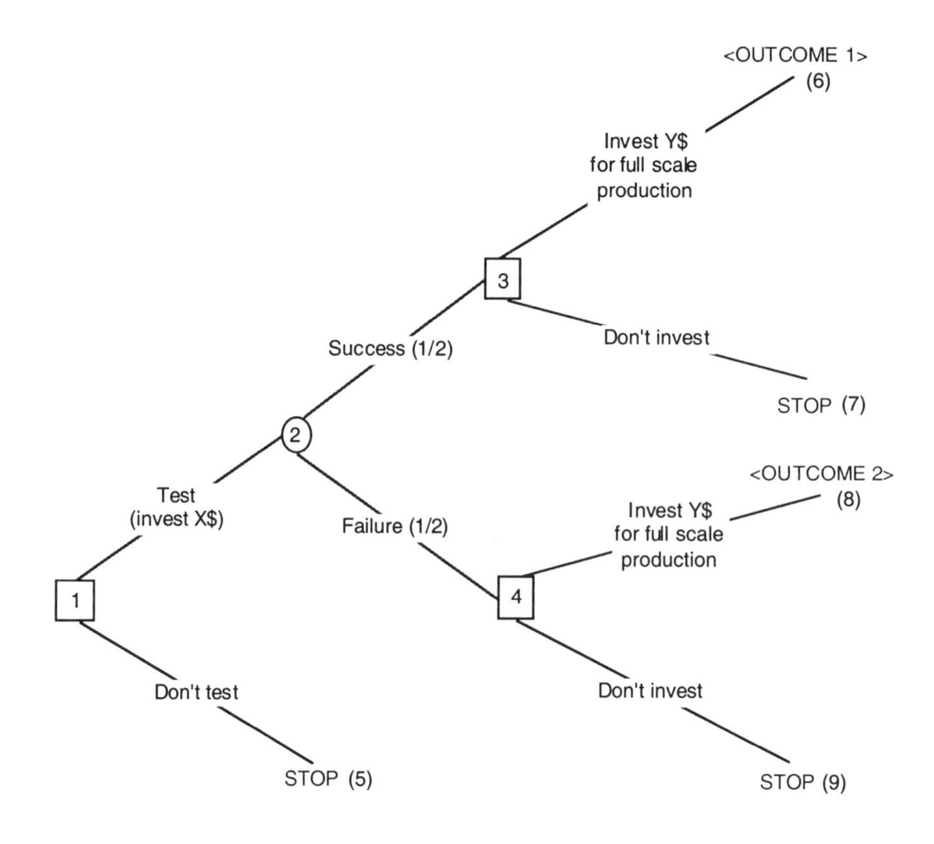

Figure 3.6: Ambiguous graph: undirected graph intending to represent a 'decision tree' (key not supplied at source)

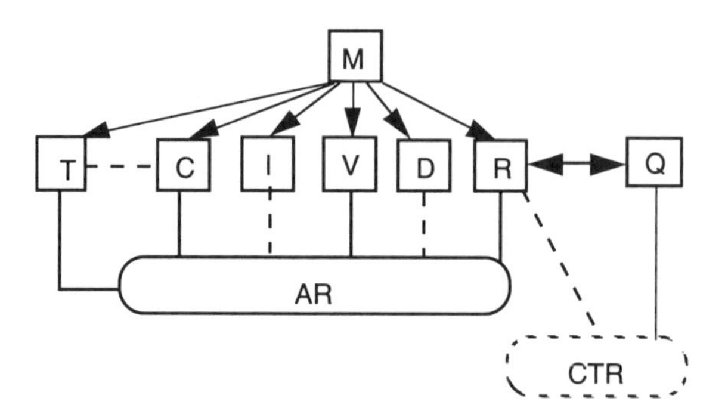

Figure 3.7: A diagram intended to represent the organization of a company. Extract from company documentation (only partial key supplied)

Figure 3.4a is a labelled directed graph: a variant of figure 3.4. Arcs are labelled by lower case letters and nodes – including the node of confluence just below the 'start' node – by capitals.

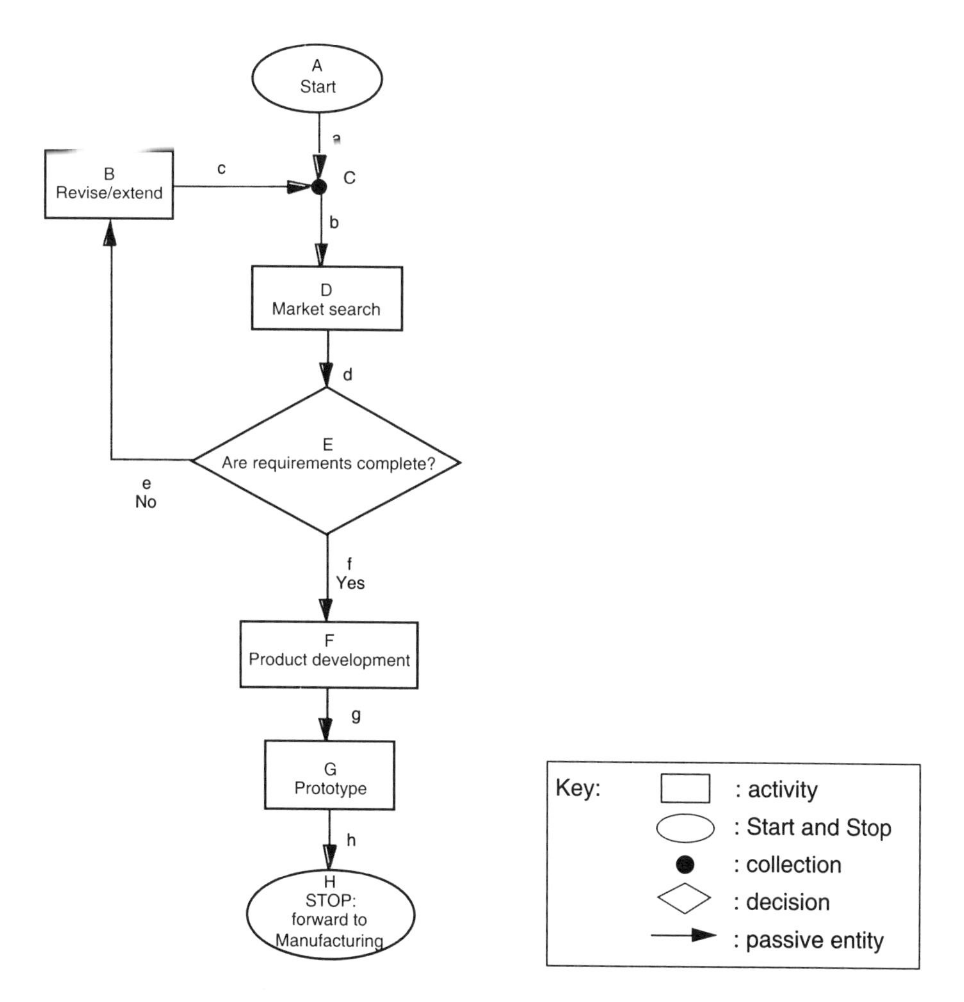

Figure 3.4(a): The flowchart of figure 3.4 as a labelled directed graph with key

USES OF GRAPHS

Directed graphs have been found extensive use in science, engineering, management, computing and other practical domains as helpful representations of the flow of information and materials. Where undirected graphs are used, direction is often implicit. This is the case in figure 3.6 where the graph is apparently undirected, but flow from left to right is tacitly assumed. Another example is the undirected organization chart where the person in charge is shown at the top, implicitly relying on people's interpretation of this to mean the line of command.

To enrich the language of graphs, one may use several kinds of nodal and arc or edge) symbols, thus distinguishing different sorts of real life entities.

- In the graph of figure 2.1, two sorts of nodal and three sorts of arc symbols were used whose meaning will be clarified in chapter 4.

- Figures 3.4, 3.5, 3.6 are graphs adopted from standard textbooks. They show languages in professional use: flowchart, block diagram representation of hardware systems, and graphical representation of decision analysis, respectively. All three graphs use one sort of arc and several kinds of nodes:
  - Figure 3.4 has four kinds of nodal symbols: ellipse, rectangle, diamond, and the unmarked node of confluence just below the Start node; in addition, there is an unmarked but labelled node at the exit. All but two of the arcs are unlabelled.
  - Figure 3.5 has two sorts of nodes: the rectangle and the unlabelled node marked by a blob. All arcs are unlabelled.
  - Figure 3.6 is a graph that might be found in many textbooks on finance and management. It has three kinds of nodes: some nodes are marked by rectangles, one is marked by a circle, and some are labelled, but are otherwise unmarked. All arcs are labelled, but labels are not unique. As we noted before, the *appearance* is that the graph is undirected: a set of nodes linked by arcs without arrows. However, the caption shows that the *intended meaning* contradicts this appearance. The graph seeks to show a decision tree: a sequence of decisions, starting from node 1 and proceeding from left to right to one of five conclusions (nodes 5 to 9). Once the decision maker is committed to a position shown in node 4 for example, only two possible conclusions are available: those at nodes 8 and 9, all others have been forfeited, there is no way back to nodes 1 and node 2. The undirected graph cannot show this.
- Figure 3.7 is a cautionary tale. It originates from official company documentation: the Quality Manual of a multinational corporation. There are four types of nodes and four types of arcs (including the bidirectional arc between nodes R and Q). All nodes are labelled but none of the arcs. The Manual includes an associated key, not shown here, which explains some of the nodal symbols, although not all; however, neither the key nor the associated text gives any indication about the meaning of the various sorts of arcs. The result is a diagram devoid of meaning, a waste of space.

MISUSES OF GRAPHS

The most common misuse of graphs is the *complete omission of the key*, or supply of an *incomplete key*. The are at least two explanations for the lack of a proper key.

The first explanation is laziness. Beware the ‘it’s obvious, they will know what I mean’ syndrome: it usually means ‘I am not sure what I mean, and I leave it to the recipient to struggle finding the hidden meaning and the missing information’.

The second explanation is that the formulator *tried* to provide a key and could not do so. Perhaps there was no single symbol that could identify what each type of node represented. Perhaps the arcs had multiple interpretations. Perhaps the inability to provide a key was a symptom of the concept behind the message being confused.

None of these reasons are acceptable. We must remember that graphs are a language for facilitating communication, not for confounding colleagues and confusing collaborators. The absence of a key, or the deficiency of the key, should alert the originator of the graph that the quality of representation is inadequate, and work is needed to put the matter right.

Another kind of misuse is the *inconsistency*: disobeying the rule given by the key. Examples of poor use of graphs include stating in a Quality Manual (!) that each node of a graph stands for an 'organizational unit' of the company, such as a department or a group, but immediately contradicting this statement by designating one of the nodes as 'Computer room', another as 'Matron's office', and yet another as 'Quality Manager'.

Figure 3.6 demonstrates a different sort of misuse, to which we have referred already: a directed graph masquerading as an undirected graph. The arrows are implicit, assuming the convention of contemporary Western culture where we read from left to right, and from the top of the page towards the bottom. There is no excuse for omitting the arrows from a directed graph, especially since the reading convention is not universal. (For example, Arabic and Hebrew script proceeds from right to left, Chinese script is vertical, and the classical boustrophedon script of the Greeks travels like a snake down the page, alternating left-to-right and right-to-left rows!)

FIRST SIGHT OF PRODUCT/PROCESS GRAPHS

Product/process graph – or P/p graph for short – is the name given to a special kind of directed graph: the graphical language used throughout most of this book. A P/p graph is a directed graph that designates products by arrows and processes by nodes. In its simplest form the graph has only one kind of node: the rectangular box, and one kind of arc: the continuous line. Figure 3.8 shows an example of such a graph, together with its key. Figure 2.1 is another, more elaborate example of a P/p graph, using different sorts of arrows to allow distinction among several types of products, and using various kinds of nodal symbols to indicate several types of processes.

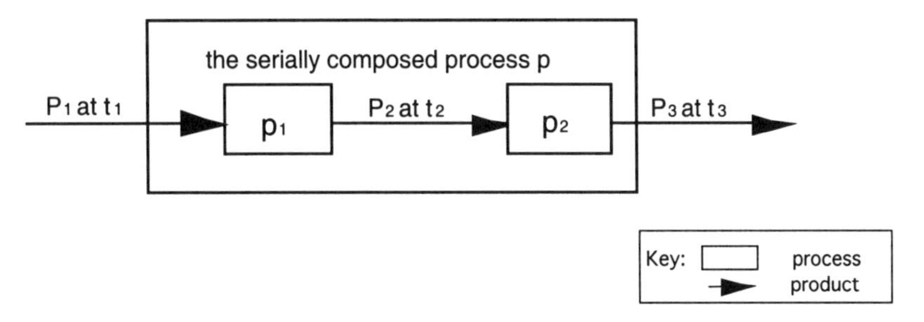

Figure 3.8: A simple P/p graph

Introducing the P/p graph as a language of system representation, together with its use in system documentation, design and quality assurance, will form most of the contents of this book. As we shall see in subsequent chapters, three versions of the P/p graph will be in use: the P/p *network*, the P/p *framework*, and the formal P/p *model*, each carrying more information than the previous.

3.10 Modelling

Some simple problems may be solved by trial and error: manipulation of the problematical referent in the hope of hitting on a solution that would relieve the adverse situation.

Example 3.21

Here is a true tragicomic story. We once employed a burly builder, let's call him Mr Brawn, who had little use for floorplans; instead, he devised the kitchens and bathrooms of houses by placing into position the various fitments, including the cast iron bath. A good natured man, he had no objection when the prospective owners wanted to vary the design: he simply moved the objects into new and new positions until everyone was satisfied. Not much later, Mr. Brawn suffered a heart attack and went to an early grave.

For the solution of most problems, trial and error is not a viable course of action: it is a costly, lengthy process of random meandering, leaving the outcome to chance.

The alternative is problem solving by deliberation and forethought: manipulation not of the referent itself but its *representation*. We define:

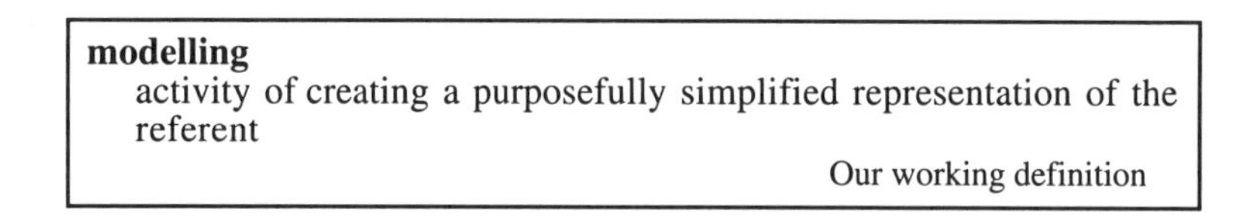

modelling
activity of creating a purposefully simplified representation of the referent

Our working definition

For the modelling activity to be meaningful, the representation must have a known referent. As a crude approximation, we may represent the modelling in a directed graph, such as figure 3.9.

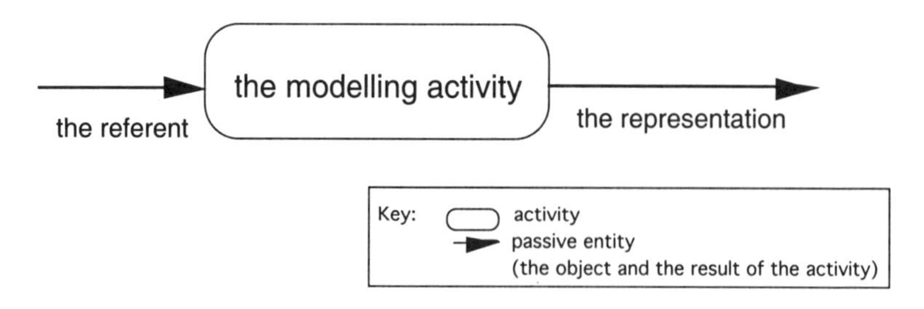

Figure 3.9: A representation of modelling

As the modelling activity maps the referent into a representation, it expresses in some suitable language the problem solver's observations of reality. If the language is formal and supports manipulation, the problem can be all but solved in the domain of the model; the remaining tasks are the realization and validation of the solution.

Reality is boundlessly complicated and admits to an infinite number of valid representations. Each representation can only preserve a few of the countless characteristics of the referent. To be of use to the problem solver in a particular situation, the modelling process must be *purposeful* and *selective*. Clarifying and articulating the purpose will guide the problem solver in identifying the relevant characteristics of the referent for the given situation, suppressing – or setting aside for later consideration – all others which would only cloud the issue and detract from the quality of the representation.

Example 3.21 revisited

The problematical referent is the bathroom of a house under construction, the prospective owner requiring a comfortable, well designed, well built, functional bathroom. The shape and dimensions of the bathroom are fixed, as are the position of the door and the window. The fitments (bath, toilet, wash basin, bidet) have been ordered, and they form part of the referent.

The problem is simple: find a suitable position for the fitments.

- *The modelling activity will comprise choosing the relevant features and a suitable language of representation. Many features of the referent are irrelevant from the viewpoint of the problem. Among these are the price of the fitments, the colour of the fitments, the finish of the walls, the height of the ceiling. The important features are the floorplan of the room and the 'footprint' of the fitments. A scaled-down graphical representation of the entities is the obvious answer: draw the floorplan of the bathroom; draw and cut out the footprints of the fitments. Ensure that all entities are to the same scale.*

- *Realization involves checking that the correct fitments are delivered, placing the fitments into the position shown in the plan, and plumbing them in.*

- *Validation amounts to inspecting the finished bathroom, assuring the adequacy of the workmanship of the realization, and checking the result against the owner's original requirements,.*

Note that quite a different representation would be used when choosing the fitments. Here the key parameters would include such features as price, delivery, colour, finish and possible guarantee of the taps.

Representations, models and formal models

In this chapter the term 'model' is used in its popular sense of representation. In the next chapter a distinction will be made between 'model' and 'formal model'. To qualify as a formal model, a representation must be expressed in a formal language and characterized not only by its well defined attributes but also by the *measure* of the value of each attribute. By contrast, representation (informal model) is a much wider notion: although a representation may include the measure of one or more attribute, this is not a general requirement.

3.11 Summary

This chapter explores key ideas of the preliminary phase of problem solving, among them:

- the *boundary* between the entity of interest and the rest of the real world,
- the significance of *definitions*,
- the need for properly defined *attributes*,
- the notion of *measures* as problem solving fundamentals,
- descriptive, predictive and prescriptive *representations,*
- *languages* in everyday and professional use, and the language of *graphs,* among them Product/process (P/p) graphs,
- *modelling,* an essential tool in problem solving.

3.12 Exercises

Exercise 3.1

Write a brief note to yourself on a situation which annoys you, such as receiving junk mail by post or on a fax line, being frequently left at the bus stop in the rain by an inattentive bus driver, having to work with an unhelpful or thoughtless colleague, or whatever.

(i) What could you consider the referent in the situation?
(ii) What is the boundary of the referent?
(iii) What are the key attributes?

Exercise 3.2

Explain the difference between designation and representation.
Provide an example from your own experience.

Exercise 3.3

The text of the chapter points out that ambiguity arises when two or more concepts are designated with the same term.

Is the converse – when two or more terms designate the same concept – also ambiguity?

Exercise 3.4

Example 3.4 quotes the definition in the Oxford Dictionary of the word 'sanction', to demonstrate ambiguity. The term is used in the Quality Manual of your company.

Describe a situation when this could cause difficulties. What steps would you recommend to eliminate the ambiguity?

Exercise 3.5

Two definitions of the term 'censor' are quoted below:

(i) The Oxford Dictionary:
"An official whose duty is to inspect books, journals, plays, etc., to secure that they shall contain nothing immoral, heretical, offensive, or injurious to the State."

(ii) Student Society leaflet:
"An officious busybody; a self-appointed killjoy who puts himself/herself above others, and claims the right to interfere with every citizen's right to free speech and self expression."

Compare and evaluate the definitions, adopt one or the other, or, if neither meets your quality criteria, propose a third. You might wish to consult other dictionaries.

Exercise 3.6

What are the three types of representation needed by systems professionals? From your experience, provide an example for each.

Classify the following according to your types:

(i) a railway timetable,
(ii) the tag of washing instructions in your shirt,
(iii) your sister's (daughter's) school report,
(iv) your holiday snapshot.

Exercise 3.7

What concept do the two following phrases share:

(i) stipulative definition,
(ii) stipulative semantics?

Exercise 3.8

"The *outer* or *acromial* extremity, directed outward and forward, presents a small flattened, oval facet, which looks obliquely downward, for articulation with the acromion process of the scapula."

Who is communicating with whom? What is the passage about? What gave you the clue? Can you honestly say that you understand this passage? If not, why not? If understanding would be essential, how would you go about obtaining the necessary information?

Exercise 3.9

Why is figure 3.7 not a graph?

Exercise 3.10

The ISO 8402 (1994) quality standard gives the following definitions:

product
the result of activities or processes,

process
set of interrelated resources and activities which transform inputs into outputs.

The Draft ISO/FDIS 9000:2000 gives slightly modified definitions:

product
: the result of a process,

process
: set of interrelated or interacting activities which transforms inputs into outputs.

Using directed graphs, or otherwise, analyze these definitions, and comment on their quality.

Exercise 3.11

Mark the following as either true (T), partially true (PT) or false (F).

(i) At least two parties are necessary for communication to take place. ___
(ii) A message is a written communication. ___
(iii) Ambiguity is caused by a careless attitude. ___
(iv) A common culture guarantees mutual understanding. ___
(v) All experts have the necessary communication skills to explain their subject ___

In each case, justify your answer to someone who disagrees with you.

Exercise 3.12

Give several ways of representing the concept behind the word 'stack', commencing with entry from a general purpose dictionary such as the Shorter Oxford Dictionary. Use representations suitable for:

(i) a farmer,
(ii) a waiter,
(iii) a programmer,
(iv) another specific purpose, specified by yourself.

Exercise 3.13

(i) Can you envisage measurement:
- without comparison?
- without numbers?

Explain your answer.

(ii) Market data is being collected at the supermarket checkout, and representatives are canvassing the opinion of customers about certain product lines.

Are they carrying out measurement? Explain your answer.

Exercise 3.14

The document "The universe of engineering – a UK perspective", issued by the Royal Academy of Engineering in June 2000, defines 'engineering', and offers a graphical representation of the 'engineering process'. The representation is reproduced in figure 3.10. Comment on the figure.

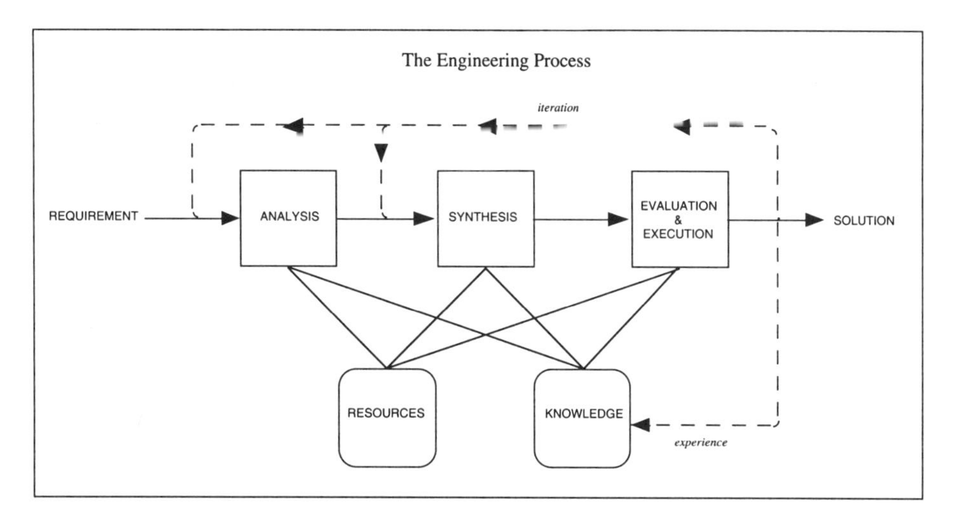

Figure 3.10: A graphical representation of the 'engineering process'

Exercise 3.15

As a famous architect, you have been commissioned to build a new cathedral. Suggest several types of model you need:

(i) to obtain the contract,
(ii) to show how the building will blend into the environment,
(iii) to satisfy the building regulators that the building will not collapse,
(iv) to give instructions to the builders,
(v) to cost the building.

Which of these were available to the mediaeval cathedral constructors? What happened?

3.13 Footnotes and References

1 At the time of writing ISO 9000 series of standards is under revision. We refer to the definitions of the final draft of the new standard (ISO/FDIS 9000:2000), or, when appropriate, to ISO 8402, the Vocabulary of the currently valid ISO 9000 Quality Standard.

2 Although recently the term 'bandwidth' has entered into everyday language, for example when referring to the speed of accessing multi-media on the internet.

3 The ISO/FDIS 9000:2000 draft standard defines 'characteristic' as "distinguishing feature". We don't adopt this usage, since it adds little to the lexical meaning of 'characteristic'.

4 The full definition will be given in chapter 8.

5 See e.g. "Words and Phrases Legally Defined", ed. J B Saunders, Butterworth, 1969.

6 M Bunge: "Scientific Research". Springer Verlag: "Studies in the foundations, methodology and philosophy of science", 1967.

Chapter 4 Systems concepts

It is to be expected that complex problems will demand complex solutions: elaborate arrangements requiring substantial resources, long-standing commitments, extensive multidisciplinary collaboration. Embarking on the solution of a complex problem is a risky undertaking: a potential source of confusion, delay, and financial loss, and at times even calamity. To avoid this, the successful problem solver uses a repertoire of general concepts, complemented by systems concepts and methods as guides for managing complexity.

This chapter gives the background to the systems approach pursued in this book, and presents systems concepts and methods for dealing with complex systems.

4.1 Systems approach – a historical perspective

"The systems approach is one of the methodological trends in modern science that was born of the need to find a way out of the crisis in scientific knowledge at the turn of the century" [1]. The aim of early workers in the field was to formulate new guiding principles of scientific investigation in all fields, including sociology and biology, the natural sciences and psychology, economics and linguistics. Later, interest extended to the investigation of complexity, and development of principles for solving complex problems.

A method of classical science was attempting to *reduce* complexity by dividing the whole into its 'atomic' parts, great importance being attached to finding and studying the smallest component. Nevertheless, some thinkers realized that the reductionist approach is inadequate in itself, and, while studying the parts, sought also to identify the specific properties of the *whole.*

Two other early approaches were important: *functionalism,* concentrating on the operation of the whole and formalizing this mathematically, and *structuralism* [2], exploring the organization of the entity. Structuralists recognized that the whole can have many different parts, and postulated the importance of penetrating this variety by *interdisciplinary study.*

The *systems approach* originated in biology [3] and modern technology (in particular, cybernetics) [4]. Initially research in the two fields had little or no contact, but common fundamental principles soon became apparent, leading to a unified methodological trend by the middle of the century [5]. Among the main achievements of Ross Ashby, Bertalanffy and other pioneers [6] is that they saw wholeness and structure not as opposites but two sides of the *same* coin. They recognized the role of interdisciplinary cooperation in the solution of complex problems, and the need to transfer principles and concepts from one sphere to another.

By the late 1960s, several directions of development were noticeable:

- development of *mathematical foundations* for the theories of general systems [7],
- extension of systems concepts *and methods* through their application in control and other scientifically well established fields [8],
- application of systems concepts (without methods!) to *newer fields*, such as psychology [9] or social science [10].

Not all of these developments produced unqualified success. Uncompromizingly rigorous, the 1960s vintage of new mathematics of systems proved to be incomprehensible to most, and almost inapplicable in practice. A more practical systems approach, advocated by far sighted engineers, such as Harold Chestnut, later degenerated into control theory: a specialist field of engineering. Lacking methods, social scientists could *talk* about systems, but not apply their ideas effectively in their field.

In the 1970s and 1980s, a particular version of systems approach was introduced to management, based on some of the earlier ideas and diagrammatic explanations [11]. During the same period, the underlying concepts were developed further, strengthening the methodological foundations [12], and linking them with the theories of computing [13]. Computing professionals continue to take an interest in a systems approach [14], but the scope is usually confined to computer systems.

We build on the foundations and experience of systems theorists and systems thinkers, and contribute to these the methods of Product/process (P/p) modelling and model-based measurement [15], [16]. Our contributions make available the advantages of a disciplined systems approach to problem solvers, problem owners, and other concerned and interested members of the community. The concepts, principles and a notation are accessible to all, and those mathematically inclined can also avail themselves of rigorous methods of systems analysis, design and verification. All can progress to understanding complex systems, both existing and planned, and manage them according to sound engineering principles.

4.2 Classifying referents or representations?

We know now that systems concepts can be used in seemingly limitless ways, for describing simple situations, prescribing standards, predicting outcomes, explaining the operation of complicated organizations, focusing on parts of a whole, or viewing the whole in a wider context. Systems concepts can relate to individuals or groups, tangible objects such as a piece of fruit or a motorcar, or abstract items, such as an idea, a social group, or a theory. To cover such variety, we adopt the notion of 'referent', based on the ISO 8402 standard's definition of 'entity', introduced in Chapter 3.

Active and passive referents

In life, everything changes. The change may be slow, such as a plant growing or paint drying, or fast, such as an athlete in action, an explosion, or a flash of lightning. No matter how fast or how imperceptibly slow the *activity*, we can track its progress by a sequence of observations at appropriate intervals throughout the *time period* of interest.

The active and dynamically changing referent may also be viewed as a *passive* entity. We can arrest the change by taking a snapshot at a *time instant* of the athlete, the plant or the flash of lightning; or else we may compress the change into a single representation of the complete process of events. The entire nighttime traffic in the Champs Elisée can be displayed in a single picture by time-exposure photography. The year's activity of a business is summed in the annual report.

Although in practice we frequently distinguish between active and passive referents, the distinction is not inherent in the entity itself: it is merely one of viewpoint and representation. Depending on our interest, and on the resolution of the passage of time, the same real life entity may be viewed as active or passive, static or dynamic.

Example 4.1

A message may be regarded as a passive entity to be processed or sent, or as an activity: a sequence of sounds or characters being delivered over a period of time.

Consider someone buying a factory. What is the referent: the real estate – the buildings, the equipment and other resources –, or the going concern – the manufacturing, business and other processes? By the former view the factory is a passive, by the latter it is an active entity.

Regarding a referent as an active entity loosely corresponds to considering it as 'activity or process' in the ISO 8402 definition quoted in Exercise 3.10. Conversely, taking it as a passive entity on which the process acts corresponds to 'product' in ISO 8402. The ISO/FDIS 9000:2000 standard, also quoted in Exercise 3.10, makes the same distinction between active and passive entity, product and process.

To the problem solver, clear differentiation between product and process is essential. The distinction is explained more fully later in this chapter, and the terms will be defined formally in Part 2 of the book. Meanwhile the terms 'product' and 'process', being convenient, will be used on the basis of the above explanation.

Referents as wholes and as structures

In real life all entities, no matter how small, are made up of parts. Unlike physicists, systems thinkers don't search for the ultimate building elements of the universe; instead, they adopt the philosophy that any entity of the real world can be viewed in two ways:

- as a *whole*, in the context of its environment, and
- as a *structure*: a composition of parts which are systems in their own right, and can be viewed either as wholes or as structures ultimately composed of 'atomic' parts which are *deemed* indivisible.

As in case of active and passive referents, here too the distinction is not an inherent characteristic of the referent, but one of viewpoint. The referent is the same no matter which view we take; hence, as far as the environment and the external observer are concerned, the 'holistic' and the 'structural' view should yield the same information about the characteristics of the entity. As far as the problem solver is concerned, however, there are major differences between the two views.

- The holistic approach characterizes the referent *directly*, by measures of its interrelated externally observable attributes. The internal composition of the referent is unknown, or is deemed irrelevant. In systems terminology this is called the *black box* (or *holistic*) representation of the referent.
- In the structural approach, the referent is characterized *indirectly*. It is decomposed into its interrelated parts, and reference is made to the black box representation of each of the component parts. In addition, the structural interrelations among the parts are defined, such that it should be possible to deduce the black box representation of the referent.

We now need to define:

interrelation
a way of grouping two or more entities in accord with some common concept
Our working definition

and

well defined interrelation
an interrelation which is meaningful, grounded and free of circularity
Our working definition

In many problem solving situations, such as when one adopts a strategy of procuring a ready-made entity as a solution to the problem, there is no need for the structural approach: the black box representation is sufficient. However, in most cases it is not feasible to obtain a black box representation directly, and the problem solver must resort to a structural representation. Even so, the obligation to find the black box representation remains; thus, the structural representation should be viewed as a step towards gaining the holistic, black box characteristics of the referent.

When opting for a structural representation containing n number of parts, the problem solver exchanges a single problem – the direct representation of the referent as a black box – for a fistful of problems, (n+2) to be precise:

- n tasks of defining the *black box* representation of each *of the n parts* of the referent,
- a further task of defining of defining the *structure* into which the n parts fit: the way in which the parts are composed to form the referent as a whole,

- the final task of *deducing* the black box representation: calculating the measure of each attribute of the referent from the structural interrelation of the parts and black box representation of the parts.

On this basis, should one conclude that structural representations are to be avoided in favour of black box representation?

Most complex problems call for customized or design–and–make solutions, requiring both black box and structural representation. The problem solver must understand both, should know how to choose between them, and how to use both of them effectively.

Whichever representation is used, it must provide a *coherent* picture of the referent. All the attributes in the black box representation, and all the parts in the structural representation, must belong to the *same referent*, and characterize it *at the same time*. We shall return to the notion of coherence later, and will define it in greater detail.

4.3 Referent as a black box

As we noted earlier, reality is boundlessly complicated, and any entity has an infinity of attributes. When representing the entity as a whole, we must be selective, choosing only those features, which are essential for the given purpose, suppressing all features that are secondary or irrelevant. Selectivity is the problem solver's friend: it allows attention to be focussed on the key attributes of the referent. Selective representation amounts to controlling complexity: keeping to a minimum the number of 'dimensions' of the problem and the 'size' of the 'problem space'.

These ideas need further explanation, and we shall return to them in subsequent chapters; meanwhile we concentrate here on defining:

> **black box**
> representation of the referent as a set of interrelated attribute values
>
> Our working definition

Note that the term 'black box' denotes the concept of wholeness: the representation of the referent as an indivisible entity; it has no graphical connotation.

Examples 4.2

Should the referent be a man, we would assume – unless otherwise stated – that the usual attributes and attribute values apply: the normal number of arms and legs, eyes, some aspects of character associated with maleness. These are the customary attributes to members of the class 'man' to which our particular referent belongs. When seeking to point out a particular man in the crowd, we might add the adjectival phrase 'in the yellow pullover', and we have offered another attribute (colour of clothing) and attribute value (yellow) worthy of mention.

Carefully chosen collections of attributes are required to characterize uniquely each person on the company payroll, or to identify from forensic evidence a criminal beyond reasonable doubt.

The details entered in a passport are those attributes which, the State decrees, are sufficient to represent the holder of that passport. Number of arms, legs etc. are not considered relevant attributes unless they deviate from the norm, whereupon it would be entered under 'distinguishing features'. Attributes of lesser or no consequence are omitted; these would not only create unnecessary clutter, but may be harmful, distracting attention from the key attributes.

When entering into a contract, such as buying a ready made object, ordering a bespoke item, or engaging a service, it is in the interest of both purchaser and supplier to select and document the full range of relevant attributes and attribute values. This information, usually complemented by the target date of delivery, constitutes the *customer's specification* of the entity against which the attributes of the finished item will be compared. The specification naturally reflects the viewpoint of the user, focusing on the externally observable black box attributes of the entity, rather than on the way in which it is internally constructed. However, structural characteristics might also be included in the customer's specification for guidance, or for marketing/public relations purposes, such as when describing stationery as being made of *recycled paper*, specifying that chocolates are *hand made*, referring to a radio set as *transistor*, describing poultry as *corn fed*, etc.

Example 4.3

The matrix below is the catalogue description of a doormat, showing key attributes and their values. The matrix is also printed on a label attached to the mat, offering the purchaser an opportunity to test an individual item against the description.

Attribute	Value
Length	230 cm
Width	170 cm
Edges	bound
Backing	Latex non-slip
Material	sisal

Example 4.4

The first two columns of the matrix below are published in the manufacturer's catalogue description of office shelving. With one exception, the validity of the attribute values cannot be ascertained by objective observation and measurement. The third column of the matrix lists some of the queries of the potential purchaser.

Attribute	Value	Customer's queries
Assembly	Easy	For whom?
Adaptation	Easy	For whom?
Freestanding	Yes	Generally accepted definition
Quality	Tested	Define quality; what is it tested for? how was it tested?
Durability	Tested	How long is projected life? For what type of usage?

Remember that the black box representation must be coherent, and must be given in measurable terms, such that its validity could be established by objective testing. Remember also that the measures need not be numerical. As we know, many attributes might be adequately characterized by qualitative measures, but it is essential that the attributes should be properly defined, the scale of the measures should be given, and, within the limits of tolerance, repeated measurements should yield the same result.

We shall see later in this chapter how one would use the two aspects of time mentioned in chapter 3 (real time and elapsed time) for distinguishing between the black box representation of active and passive entities, to be characterized as 'processes' and 'products'.

4.4 Referent as structure

It is not always easy, and in many cases it may not even be possible, directly to characterize the entity as a whole. Where some of the black box attributes of the referent are not readily observable, a task of the problem solving process would be to determine them by analysis and deduction. In these cases one would build up a black box picture of the referent from knowledge of its *structure*. We define:

> **structure (or structural representation)**
> representation of the referent as a set of interrelated components, each component being represented by a unique label
> Our working definition

Examples 4.5

A house is a structure of communicating rooms. Its suitability as a home for a family of five will depend not only on the number and size of rooms but also on the arrangement of rooms in relation to each other.

A wall is a structure of bricks. The stability of the wall will be strongly influenced by the interrelation among the bricks, an overlapping structure being favoured compared with laying bricks face to face, rather than on top of one-another.

A year of a university course is a structure of lectures, assignments, tutorials and examinations, linked by a schedule. The effectiveness of the education depends on the quality of each activity viewed on its own, as well as on the scheduling. For example, lectures should be preferably given in the mornings rather than in the afternoon, tutorials should follow lectures closely to consolidate the material taught, theoretical and practical classes on a given topic should be closely related in time, etc.

A hierarchically organized company is a structure of divisions, each division being a structure of departments, each department a structure of groups, each group a structure of sections, each section a structure of individuals. Reorganization of the copany, for example into a matrix structure, may not affect the attributes of the individuals immediately, and yet the performance of the organization may change significantly.

A computer application program is a structure of coordinated modules. The performance of the program may be changed considerably by keeping the modules invariant but rearranging the order in which they are executed.

An evening meal is a sequence of courses: soup, main dish, desert, coffee, the 'courses' forming the parts, 'sequence' being the interrelation. The main dish of the evening meal is a further structure: the combination of meat course, potatoes and two vegetables. The meat course itself will be made up as a structure of ingredients, in accord with the recipe. The evening meal is an element of the diet for the day, other elements being breakfast and lunch, in a sequence.

Let us draw attention to the most important issues regarding structural representations of a referent.

Set or system?

When describing the referent as a structure, it is not sufficient to characterize the component parts. Without knowing the *interrelations* that hold them together, the parts remain a *set*: a disjoint collection of entities, a meaningless heap. The structural interrelation specifies *how* the parts are linked together to form the entity as a whole.

Black box or structure?

Black box and structure are different forms for representing the *same referent.* Reality does not depend on representation: whatever the representation of a given referent, the whole will display the *same attributes* towards the environment. The difference is that the black box representation defines the attributes of the whole *directly,* whereas the structural representation defines them *indirectly*, through the attributes of the parts and the interrelations among the parts.

Black box characteristics are always necessary: these define the referent for its environment. Structural representation can be seen as auxiliary: supplementary to the black box representation, or a stepping stone towards obtaining the black box representation.

Constructivity

Indirect characterization means that, in theory, it should be possible to deduce by calculation the black box attributes of the system as a whole from the black box attributes of its parts and the structural interrelationships among the parts. This is trivially true in some cases, such as the cost of a complete meal being the sum of the cost of the various courses of the meal, 'sum' being the interrelationship among the part-costs to form the cost of the whole. If all the required attributes of the whole can be deduced from the structure then we say that the system is *constructively defined.* We shall return to the concept of constructivity in later chapters. Here it is sufficient to define the concept, and note that constructivity relies on the representation of the structure in a mathematical model.

> **constructivity**
> the attribute of a structural representation that its interrelations are well defined, its atomic components are characterized as black boxes, and it is possible to derive from it the black box representation of the referent
>
> Our working definition

Where constructivity does not obtain, there may be several reasons:

- some information may be missing (one or more key attribute of the parts may not be given, the structure may not be adequately defined),
- the characterization of the parts may be inconsistent (the mathematical models of the parts may be incompatible, such as some electronic components being modelled as analogue, and others as digital),
- the theoretical foundations of the subject may not be sufficiently mature, hence a mathematical model may not be available.

Since black box representation is needed in all professional practice, engineering and science demand knowledge appropriate to constructivity. Other fields, where currently soft methodology is the norm, should work towards the goal of formality and constructivity; otherwise they may only describe a set rather than a system, or structure, but not the black box representation of the referent.

A further comment on black box and structure

Let us assume that we have a constructive structural representation of our referent. This gives *more information* about the referent than the black box representation.

- As we have seen, it defines, indirectly, the black box characteristics of the referent. This means that, from the structure and the black box definition of parts, we can deduce mathematically the black box characteristics of the whole. Engineers refer to this as *analysis.*
- The same black box characteristics might be obtained from many different structures. The structural representation identifies one of these. It defines a particular choice of parts and a specific configuration of the selected parts: one of many possible *designs* that delivers the black box characteristics.

4.5 Graphical representation of structure

As we have seen in chapter 3, graphs are helpful representations. Used in a disciplined manner, they are powerful aids to understanding complex systems, and can show many different aspects of them. The graph may be *undirected* or *directed.*

- *Undirected graphs* can represent the structure of objects as well as the composition of ideas. For example, they can show the construction of a washing machine built of subassemblies and component parts, the structure of a company, the composition of concepts forming a theory, the underground network of a city with all its lines and their junctions, the roadmap of a country with the totality of possible routes.
- *Directed graphs* may be used to show, for example, flow of information and flow of material through a referent, represented as an active entity. They can display a specific route through a structure of many possible routes on a map, the connection of a particular customer to the mains distribution network of public utilities such as gas or electrical power, the progression of the assembly process along a production line, or the operations performed on information from the source of the message to its destination. They may take several forms, among them flowcharts – a type of directed graph in wide general use.

In view of their value in problem solving, directed graphs are employed extensively throughout this book. Here we describe three kinds of directed graphs, in order of increasing precision and information content: *(i) networks, (ii) frameworks* and *(iii) (formal) models* [17]. All three are purposefully simplified representations of complicated reality.

- Frameworks inherit all the characteristics of networks, with additional features.
- Formal models inherit all the characteristics of frameworks (and hence of networks), with additional features.

As all representations, networks, frameworks and formal models may be used:

- to *describe* an existing referent,
- to *prescribe* standards and norms which a referent must satisfy for it to be classed acceptable,
- to *predict* the characteristics of a future referent.

Graphs as networks

Networks are directed graph representations of their referent, showing the flow of activity within the network, as well as the interaction between the referent and its environment by inputs and outputs.

We define:

network
structure of a referent or a class of referents as a *labelled, connected, directed* graph with one or more inputs and one or more outputs, such that there is at least one path linking each input to at least one of the outputs, and each output is accessible from at least one of the inputs
Our working definition

This definition uses some terms already defined, as well as the terms:

input
passive entity representing the effect of the environment on the referent
Our working definition

and

output
passive entity representing the effect of the referent on the environment
Our working definition

In a network:

- each node and each arc is uniquely identified,
- each arc has an arrow indicating direction,
- no part of the graph is disjoint: there is at least one arc linking each input and output to the rest of the graph,
- there are at least two arcs linking each *internal* node to the rest of the graph.

Networks characterize a structure in terms of two kinds of features:

the *elements* contained in the structure, and

the *interrelations* (interconnections, interactions) among the elements.

The person devising the representation can choose to represent the elements as nodes of the graph and the arcs as the interrelations, or the other way around. The meaning of the arcs and nodes must be explained, either in words or by a graphical *key*.

Example 4.6

Figure 4.1 is a network, showing the construction of the apparatus A in terms of different types of components. As the figure shows, A is made up of component types B, C and D, B in turn is made up of E-type parts, and C requires part types E and D. The network gives no indication at all about the number of parts of each type necessary for constructing the apparatus. Such a graph is also called a 'resource dependency network': for achieving A, resource types B, C, D, E are all required.

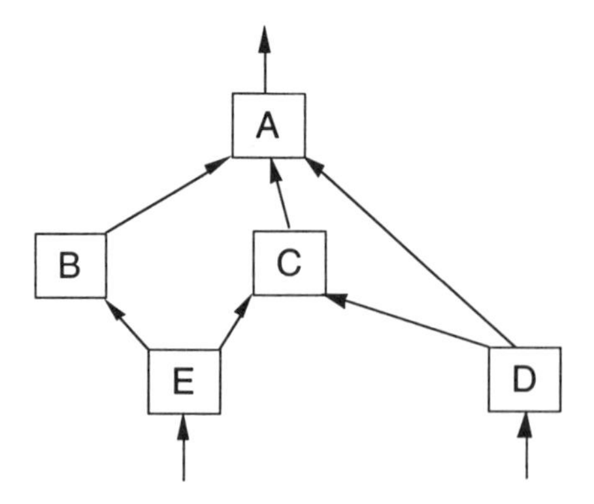

Figure 4.1: Network showing use of components in an apparatus A (arcs are not labelled; key to be drawn up by the reader as exercise)

Example 4.7

Figure 4.2 is a directed graph: the usual representation of computer circuits (finite automata). Arcs show state transitions, with arc labels identifying inputs (I) and outputs (O), and nodes showing states. The reader is invited to decide why the graph is not a network.

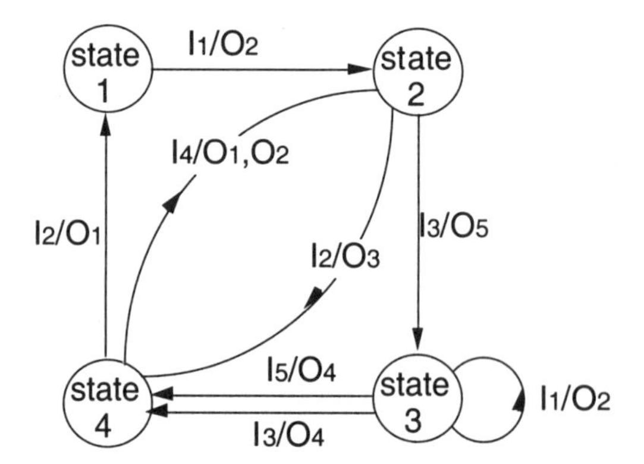

Figure 4.2: Directed graph representing a finite automaton (key in text)

Example 4.8

Figure 4.3 is taken from the Quality Manual of a major multinational organization. The figure is an undirected graph, sometimes referred to as an 'organogram', representing the top management levels of the organization. It is implied (although not stated explicitly in the Manual) that the nearer the node is to the top of the page, the higher the position of the individual in the organization. Note therefore that, although the graph appears to be undirected, direction is implied by the position of the nodes on the page. As seen in chapter 3, this kind of implicit representation of meaning can lead to confusion, and should be avoided.

As an exercise, the reader might show how the graph can be turned into a network. (Identify inputs and outputs and draw up the key of the graph showing the meaning of boxes and arrows. Then reverse the arrows, draw up the corresponding key, and satisfy yourself that the new graph is also a network.)

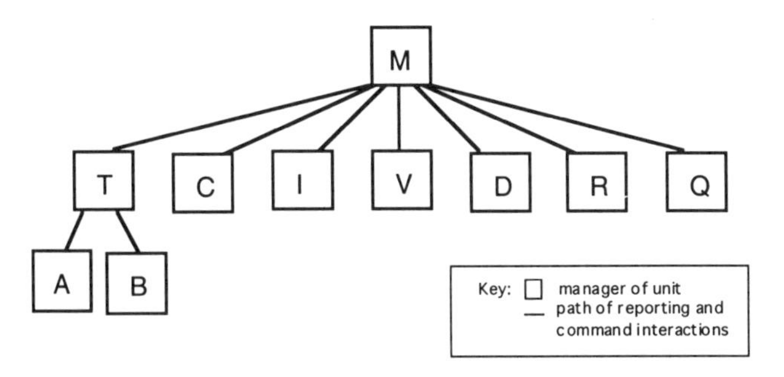

Figure 4.3: Undirected graph showing the 'organogram' of an organization

A-TYPE AND B-TYPE NETWORKS

When using networks for representing flow, we distinguish between active entities and passive entities. Passive entities are inputs, initiating the operation of active entities, and outputs emerging from active entities. Active entities perform operations on inputs, and generate passive entities as their outputs. We define:

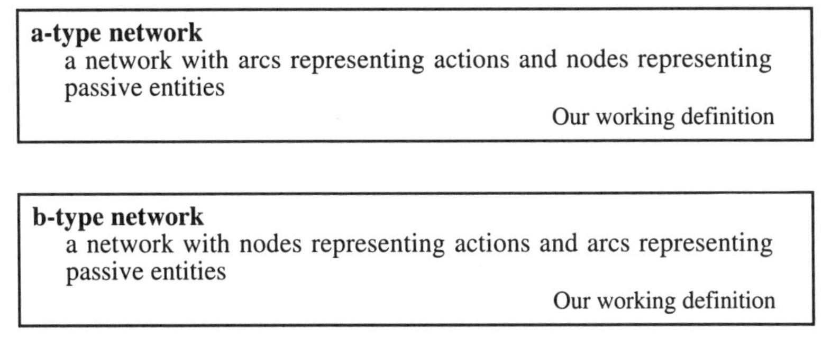

a-type network
a network with arcs representing actions and nodes representing passive entities
Our working definition

b-type network
a network with nodes representing actions and arcs representing passive entities
Our working definition

In use, b-type networks afford greater flexibility, and in our further discussions we focus attention on these.

Example 4.9
The networks below carry the same information in a-type and in b-type representations.

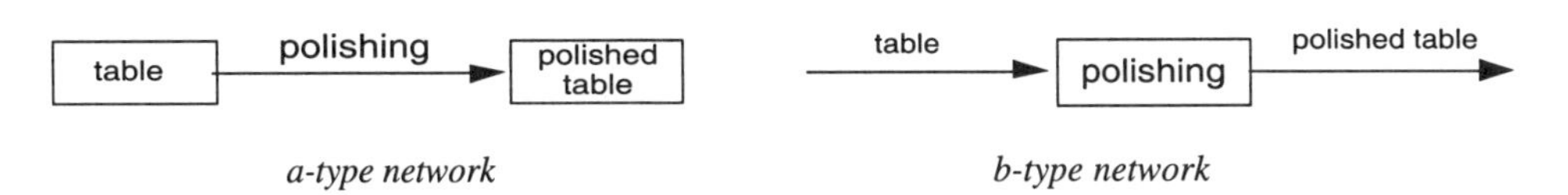

Figure 4.4: Representing the same information in a-type and b-type network form (key in text)

A comment

Here we must mention a technicality. Recall the definition of 'graph', given in chapter 3 as 'a finite set of arcs that connect pairs of nodes'. By this definition, the a-type network is a graph: it has two nodes ('table' and 'polished table'), connected by the arc labelled 'polishing'. Strictly speaking, the b-type network would only be a graph if both ends of each of its two arcs would be anchored in a node, as in figure 4.4(a). The two nodes are 'phantoms', playing a purely formal role, and having no referent in reality. In this book we use b-type graphs throughout, omitting phantom nodes.

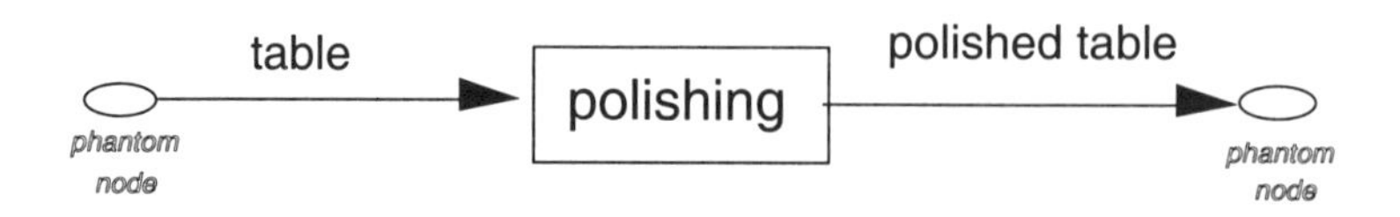

Figure 4.4(a): b-type network of figure 4.4, with phantom nodes shown explicitly (key in text)

Example 4.10

Figure 4.5 is a b-type network, representing the activity of assembling and polishing a table. Both 'assembling' and 'polishing' are activities, but 'assembling' has several inputs, and will be called a 'cactus' [18]. The 'polishing' activity has a single input and a single output.

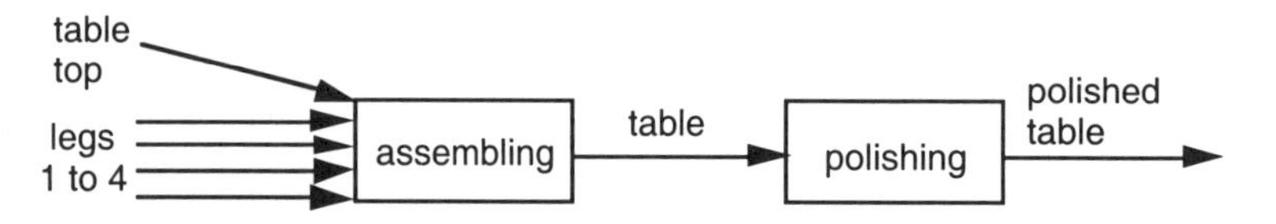

Figure 4.5: A b-type network (key described in text)

We reserve the term 'process' for representing an active entity as a single input/single output node. 'Cactus' is the name given to representation of active entities by nodes with more than one input and/or more than one output. The first box in figure 4.5 is a cactus, the second a process.

Let us summarize. Networks are labelled, directed, connected graphs with a key explaining the meaning of symbols. They have one or more input and one or more output, there is at least one path connecting each input to one of the outputs, and along each path passive and active entities alternate (see e.g. figures 2.1 and 3.8). Networks allow freedom for the problem solver:

- to choose an *a-type* or a *b-type* representation,
- in case of b-type representation, to show activities as *processes* or as *cactuses,* and incorporate both in the same graph, if required,
- to include in the representation any *attribute definition* and any *attribute measure* which may be at hand (or none at all).

Graphs as frameworks

We define:

> **framework**
> b-type network where active and passive entities are characterized by well defined attributes
>
> Our working definition

The characteristics of frameworks are summed up as follows:

- A framework is a *b-type network*, showing activities in boxes and passive entities in arcs.
- In a framework, all activities are represented as *processes,* cactuses having been resolved to a structure of products and processes.
- A framework has *at least one process.* Each process has exactly one passive entity as its input and generates exactly one passive entity as its output.
- In a framework, all nodal elements (processes) and all arcs (products) correspond to entities characterized by a *set of selected attributes,* each item of the set having an *attribute definition* of adequate quality. Since the definitions would clutter up the graph, this information is usually provided in a separate *attribute table* and *glossary* for each nodal element and each arc element of the framework.

The framework allows freedom for the problem solver to include any *attribute measure* that may be to hand, but this information is optional.

Graphs as formal models

'Model' is a popular word in everyday usage, to which systems terminology assigns a particular meaning. We define:

> **model – popular usage**
> a purposefully simplified representation of the referent which preserves its selected characteristics
>
> Our working definition

Models may take several forms. Scientists and engineers are particularly interested in *formal models* since these offer unambiguous representation, afford constructivity, and support secure reasoning about the referent. We define:

> **formal model ('model' for short)**
> black box with all attributes given as measures, or a constructively defined structure
>
> Our working definition

and

> **graph model**
> framework where all active and passive entities are characterized by their formal model
>
> Our working definition

As in case of frameworks, for practical purposes information about attribute definitions and measures is seldom included in the graph itself, but is usually given in an attached table.

Example 4.11

Fred is getting married and goes to the tailor for a new suit. The tailor measures Fred's chest, waist and the length of his arms and legs. These measurements are entered on a record which bears the date and Fred's name. The record is the tailor's model of Fred's suit.

The tailor is not only concerned with modelling the suit: he must also assure payment. For this, he needs to model Fred himself. For the tailor's purposes, Fred's measurements, together with his address, telephone number and credit details are an adequate model of him as a customer.

We could extend our example beyond all bounds. Fred would also be modelled by his employer, his doctor, the building society providing his mortgage, the travel agent where he books the honeymoon, not to mention his best man. Each would have a different purpose, and each would arrive at a different model. The modeller has the responsibility to choose which aspects of Fred's countless characteristics to represent and which notation to use that best serves the given purpose.

Product/process (P/p) graphs

The distinction between network, framework and (graph) model will be valuable when discussing and using Product/process (P/p) graphs in chapter 5, and again in Part 2 and Part 3 of the book. We shall encounter three types of P/p graphs: P/p networks, P/p frameworks and P/p (graph) models. These will be progressively defined: P/p frameworks inherit the characteristics of P/p networks, and P/p models inherit the characteristics of P/p frameworks, each with additional defining features.

4.6 Graphs as black box representations

Graphs are primarily structural representations; nevertheless, it is necessary to consider their use in portraying black boxes, not only because the structure is built of these, but also because the black box representation is of primary interest to the customer. As we have noted before, in many applications the structural representation is but an intermediate step: the main purpose is to obtain the model of the referent as a whole. We have also seen that the structural representation needs the black box representation of each part of the structure, together with the constructively defined interrelations among the parts.

Consider the b-type graph in figure 4.4. This is a black box representation of the table polishing activity, and, depending on the information attached to the graph, the representation may be a network, a framework or a model. In practice the table polishing activity may be a composite of several subactivities, such as cleaning the surface, oiling it, polishing it with emery paper, oiling it again, polishing it with a rough cloth, etc., etc. The detailed structure of the process would have several arcs and nodes, each node showing a subactivity. The black box representation in figure 4.4 suppresses these into a single composite activity, showing it as a node wedged between two arcs.

Simple as they are, black box representations such as the b-type graph of figure 4.4 can be simplified even further.

Assume that we are not interested in the activity itself, only in its output: the polished table. Now we have a to represent in a b-type graph a passive referent on its own: a single arc, wedged between two phantom nodes, usually not shown explicitly (figure 4.4(b)). If this degenerate graph is properly endowed with attribute definitions, measures and time signature, it amounts to a model; otherwise it is a framework or a mere network.

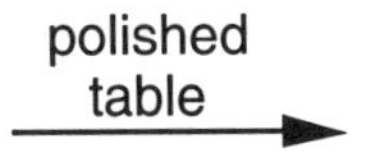

Figure 4.4(b): A degenerate b-type network representing a single passive entity

Example 4.12

As a simple example, consider one of our great Group of Companies listed in the electrical and electronics sector of the Stock Exchange.

The Annual Report of the Group shows three constituent companies, with details of locations, employees, product lines, profits and trends of each. In assessing the value of the shares of the Group, one must aggregate attributes of all three constituent companies, and combine them in a suitable way. The simplistic aggregate is by addition, the more sophisticated will take into account interaction between the groups and the advantages of a single overall Board with its stated Mission.

4.7 Systems

A system is a distinct entity, a unified whole with its own identity. The concept of 'system' is universal: anything can be regarded as a *system* and represented by a coherent collection of its *attributes*, or as a collection of its related *parts*. Systems may be as enormous as galaxies, as minute as atoms, as simple as a brick wall, or as complex as a human cell.

The system of interest may *exist*, irrespective of the observer, just as the solar system exists. A system may be *planned* and built purposefully and constructed deliberately and rapidly, or the man-made system may evolve gradually, as the road system of a continent. A system may *evolve* naturally over a long time period, like the nervous system of a species, the food chain in a forest, or human society. The parts of the system may be systems in their own right, on many levels. For example, a school, which is part of the education system of a district, is composed of functional and physical units, such as the various classes, classrooms, staircases, the central facilities such as the library and the refectory, each part being further decomposed, for instance a class to its members: human beings, themselves multilevel complex systems. Systems may be tangible as a skyscraper or abstract as the theory of electromagnetism.

System hierarchy

We know that a system may be represented by the attributes it displays to its environment, or characterized as a constructively composed collection of parts, the parts may themselves being composed of other parts, forming a multilevel hierarchy. A system can also be seen as one of many components of another system. Thus, the hierarchy extends upwards – towards the universe – and downwards – towards the ultimate subatomic components of our world.

For practical purposes this seemingly infinite two-way hierarchical expansion must be halted, and the problem solver must take responsibility for declaring the limits.

- The *upper limit* of the hierarchy will be the black box representation of the referent. At this level the referent acts in interaction with its environment, as observed at the boundary between the two.
- The *lower limit* is formed by the set of components of the structure for which ready-made solutions are deemed available.

Defining 'system' and interpreting the definition

Our definition of 'system' is simple, and since it is based on the notion of 'entity', it is quite general:

system
a set of interrelated entities

Our working definition

The definition can be interpreted for any kind of assembly of entities, and for both black box and structural representation.

- When the system is defined as a structure, the elements are the *component parts* whose interrelations yield the system as a whole.
- When the system is viewed as a whole, then the elements are the coherent set of *attribute values* which, viewed together, represent the system [19].

Hard systems, soft systems, system spectrum

In popular parlance, systems have been referred to as either 'hard' or 'soft'. It is assumed that attributes of the former are well defined, measurable, and the interrelationships between their components are rigorously characterized, whereas not all features of the latter are measurable, many are weakly defined, and some may not even be clearly understood. Examples of hard systems arise in engineering, mathematics and the natural sciences, whereas examples for soft systems include political, religious, societal, economic systems, as well as some systems of the life sciences – fields of science dealing with sophisticated referents for which no 'hard' theories are available.

Not all systems lend themselves easily to such hard/soft categorization. 'Cognitive' systems could comprise knowledge of facts, understanding of concepts and theories, consciously held ideas such as a structure of beliefs, a network of subconscious notions, prejudices, preconceptions, attitudes.

Modelling real life entities as systems yields a veritable spectrum: some attributes admit to hard and measurable definition, some are less precisely expressed, and some may not be expressed at all, being locked in someone's mind. Cognitive systems and hard systems lie at the extremes of our *system spectrum* shown in figure 4.6.

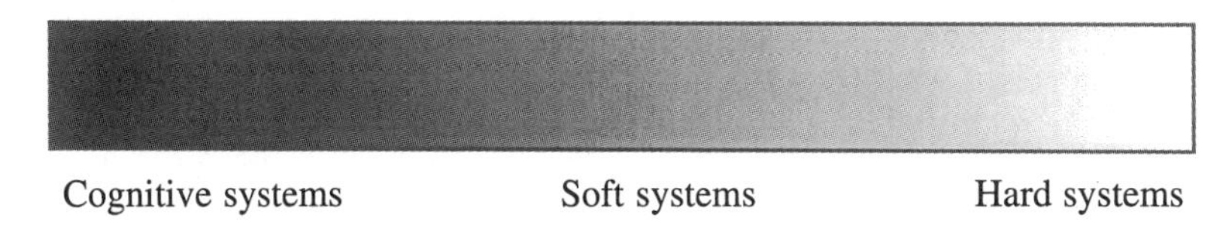

Cognitive systems Soft systems Hard systems

Figure 4.6: The 'system spectrum'

The modeller chooses the referent and the attributes of interest.

- If all chosen attributes are defined and measurable, the system is *hard.*
- If all attributes are defined in the mind of the modeller but are not expressed explicitly then the system is *cognitive.*
- If all attributes are defined and explicitly expressed but only some are measurable then the system occupies some intermediate position in the spectrum of figure 4.6. Such systems are called *soft.*
- If some or all of the attributes of interest are undefined then we have no system at all.

4.8 Products and processes

When discussing definitions in chapter 3, we observed that if the definition of some entity A is *circular*, entity A being defined in terms of entity B and B in terms of A, nothing is defined. Similarly, if entity A is defined in terms of entity C and D which themselves are undefined then the definition of A is *open-ended,* and nothing is defined. At the same time, the definitions of a scientifically well founded domain must be clearly *related;* otherwise they fail to provide coherent foundations.

The distinction between product and process is fundamental for the problem solver. In the following, we offer definitions for product and process that are coherent, do not suffer from the flaws of circularity or open-endedness, and rely on *measurement* for drawing clear distinction between 'product' and 'process'.

- The notion of both 'product' and 'process' is based on the concept of 'system'.
- 'Product' is defined autonomously, without reference to the process that brought it about.
- The definition of 'process' relies on the definition of 'product'.
- Distinction between 'product' and 'process' is based on the measure of time duration, 'product' being instantaneous (having zero duration) and 'process' having finite non-zero duration.

4.9 Products as systems

As we know, attribute values are liable to change. The slim young man with the blond hair may in time become the fat man with gray hair, or even the man with no hair. Hair colour may be a suitable distinguishing attribute in the short or medium term, but is not a suitable attribute for characterizing a man over his entire lifetime. As the car's tires wear out and the lubricating oil is used up, at a given time instant the previously safe car will become unsafe. The combination of attribute values of an entity from different time instances is likely to be misleading, or even meaningless. Similarly, it may be misleading to combine the attribute values of different individuals: they may not amount to the characteristics of any of them.

When we choose to represent a referent as an instantaneous entity, we need to define the *time instant at* which the representation is valid. A further stipulation is that all the attribute measures are features of the *same referent*. When those two provisos as mandatory interrelations are obeyed then we can represent the entity as a product.

Defining 'product'

Bearing in mind that 'system' is a set of interrelated entities, we give a simplified definition of 'product' as a black box [20]:

product
representation of a passive referent by an attribute set containing no time duration attribute (or a time duration attribute whose value is zero), and an interrelation set that includes
(1) the measure of the real time instant at which all attributes are valid, and
(2) the coattribute interrelation asserting that all attributes characterize the same referent

Our working definition

Classifying products

Hard, soft and cognitive (cloud) products will be treated formally in Part 2. Here just enough elaboration is added to enable their introduction into P/p modelling.

HARD PRODUCTS

A hard product is a formal model: a system comprising measures of a set of properly defined attributes chosen for a purpose, together with a set of relationships binding those attributes to a single referent at a single time instant. There are three kinds of hard products: *material* products, *information* products and *hybrids*.

Material products

Attributes of these products arise from the real world, and are measured in the base or derived units of SI [21].

Information products

These products have measurable attributes but the units of measurement – except for time – are not SI units. For some purposes, such as manufacture and transportation, a useful model of a computer disk would be a material model: its weight, thickness, diameter and the like. However, for most users such details would be irrelevant; more important would be the number of bits of information the disk stores. An article on the finance page of a newspaper may be modelled as a material product, with attributes such as the number of square inches covered and the weight of the ink. The reader of the article would consider other attributes more important, such as the number of entries in the stock exchange listing, and the date and time at which the list was compiled.

Hybrid products

These contain both SI and information-attribute measures. We exclude these from further consideration here.

EXPRESSED (SOFT) PRODUCTS

A soft product is a representation, but not a model. It carries some but not all of the characteristics of models: the representation is valid, it is instantaneous (the time signature is specified), and the coattribute interrelation applies. Attributes may be properly defined, more weakly described, or merely represented in some observable form. Measures might be given for some attributes, but not for all. Expressed products may also be referred to as 'soft' or 'conceptual' products.

UNEXPRESSED (COGNITIVE) PRODUCTS

A cognitive product is an unstated notion: it exists only in the mind of an individual. Since such products have no representation, their validity cannot be ascertained. Nevertheless, cognitive products share with other types of products the property of having a time stamp, and they also posses a version of the coattribute relation: attributes of the referent are held in the mind of the same individual. A cognitive product may also be referred to as a 'cloud product'.

BASIC PRODUCTS

Collectively, hard, expressed or unexpressed products are 'basic products'. Table 4.1 summarizes their classification. The table also shows a graphical representation used for each type of basic product in P/p modelling.

Class of basic product	Representation	Graphical Symbol
Material – 'hard' product	Interrelated attributes, measured in SI units, or measurably defined	——►
Information – 'hard' product	Interrelated attributes, measured in non-SI units, or measurably defined	——►
Expressed – conceptual or 'soft' product	Statement in some language (verbal, pictorial, material, etc.)	– – –►
Unexpressed – cognitive product or 'cloud' product	Internal to an individual, has no representation, is inaccessible to others	~~~►

Table 4.1: Classification and representation of products

COMPOSITE PRODUCTS

Hard and soft basic products can appear in combinations, and these are called 'composite products'. Composition is a mental rather than physical process: the composite product retains the characteristics of its constituents.

COMPOSING PRODUCTS

One may suggest an 'algebra' of product composition over hard and soft products as follows:

Hard product *composed with* Hard product = Hard product,

Hard product *composed with* Expressed product = Expressed product,

Expressed product *composed with* Expressed product = Expressed product.

Generalizing this, in any composition of products the type of the composite will be that of the leftmost constituent in the spectrum of figure 4.6. Thus,

Unexpressed product *composed with* any type of product = Unexpressed product.

Product structure

A product P may be regarded as 'atomic' – a single indivisible black box entity –, or as structures of subproducts P_1, P_2, ..., P_n. In turn, each subproduct may be atomic, or may itself be composed of subproducts, such that the structure of product P is a 'multilevel hierarchy', finally resolving to atomic component products. A tree conveniently represents such a hierarchy. Trees are an important class of directed graphs which we shall meet repeatedly. We define:

tree

a directed graph without cycles which has exactly one node called the 'root' with no incoming arc, (or no outgoing arc), every other node has exactly one incoming (outgoing) arc, and every node other than the root is on a path from (to) the root
NOTE: nodes without outgoing (incoming) arcs are called leaves.

Based on D F Stanat, D F McAlister:
Discrete mathematics in computer science, Prentice Hall, 1977

Example 4.13

Observe the two directed graphs emerging in Example 4.8. Check that they conform to the definition of 'tree'. The root of the tree can represent the complete organization as a product, for example the assets, liabilities and performance indices of the company on the day shown as the date of the annual report. The data in the company's annual report would be based on the annual reports of its departments and their subdivisions.

Recall that products represent a referent as instantaneous. This means that the same time stamp must be valid for all elements of the structure, from the product at the root to its ultimate atomic components.

4.10 Processes as systems

Let us remind ourselves again that, over time, attribute values of all entities are liable to change. The change may differ:

- It may be *intentional,* such as *growing* tomatoes, *baking* bread, *polishing* a table, or else *unintentional,* like *fading* of textiles, or *wearout* of a machine part.
- It may be *natural,* like *aging*, or *artificial,* like *developing* photographic film.
- Some changes, such as a chemical reaction causing explosion, are so *fast* that they can only be recognized by their effect. Others are so *slow,* such as the leaning of the tower of Pisa, that over a short time period they may be regarded as negligible.

What all these processes have in common is that they are associated with *passage of time*. Processes are means by which an input product – an instantaneous system –

is converted into an output product – another instantaneous system. The process has a single input product and a single output product, and the duration of the process is the time *distance* between the time *instances* of its input and output products.

Defining 'process'

Like products, processes are systems, and their representation as a black box is characterized by an interrelated collection of attributes. The simplified black box definition is as follows [21]:

process

representation of an active referent as a *set of interrelated attributes,* transforming an input product into an output product over a period of time.

The attributes characterizing a process must include:

- the *duration*: the time period of the operation, given as a constant or as a variable,
- the *domain* of valid input products,
- the *transfer function*: a function over the measures of the attributes of the input product to produce the measures of the attributes of the output product,
- *status*: whether the process is free or busy – open for business or not – at the time of arrival of the input product,
- the designation of the *owner* of the process, if man-made,
- the *cost* incurred by executing the process, if the process is man-made,

and the interrelation set includes two mandatory elements:

- the *coattribute* interrelation: the assertion that all attributes characterize the same referent.
- the *time stamp*: the real time instant at which the input product arrives, or when the attributes are valid.

In case of man-made processes other attributes might be usefully specified, among them

- the *agent*: the means by which the process is executed.

Our working definition

Attributes

DURATION

Since all real life processes take time, non-zero duration distinguishes processes from products. Unlike processes, products are instantaneous.

DOMAIN

Every process has its limitations. The meat grinder will function correctly regardless of its 'input' being a piece of chicken, beef, lamb, or even a piece of bread, but will break down when fed with slabs of metal. The car will run well on the specified grade of petrol, but will falter on the wrong sort, and will give up altogether when filled up with water. Cotton fabrics may do well in the washing machine, but woolen garments may shrink, and silk shirts may disintegrate altogether. Entry requirements for academic courses and training programmes are specified in the interest of candidates and the teaching institutions.

Defining the domain of acceptable inputs is necessary for the protection of products and processes alike.

FUNCTION (OR 'TRANSFER FUNCTION')

The transfer function defines the relationship between the attributes of the incoming product and the attributes of the outgoing product. As we shall discuss in more detail later, processes may:

- *change* the *value* of attributes,
- *generate new* attributes,
- *suppress* attributes,
- perform some combinations of the above.

A class of process which is of particular interest is the *null* (or *storage* or *waiting)* process whose transfer function is the identity function: the attribute set of the input product is identical to that of the output. The process is essential in assuring synchronization of two or more products that may have been created at different times, but must be input to a process simultaneously. It is an idealized representation of storage without deterioration, or transportation of goods without damage. Because of its frequent use, the waiting process has a specific symbol, shown in figure 4.7. P_1 and P_2 in that figure have identical attribute sets and differ only in their time stamps.

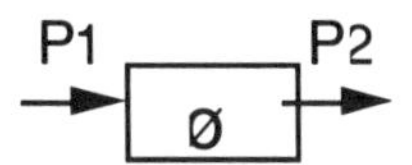

Figure 4.7: The waiting process (b-type process, key as before)

STATUS

At the instant of arrival of the input product, a process must be free, rather than being engaged in an operation on a previous input. The status parameter is a binary number: its value is 'free' when the process is free, and is set to 'busy' for the period in which the process is unable to accept a new input.

PROCESS OWNER

Remember the famous notice in the Oval Office during President Truman's era, which read: "The buck stops here". It is, or should be, a fundamental principle of management and quality assurance that responsibility must be shouldered by the person on the top, and cannot be *divided.* The owner of a process must always be an individual (not a committee, not a group).

Most processes are too complex for the owner to execute all the tasks single-handedly, especially as the process owner may not always be the most competent person to perform each one of them. Practicality demands that tasks be *delegated*, and different owners may be appointed for various subprocesses, while the owner retains overall responsibility. The Government Minister or the Managing Director who claims at the time of trouble that he/she "did not know" of the circumstances that led to the calamity is either the truthful but incompetent owner of the processes of which he/she is in charge, or is dishonest.

OTHER PROCESS ATTRIBUTES

An important process attribute, not included in the mandatory list but frequently stipulated, is the *agent*: the human operator, team, department or apparatus selected by the process owner to perform the task of carrying out the process.

In a given situation other process attributes may be relevant, such as the location of the agent executing the process, and the cost associated with the execution.

A COMMENT ON THE VALUE OF PROCESS ATTRIBUTES

In many cases it is sufficient to assume that the attributes of the process remain constant during the process. If not, then the process is to be resolved into a structure of subprocesses rather than being characterized as a black box, with each constituent subprocess being given as a black box, having constant attributes over its duration.

Interrelationships

MANDATORY INTERRELATIONSHIPS

To ensure coherence, the complete attribute sets of processes are interrelated by two mandatory relationships: the *time stamp* that defines the instant at which the process attributes are valid, and the *coattribute* interrelation which binds all the stated attributes to a single referent. Since process attributes are constant during execution, the time stamp may mark the real time instant at the beginning of the process, or any time instant during execution.

NON-MANDATORY INTERRELATIONSHIPS

If the attributes of a process are not independent (the attribute set contains redundancy) then interrelationships will exist which link the attributes. Such interrelationships may be deliberately defined over the complete set or subsets of attributes, the redundancy being used for error detection.

Example 4.14

An example of such a nonmandatory interrelation would be between agent and duration. If the process agent is stipulated as an attribute and the agent executing the process is a computer then the duration of an elaborate calculation will be markedly less that if the agent is a human calculator.

A further example occurs in chapter 8 where the process attribute 'financial effectiveness' is a relation over the transfer function and duration attributes of the process.

Classifying processes

Similarly to products, we discriminate between *hard, soft* and *'cloud'* processes. Unlike 'product' whose definition is autonomous, 'process' is defined with reference to its input and output products. This gives us the key to the classification of processes. Since processes convert input products to output products, one may classify processes by the nature of the conversion from each class of basic input product to all other such classes. There are four basic product types, and this gives 4 x 4 = 16 possible conversions. Table 4.2 shows these and their graphical symbols, together with some examples of their occurrence.

SYMBOLIC REPRESENTATION OF PROCESS CLASSES – A NOTE

The sixteen process classes are quite distinct. It would be too simplistic to represent them all with the same graphical symbol, whereas it would be too clumsy to use 16 different symbols to distinguish them. The symbolic representation in table 4.2 is a compromise, using only three different symbols. Subclassification in accord with Table 4.2 is implicit in their input and output symbols

- All *four types of hard processes* are designated by solid rectangles. Their symbol is a solid rectangle, and their common characteristic is that they all operate on hard products and deliver hard products. They deal with the subject matter of traditional science and engineering.
- The common characteristic of the *four kinds of soft processes* of the table is that they convert soft products into hard products. All soft processes move the product *to the right* of the product spectrum, making the output product *harder* than the input, characterizing it by measures, increasing its information content. The graphical symbol of these process types is a round-cornered rectangle.
- The *remaining eight processes* are called 'cloud processes'. Five of them actually *soften* product representations, moving the output *to the left* of the scale compared with the input. All are designated by the graphical symbol of a cloud, and their sub-classification.

Example 4.15

The examples below are taken from the world of business with an analysis of input, output and consequential process classes.

Simultaneous translation:
Expressed-to-Unexpressed cloud process, followed by
Unexpressed-to–Expressed cloud process.

Major management functions may be perceived as:
Planning – a soft process (Information composed with Expressed) input and Information output,
Organizing– a hard process, Information-to-Information,
Motivating– a cloud process, Expressed-to-Unexpressed,

Controlling– a hard process, hybrid (Material composed with Information) input, Information output.

Decision making

hard process, Information-to-Information,
or else (Soft composed with Information)-to-Information,
or, in less mature organizations, Cloud process Information-to- Expressed.

Quality assuring

hard process, Information-to-Information,
or (Material composed with Information)-to-Information,
or, in less mature organizations, Cloud process, Information-to-Expressed.

I/P product class	O/P product class	Class of process	Example	Symbol
Material	Material	M-to-M, Hard process	Manufacture	
Material	Information	M-to-I, Hard process	Modelling, measurement	
Material	Expressed (soft)	M-to-E, Cloud (cognitive) process	Expressing value judgement	
Material	Unexpressed (Cognitive)	M-to-U, Cloud process	Forming opinions about material item	
Information	Material	I-to-M, Hard process	Implementing strategy, introducing methodology	
Information	Information	I-to-I, Hard process	Information processing, Decision support, Expert systems	
Information	Expressed (soft)	I-to-E, Cloud process	Theory formation, heuristic	
Information	Unexpressed (cognitive)	I-to-U, Cloud process	Forming opinions in response to information received	
Expressed (soft)	Material	E-to-M Soft process	Craft Heuristics	
Expressed (soft)	Information	E-to-I, Soft process	Modelling, measurement	
Expressed (soft)	Expressed (soft)	E-to-E, Cloud process	Philosophizing, verbal reasoning, reasoning without adequate models	
Expressed (soft)	Unexpressed (cognitive)	E-to-U, Cloud process	Forming opinions in response to pictures seen, reading, learning	
Unexpressed (cognitive)	Material	U-to-M Soft process	Artistic creativity	
Unexpressed (cognitive)	Information	U-to-I Soft process	Inventive creativity	
Unexpressed (cognitive)	Expressed (soft)	U-to-E, Cloud process	Articulation, communication	
Unexpressed (cognitive)	Unexpressed (cognitive)	U-to-U, Cloud process	Learning, understanding (to test the efficacy of the learning process, the ideas must first be 'externalized' by representing them as Soft products)	

Table 4.2: Classification of processes by their input and output products

4.11 Systems methodologies

We adopt the definition:

> **methodology**
> definition of the aims, concepts, methods, principles of reasoning and domain of discourse of some discipline, and the relationships between its subdisciplines
> Based on The Fontana Dictionary of Modern Thought, Fontana Press, 1988

In this book we are specifically concerned with *systems methodologies*: those which deal with the representation, analysis, design, development and management of systems. In view of the universal nature of the concept of 'system', the domain of discourse of a systems methodology is virtually unlimited.

Nowadays it is customary to divide systems methodologies into two classes: 'hard' and 'soft' systems methodologies. To understand the difference, we must briefly examine how scientific disciplines develop.

Science or common sense?

All science, with the possible exception of the abstract science of pure mathematics, grows out of common knowledge. Common sense is the generalization of repeated observations. The shepherd's weather predictions and the old wives' tales of housekeeping and child rearing offered useful guides to the events and activities of everyday life, but in time limitations became apparent: common sense failed to explain many important phenomena. It proved inadequate even for posing some questions, let alone for answering them. To make progress, observations had to be systematized, such that results could be enriched, refined and classified. In due course some classes of common knowledge became enforced and codified into scientific theories, others were superseded or rejected altogether.

Critical and methodical review of common knowledge marks the start of scientific development. As science develops further, it does not only provide explanations for phenomena observable by the layman: it *widens* our domain of observation. Scientific instruments extend our senses. Special techniques enable us to make many accurate observations and record them accurately by means of measurement. The results allow us to perceive causal links between previously unrelated entities. Based on these, scientific conjectures are formed, to be tested and validated by measurement, and hypotheses become established as scientific theories. The domain of scientific theories far exceeds the scope of common sense. Whereas common sense had to be based on scattered bits of knowledge, science inspires, and facilitates, search for a coherent 'world view'.

The 'scientific method'

Scientific development never stops. Each new problem challenges the body of available knowledge, calling for the creation and objective testing of new scientific hypotheses. Each successful solution is of specific value to the 'owner' of the problem, but it is also of general value to the scientific community. The scientist consolidates the newly acquired knowledge, combining it with the old, forming the extended body of knowledge available for solving the *next* problem. Where the new knowledge proves inconsistent with old theories, those theories are refined, revised or rejected, to be replaced by new, more powerful theories. These in turn are tested in the light of experience. Scientific progress continues, distilling practical results into theory, and integrating the new knowledge with the old. The progression is termed the 'scientific method'.

From common sense to science

Bunge [22] explains that common knowledge can progress in three ways:

- It can develop into *technical knowledge*: specialized but not scientific knowledge; this characterizes the arts and crafts.
- It can evolve into *protoscience*: embryonic science, characterized by careful observation and experimentation.
- It can turn into *pseudoscience*: a body of beliefs and practices whose exponents wish to pass it for science, naively or maliciously, although it lacks the 'self-correction' mechanisms of the scientific method, and is alien to the methods, practices and body of knowledge of science.

Science can make good use of the data of protoscience, and the practices of technical knowledge, and these serve as routes to scientific development. Pseudoscience holds potential dangers for the public. Its dogmatic nature makes its teachings virtually inaccessible to scientific enquiry.

Hard and soft systems methodologies

A *hard systems methodology* has firm foundations in science. Such a methodology uses mathematical models for representing its referents, and is supported by a universal measurement system. Its concepts and principles are codified in well established and verifiable formal theories, and it can rely on the power of mathematics to reason about its entities securely. Thus, systems methodologies inspire confidence, and decisions based on them are reliable.

To balance these advantages, the scope of hard systems methodologies is relatively narrow: it effectively confines itself to hard products and hard processes, relying as it does on the definition of entities by their attributes and their measures, and on mathematical structures that interconnect them. Hard systems methodologies are used in the mature sciences, such as the natural sciences of physics and chemistry, in some areas of the information sciences, and in engineering disciplines that are based on these sciences. At the present state of scientific development, many important problems involving developing disciplines such as psychology, software engineering and management fall beyond the scope of hard systems methodologies.

Soft systems methodologies have seemingly unlimited domain, and can deal with problems of developing fields where there is no universally accepted general theory, and an internationally agreed measurement system is not yet in place. Such methodologies are still in the stage of protoscience: they lack definition of basic concepts, and have no mathematical formalisms of representation and reasoning. However, they can deal with all types of products and processes, hard, soft or cognitive. They offer help in eliciting from the human brain unexpressed feelings, intuitions, prejudices and attitudes, bring these out in language, and subject them to unbiased examination. To this end, soft system methodologies use aids such as unstructured discussions, rich pictures and influence diagrams. A soft systems methodology, where successful, will lead to the identification of attributes of interest in the system, and will guide a gradual progression towards the application of hard system methods.

Lacking formal theoretical basis for the time being, the professional working in these fields must at least institute clear and agreed attribute definitions, develop and test qualitative theories, and promote the use of measurement as far as possible. This way representation can be put on a factual basis early in the problem solving process, facilitating analysis, supporting reasoning and rational decision making, guarding against errors, and paving the way to development of the discipline. The obligation for practitioners in the field is to keep an open mind, be aware of the limitations of the soft system methodology, and to guard against falling into the trap of pseudoscience.

Cooperation is in the interest of users of both hard and soft systems methodologies. To widen their scope, researchers of hard system methodologies must track the development of soft system methodologies; conversely, those dealing with soft systems must learn from those working in hard domain. The two should interface wherever the opportunity arises, the collaboration promoting progression towards hard system methodologies over an ever widening problem domain. One of the main aims of this book is to assist this collaboration.

Systems methodology and process classification

Figure 4.8 gives a summary of process classification, and shows the interface between soft and hard systems methodology. This figure indicates where the two systems methodologies apply in process representation.

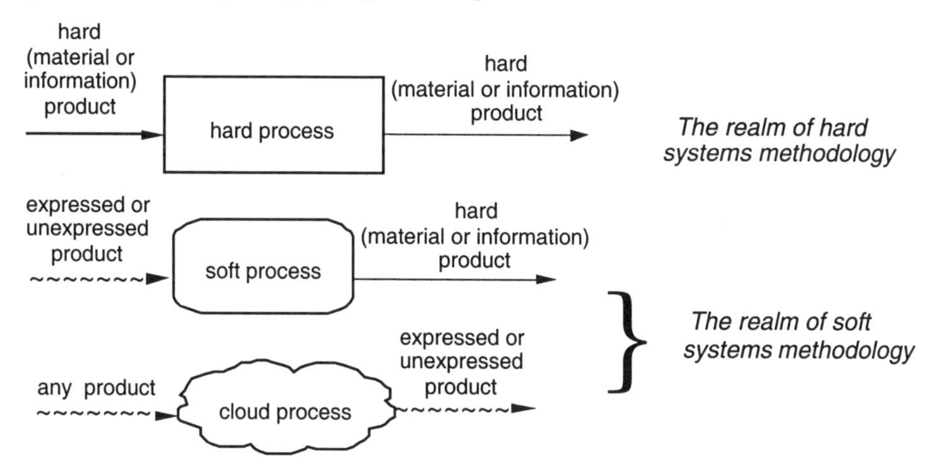

Figure 4.8: Overview of classification of processes. (All arcs and nodes labelled)

It has been said that the aims of the soft systems methodology are to obtain 'understanding' [23]. Understanding is a necessary aim for hard and soft methodologies alike, but for the problem solver it is not enough. Understanding is internal to the individual. The insight gained through understanding should be recorded and expressed in some formal document that characterizes the referent and its environment by measurable attributes. Such representation can then form the input to the problem solving process. Hard and soft methodologies are, therefore, different but not incompatible; both may need to be harnessed in the effort to solve a particular problem.

Extending the benefits of hard systems methodologies

Hard system approaches allow us:

- to *specify* systems,
- to *analyze* systems,
- to *design and develop* systems with confidence,
- to *verify* designs and *validate* implementations, providing objective proof of quality,
- to *derive* many important attributes,
- to *detect* errors and shortcomings,
- to *diagnose* the cause of such deficiencies, and
- to *protect* the system against certain kinds of adversities.

In some fields of engineering the hard systems approach goes even further:

- it facilitates *prediction* of the performance of some future system, and
- it allows the *synthesis* of new systems from extant component parts, giving reasonable confidence of the whole meeting prescribed standards and satisfying set specifications.

Although soft approaches afford valuable insights, their methods cannot provide comparable advantages.

The questions posed here are:

- Can we introduce hard system methods into the realm of soft systems, so as to improve the success rate of such systems?
- How far can we go?

A concomitant question is:

- Are we justified in so doing?

It would be foolhardy to force the use of a hard systems methodology to problem areas where it cannot apply, such as emotional problems and artistry. The many examples of inappropriate use of hard methods include a recent competition for young opera singers. The judges devised a quantitative scale for comparing the artistic merit of the performances. The result was an absurdity.

We submit that the answer to the justification question is: – Yes, we are not only *justified* in introducing hard systems methods, but *obliged* to do so by professional ethics, if they promote understanding of the problem, and enhance the quality of the solution!

4.12 P/p methodology

We can now identify the subject of this book: the methodology for products and processes, or P/p methodology for short. Using our definition of 'methodology', we may define:

> **P/p methodology**
> definition of the aims, concepts, methods, principles of reasoning and domain of discourse of products and processes as systems, and the relationships between its subdisciplines of systems theory, communications, modelling, measurement and quality management.

The definition includes two lists. The first list (aims, concepts, methods, principles of reasoning and domain of discourse) characterizes the P/p methodology as a whole. The second list (systems theory, communications, modelling, measurement and quality management) refers to the constituent parts of the methodology. Here we discuss each item of each list in turn, together with their interrelationships.

Aims, concepts, methods, principles of reasoning and domain of discourse

AIMS

The aim of the P/p methodology is to assist in the formulation and effective solution of complex problems, regardless of the field from which they may arise, and irrespective of the specialist disciplines needed for supplying the solution.

CONCEPTS

The concepts of the P/p methodology arise from systems theory, engineering, and advanced ideas of quality management.

DOMAIN OF DISCOURSE

The domain of discourse is universal. Entities of interest may be small tangible objects or large physical systems, alive or inanimate. They may also be hardware or software, individual ideas or complete theories, or any mixture of these.

METHODS AND PRINCIPLES OF REASONING

The principles of reasoning are rational, based on a systems philosophy, with firm roots in engineering. The methodology relies on the characterization of all entities, problems and solutions by means of measurement. The measures might arise from direct observation or intuition, they might represent facts or express value judgements, or else they might be derived theoretically from some specialist contribution. The concepts, models and methods of the P/p methodology unify such contributions.

Recognizing that many aspects of problems and problem solving situations do not lend themselves to 'hard' scientific methods of representation and reasoning, the P/p methodology allows for 'soft' representations, and can even deal with ideas *prior* to their being expressed. It is a particular strength of the P/p methodology that its concepts and methods integrate the 'hard' and 'soft' elements.

Communications, systems theory, modelling, measurement and quality management

The subdisciplines of communications, systems theory, modelling, measurement and quality management are integrated to form a coherent methodology.

COMMUNICATIONS

Practitioners of every discipline need to communicate with each other with precision and without ambiguity. The P/p methodology identifies a frugal collection of simple general concepts, defining these carefully and – as far as possible – unambiguously. It then uses these simple general concepts repeatedly and systematically in any context: for explaining complicated notions, reasoning about them, stating, analyzing and solving problems relating to them, and accounting for their solution to the problem owner and all others who might be interested.

The general applicability of the natural, graphical and mathematical languages used by the P/p methodology suits the generality of its concepts. The language of the P/p methodology facilitates its use in solving problems arising from any field, and allows interface between the P/p methodology and any specialist discipline which might be required in obtaining the solution.

SYSTEMS THEORY

The P/p methodology arises from the philosophy of general systems and the scientific theories of *cybernetics* and general *systems theory*. The P/p methodology builds on these foundations, coordinating their underlying ideas and preserving such universal notions as *system*, *black box*, *structure* and *hierarchy*.

As one of its major contributions, the P/p methodology starts from a generic representation of systems, from which the model of *any* entity is derived. The formal generic representation is presented in Part 2.

Based on the generic representation, any entity may be modelled either as a black box – a system whose elements are the attributes of the entity as a whole –, or as a structure – a system whose elements are the component parts of the entity. The black box representation is *autonomous*: the definition and value of the attributes of the system as a whole can be given without reference to the internal structure of the entity. By contrast, the structural definition of an entity is not autonomous: it relies on the resolution of the system into *atomic* components, each characterized by its attributes as a black box.

MODELLING

In the definition, the word *referent* stands for any entity of interest.

The central concept of P/p modelling emerges from the possibility to represent any real-life entity in one of two time frames: (i) at a time *instant*, showing it as a passive item termed 'product', or (ii) over a time *period*, regarding it as a 'process'. The P/p methodology employs the generic system representation for both product and process, and distinguishes one from the other by the measure of time. Products have zero duration but carry a *time stamp* designating the instant at which the attribute measures are valid, whereas processes have finite non-zero duration. The notion of 'product' is *autonomous*: products are defined without reference to the process that created them. By contrast, the definition of a process relies on the definition of its products.

Modelling may be used for three kinds of purposes: to *describe* an entity, to *predict* its characteristics, or to *prescribe* values for its attributes. The result of P/p modelling is the representation of the referent in a *directed graph.*

The black box and structural representations of the P/p methodology are used throughout the problem solving process: the same type of representation is employed in the *specification* of the problem and the *specification* of the solution, in representing and implementing the *design*, in *planning, organizing* and *overseeing* the problem solving process, and *managing* the relationship between customer, supplier and the rest of the constituency of interested parties. The P/p methodology offers the *bipartite* graph as an aid to make explicit the relationship between black box and structure.

MEASUREMENT

Rooted in engineering, in the P/p methodology deals with facts, and – as far as possible – with decisions based on facts. For this, measurement is fundamental. The need for measures arises at each step of the problem solving activity from the early stages of specifying the problem and the required solution, through the intermediate stages of generating and verifying the design, to the closing stages of delivering and validating the solution.

The P/p methodology calls for the characterization of all referents by their *measurable attributes*, and employs *measurement theory* to ensure that the measures are well defined and the scales are properly designed. By means of a unifying approach to measurement, the P/p methodology reaffirms sound measurement practice in the 'hard' disciplines, and supports the advancement of young and developing disciplines.

The P/p methodology constructs a *measurement hierarchy,* starting from the direct measurement of an individual attribute and culminating in a subjectively defined utility function which combines all attribute measures in some explicit way to yield a value judgement on the referent.

QUALITY MANAGEMENT

The P/p methodology encourages integration of general management and quality management. Its structural models can represent the project plan as well as the operation of the problem solving activity in progress. The explicit, measurement-based plans aid the prevention of delays and difficulties, and the process models support early diagnosis of nonconformance. Its process models facilitate tracking any change in customer requirements, thus avoiding deviation between conformity and customer satisfaction. The formal models of the methodology can support optimization of performance and continuous quality improvement.

4.13 Summary

This chapter offers an overview of the development of the systems approach and presents systems concepts to aid the problem solver.

- It shows how to represent a referent as a black box and as a structure, and emphasizes the importance of constructivity: the need to derive the black box characteristics of an entity from its structure.
- It indicates that the same referent can be represented as a product – a passive entity – or a process – an active entity. It explains the disciplined use of graphs for representing referents, and distinguishes between three kinds of graphs, differing in their information content: networks, frameworks and models.
- It defines 'system', and narrows down the notion of active and passive entities to 'processes' and 'products'.
- It discusses the characterization and classification of products and processes and presents an overview of hard and soft systems methodologies.
- It defines 'P/p methodology: the subject of the book.

4.14 Exercises

Exercise 4.1

We know that active entities are processes, passive entities are products. We know also that in a given context an entity must be regarded either as active or as passive.

Revisit and examine the ISO 8402 definition of 'entity' given in chapter 3. Record your comments, and attempt to classify the last two examples offered in the definition as one or the other.

Exercise 4.2

Using graphical representations only, could you distinguish between 'cactus', 'network', 'framework' and 'formal model'? If not, what extra information would you need?

If you are familiar with Venn diagrams, could you represent the four concepts on such a diagram?

Exercise 4.3

A house is being built for you to live in. Detail some attributes that the finished house should have, giving specific attribute values which could be checked in a Court of Law, in case of a dispute with the builder.

Exercise 4.4

Re-label figure 4.1 with the caption 'flow of command in an organization', specify the key, and comment on the result.

Exercise 4.5

When going to the doctor, would you rather be regarded as a whole or as a set of parts? What do you see as the advantages and disadvantages of each approach? How do you think the doctor sees you?

Suggest some interrelationships that help define you as a structural system (and prevent, as the text suggests, you being a 'meaningless heap').

Exercise 4.6

Figure 4.9 is one of the well known representations of the software development process [24].

Is this diagram a graph? If not, why not, and how would you transform it into a graph? What is the key?

If the diagram is a graph, is it a network? If not, then how would you transform it into a network?

What is the key to the diagram? What is the key to your graph? What is the key to your network?

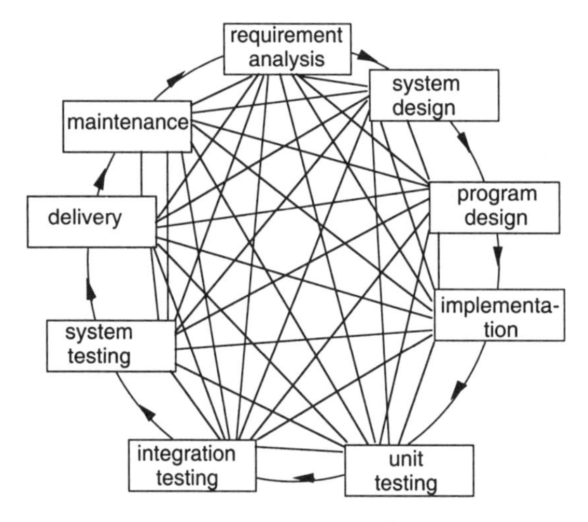

Figure 4.9: One of the popular representations of the software development process

Exercise 4.7

The saying goes: "The whole is more than the sum of the parts." Is this true?

4.15 Footnotes and References

1 I V Blauberg at al: "Systems theory – philosophical and methodological problems". Progress publishers, 1977.

2 A Angyal: "The structure of wholes". Philosophy of sciences, V6, No1, 1939.

3 L V Bertalanffy et al: "Discussion on general systems theory". Human Biology, Vol XXIII, 1951.

4 See e.g.: W Ross Ashby: "An introduction to cybernetics". Methuen, 1956; also:

W Ross Ashby: "General systems theory as a new discipline". General Systems, Vol III, 1958.

5 W Weaver: "Science and complexity". American Scientist, Vol 36, 1948.

6 L A Zadeh: "From circuit theory to systems theory". Proc IRE, Vol 50, No 3, 1965.

7 See e.g.: M Mesarovic: "General systems theory and its mathematical foundations". IEEE Trans on Systems Science and Cybernetics, Vol SSX-4, 1968.

8 See e.g.: H Chestnut: "Systems engineering methods". New York, 1967; also: "Research abstracts", Systems Research Centre, Case Western Research University, Dec. 1967.

9 See e.g.: G W Allport: "The open system in personality theory". Journal of Abnormal and Social Psychology", Vol 61, 1960.

10 N Rashevsky: "Outline of a general theory of biological and social organisms". General systems, Vol XII, 1967.

11 See e.g.: M Checkland: "Systems thinking, systems practice". John Wiley, 1981. Also: S Beer: "Diagnosing the system for organizations". John Wiley, 1984.

12 See e.g.: S A Umpleby et al.: "A science of goal formulation". Hemisphere Publishing, 1991.

13 J F Sowa: "Conceptual structures – information processing in mind and machine". Addison Wesley, 1984.

14 R Stevens et al.: "Systems engineering coping with complexity". Prentice Hall, 1998.

15 A Kaposi, M Myers: "Systems, models and measures". Springer Verlag, 1994.

16 A Kaposi, M Myers: "Systems for computer systems professionals". LSI Publications, 1996.

17 Developed in the context of Project MENSURAE, LMF-DI, Pontifical Catholic University of Rio de Janeiro, Project Director Professor A Haeberer.

18 Cactus – representation of the operation of the referent as the means of transforming input product(s) into output product(s). For definition see chapter 5.

19 Note that ISO 8402, the earlier version of the quality standard, gave no definition of 'system'. The new standard seeks to amend this deficiency by defining:

system
a set of interrelated or interacting elements
ISO/FDIS 9000:2000

20 A comprehensive definition is given in chapter 11.

21 International Bureau of Weights and Measures (1977) SI, the International System of Units, 3rd Edition, Page, C H and Vigoureux, P (eds.), London H.M.S.O. for the National Physical Laboratory.

22 M Bunge: "Scientific research". Springer Verlag, 1967.

23 View expressed verbally at the 1999 Autumn Assembly of INCOSE UK at DERA, Malvern

24 See for example M Pfleger: "Software Engineering". Prentice Hall, 1998.

Chapter 5 Product/process modelling

The aim of this chapter is to show how to represent the active and passive referents in Product/process (P/p) graphs and how to use P/p modelling in simple problem solving situations.

P/p graphs are applicable to problems in all domains, equally suited to represent the problematical *referent*, the *process* of problem solving, and the *solution* when it is introduced into service. Graphs and their specific cases – networks, frameworks and graph models – were introduced in chapter 4, as were the symbols for hard, soft and cognitive products and processes. We now show how these ideas are used to define P/p networks, P/p frameworks and P/p graph models [1] as aids for representing referents, clarifying their characteristics, analyzing them, devising them, communicating about them, and assuring their quality.

In addition to quoting some examples in the text, a collection of examples is given in a separate section near the end of the chapter.

5.1 P/p graphs

P/p graphs are b-type graph representations of the operation of active referents. Their principle is to make the characteristics of products and processes explicit.

There are three kinds of P/p graphs: *P/p networks, P/p frameworks* and *P/p models*. They satisfy the definition of networks, frameworks and graph models, respectively, with the additional common feature that all P/p graphs are *acyclic* [2]. The reason for this is logical. The products (or product-like entities) in the arcs of our P/p graphs carry an (explicit or implicit) time stamp. Along each route of the graph, products and processes alternate. As products are acted on by processes of nonzero duration, time progresses forward. Once a time instant is past, it cannot be recovered; thus, with this interpretation of the meaning of the arcs, a cyclic graph would be meaningless.

The main elements of P/p graphs are *products*, represented by the arcs, and *processes,* represented in single input, single output nodes. Figure 5.1 shows the simplest P/p graph: a single process with its input and output product. We shall also encounter two kinds of subsidiary elements: product-like entities called *product clusters,* and process-like entities called *gates.*

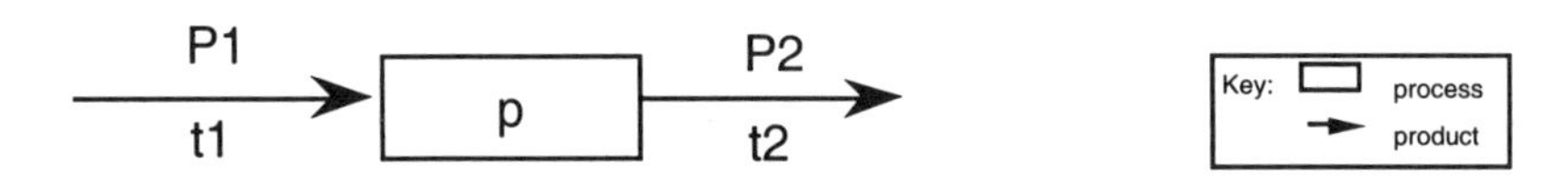

Figure 5.1: P/p network of a single process

In reality, most entities have more than one input and/or more than one output. The representation of such an entity is not a *process* but a *cactus*, of which we have seen an example in the 'assembling' activity of figure 4.5. Another cactus is shown in figure 5.2 below.

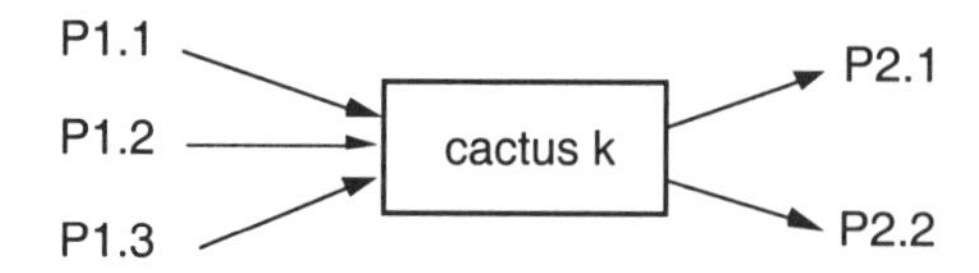

Figure 5.2: b-type graph network: a three-input, two output cactus (time stamps omitted)

We define:

cactus
nodal element of a b-type network, having two or more inputs and/or two or more outputs
Our working definition

Inside cactus k in figure 5.2, inputs $P_{1.1}$, $P_{1.2}$, $P_{1.3}$ might be collected into a single product P_1, but this is not explicit in the figure. Likewise, the outputs $P_{2.1}$, $P_{2.2}$ of the cactus might originate from a single product P_2, but this too is concealed, the internal organization of the cactus not being shown explicitly.

Figure 5.3 takes a step towards transforming cactus k into a P/p graph by making the mechanism of collection and distribution more explicit. The figure shows that process p operates on input product P_1 – an aggregate of products $P_{1.1}$, $P_{1.2}$, $P_{1.3}$ –, and generates the output product P_2 which is dispersed into products $P_{2.1}$, $P_{2.2}$. Although figure 5.3 now shows that the internal structure of cactus k contains products and processes (in this instant the single process p), there are additional nodes A and B whose definition is still not explicit. For this, we introduce 'gates': mental constructs that articulate the function of such nodes.

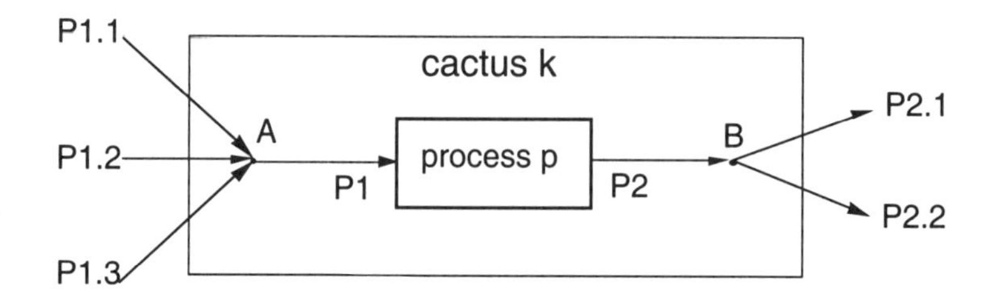

Figure 5.3: b-type graph network showing a possible internal composition for the cactus of figure 5.2 (time stamps omitted and nodes A, B undefined)

There are two types of gate: (i) *collection* gates (such as at node A in figure 5.3) designated by the letter 'c', and (ii) *distribution* gates (such as at node B) carrying the letter 'd'. The first assembles several input products to form one composite product called the *product cluster*, and the second disperses the single output product cluster into several component products. We define:

> **product cluster**
> a set of two or more products with a common time stamp
>
> Our working definition

Figure 5.4 is a P/p graph version of figure 5.3, with the role of nodes A and B made explicit. As before, process p operates on input product cluster P_1 – an aggregate of products $P_{1.1}$, $P_{1.2}$ $P_{1.3}$ –, and generates the output product cluster P_2 which is dispersed into $P_{2.1}$, $P_{2.2}$.

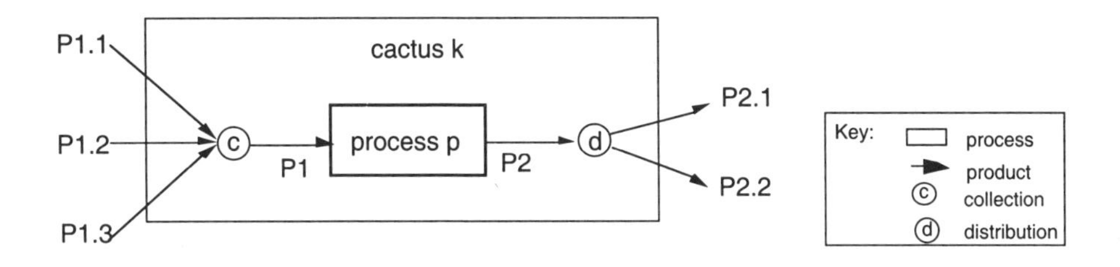

Figure 5.4: P/p network showing a possible internal composition of the cactus of figure 5.2 (time stamps omitted)

A closer look at gates

In defining the term 'process' in chapter 4, we reserved the term for a single input, single output active entity. Such a restriction is necessary for ensuring that the input and output of the process are unambiguously defined. The single-input, single-output constraint necessitates the introduction of the gates: modelling devices having *no real life referent* whose role is to make the composition of the input and output product explicit. Gates are 'virtual processes' in the sense that they are interposed between products and product clusters in the graph, but they perform no action, have no real life referents, have no duration, and absorb no resources. Their sole function is to *represent* the flow of products through the P/p network.

We define:

> **collection gate**
> gate which assembles a set of products into a product cluster, in accord with a rule
>
> Our working definition

> **distribution gate**
> gate which disassembles a product cluster into a set of products, in accord with a rule
>
> Our working definition

and, generally:

> **gate**
> modelling aid, acting instantaneously and absorbing no resources.
>
> Collection gates have in-degree 2 or more and out-degree 1. Distribution gates have in-degree 1 and out-degree 2 or more [3].
>
> Our working definition

Figure 5.5 is a generic illustration of gates with more than one input or more than one output. Gates are nodes of the P/p graph, having n+1 arcs, where n is a counter. One of the arcs is distinguished: it carries the product cluster. n is the number of arcs on the *multiple side* – the input side of collection gates, and the output side of distribution gates. Each of the arcs on the multiple side carries an individual product.

The full complement of elements of P/p graphs

P/p graphs are constructed of only the following kinds of components:

- *products* and *product clusters*, shown in the arcs of the graph, representing a referent as instantaneous, carrying a real time stamp,
- *processes*, shown as single input single output nodes, representing a referent as an activity over a time period,
- *gates*, shown as nodes of degree three or more.

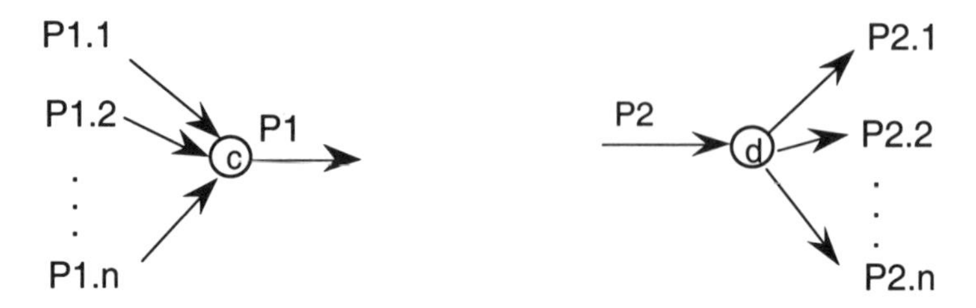

Figure 5.5: Collection gate with n inputs and distribution gate with n outputs (time stamps and key omitted)

The structure of P/p graphs

THE BLACK BOX

Figure 5.1 showed the simplest P/p graph: an indivisible single process p, with input and output products P_1, P_2.

THE SERIAL STRUCTURE

Figure 5.6 shows the serial process p, already met in chapter 3. This is a simple process, representing two activities in sequence, the product P_2 – output of process p_1 – serving as input to process p_2. In practice, the serial structure may contain more than two subprocesses in sequence, products and processes alternating along the route from input to output.

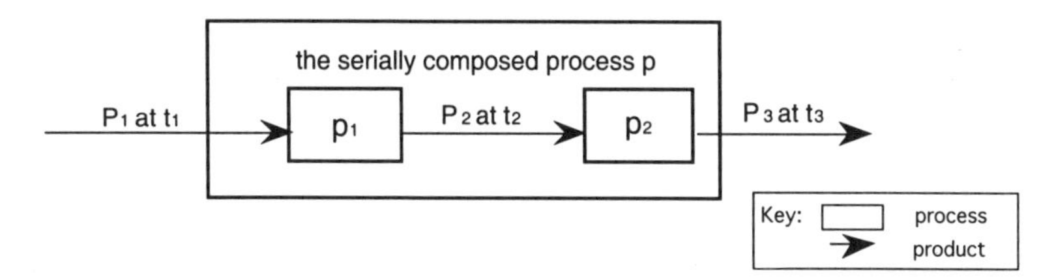

Figure 5.6: Representation of a serially composed process (key as in figure 5.1)

A NOTE ON SYNTAX

We pause to discuss figure 5.6 in more detail.

It is tempting to show structural detail by 'nesting' one structure inside another, as in figure 5.6, but this renders the figure incompatible with the syntax of P/p graphs or of graphs in general, however conceptually clear it may seem.

Figure 5.7 gives a comprehensive explanation of the relationship between the process p and its subprocesses, presenting the two levels separately, but within the same figure. In the interests of conciseness we choose, throughout the rest of this book, representations such as that of figure 5.6. This is to be regarded as a shorthand: in each case the black box process can be separated from its internal structure such as in figure 5.7, both parts being syntactically correct P/p networks.

THE SIMPLE PARALLEL STRUCTURE

Parallel structures contain two or more subprocesses. In case of a two-element structure, process p is composed of subprocesses p_1 and p_2 in parallel. When we decompose the incoming product P_1, we need to assign the product components $P_{1.1}$, $P_{1.2}$ of product cluster P_1 to the correct subprocesses of the complete process p, using the distribution gate d to accomplish this. The output product cluster P_2 of the complete process p is produced as a composition of the two products $P_{2.1}$, $P_{2.2}$. Along the route from input to output, in the parallel structure products alternate with either processes or gates.

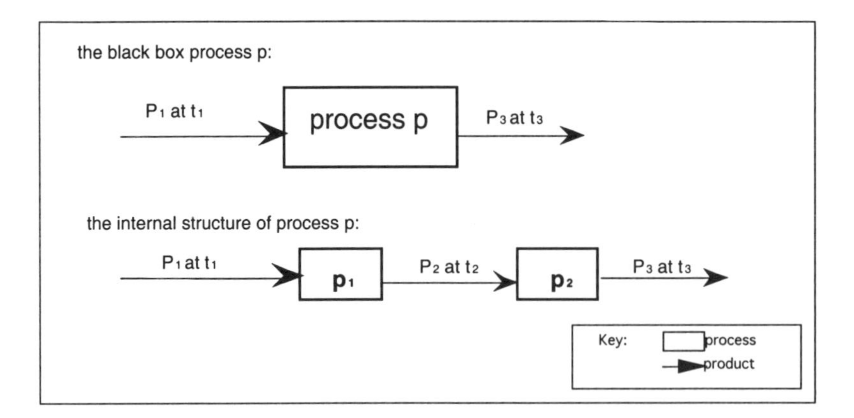

Figure 5.7: Network of a serially composed process (key as in figure 5.1)

Figure 5.8 shows a two-element parallel structure where at time instant t_1 the input product P_1 is distributed at gate d into subproducts $P_{1.1}$ and $P_{1.2}$, gate d passes these to processes p_1, p_2, and outputs $P_{2.1}$, $P_{2.2}$ appear at the same time instant t_2.

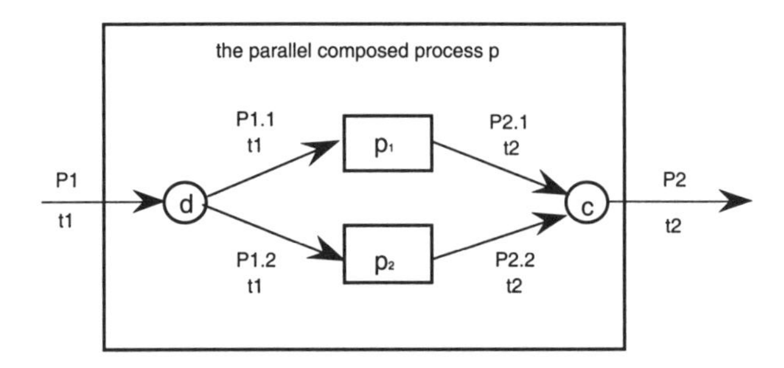

Figure 5.8: P/p network of a parallel-composed process (key as for figure 5.4)

Example 5.1

A car with an empty fuel tank ($P_{1.1}$ of figure 5.8) and dirty windscreen ($P_{1.2}$) pulls up at a garage, and while the driver fills the tank up with petrol (process p_1), the attendant washes the windscreen (process p_2). The car leaves with a full tank ($P_{2.1}$) and clean windscreen ($P_{1.2}$).

If the car also needs oil, having a near-empty sump ($P_{1.3}$), and if there is another garage attendant at hand, then the second attendant might check and supply the oil (process p_3 of a three element parallel structure) while, the other two subprocesses are carried out.

The distribution gate d of a parallel process does not always divide the input product among the subprocesses. Parallel structures might be used in other ways. For example:

- The distribution gate may pass the complete input to *either* process p_1 *or* process p_2 of the two-element parallel structure. Continuing to develop Example 5.1, the garage may have two cashiers, and if both are free, the customer might select to pay to either. (Note however, that figure 5.8 is still valid, but in this case one of the products of cluster P_1 is an 'empty' product. Chapter 11 supplies a fuller explanation.)
- Information products differ from material products in that they may be supplied in their totality to several recipients simultaneously. If the input is information then gate d may *broadcast* it in its totality to all of the subprocesses of the parallel structure simultaneously.
- Another option is that gate d *multicasts* the information input, forwarding it to m selected subprocesses of the n–element parallel structure, the remaining (n-m) subprocesses receiving 'empty' input products.

The passage of products through the distribution gate of the parallel structure is specified by the *rule* of the gate. Usually the rule of the distribution gate is matched by the rule of the collection gate at the output of the structure.

THE EQUALIZED PARALLEL STRUCTURE

The parallel structure of figure 5.8 implies that the two subprocesses p_1, p_2 have identical duration. In reality this is seldom the case. An important structure is shown in figure 5.9 when ∂t_1, the duration of subprocess p_1, is different from ∂t_2, the duration of p_2, for example process p_1 finishing ahead of p_2.

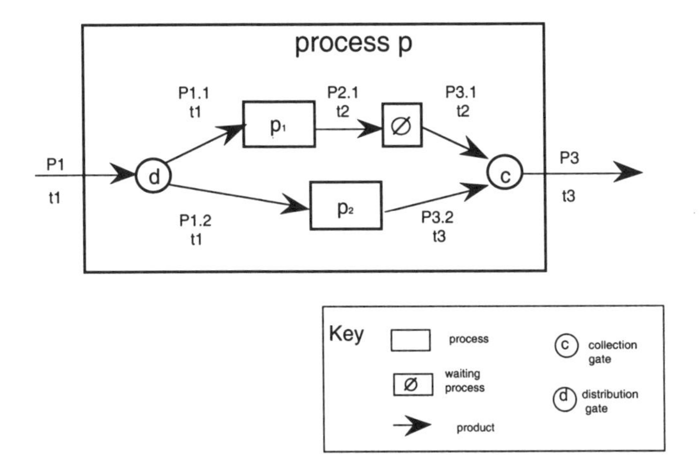

Figure 5.9: P/p network of parallel-composed processes with equalized duration

If the rule of collection gate c in figure 5.9 shows that the outputs of the two subprocesses must be present at the same time instant then the structure must contain the familiar auxiliary waiting process ø which stores P_2 for the period $\partial t = \partial t_2 - \partial t_1$. The waiting process preserves the attribute measures of product P_2, but adjusts the timing to match that of subprocess p_2, generating the product $P_{3.1}$.

When both components $P_{3.1}$ and $P_{3.2}$ of the cluster P_3 are ready for collection, the cluster can pass through gate c.

Example 5.1 revisited

Filling up the car with petrol takes more time than cleaning the windscreen. The car stays on the forecourt until the slower process is completed.

NESTED STRUCTURES

In addition to serial and parallel compositions, elements of P/p networks can be combined in many ways to form complicated structures. However, one can frequently simplify these by analyzing the structure to reveal serial or parallel substructures.

A simple case of this is represented in figure 5.10. Close examination makes it evident that the structure contains two subprocesses p_2, p_1' in parallel, p_1' itself being composed of two sub-subprocesses p_1 and ø, which are in series. Figure 5.10(a) makes this clear. This P/p graph may be simplified, showing only the two subprocesses p_1', p_2 (figure 5.10(b)). The P/p network (p_1 in series with ø) is *nested* inside p_1', and details of this can be supplied when required.

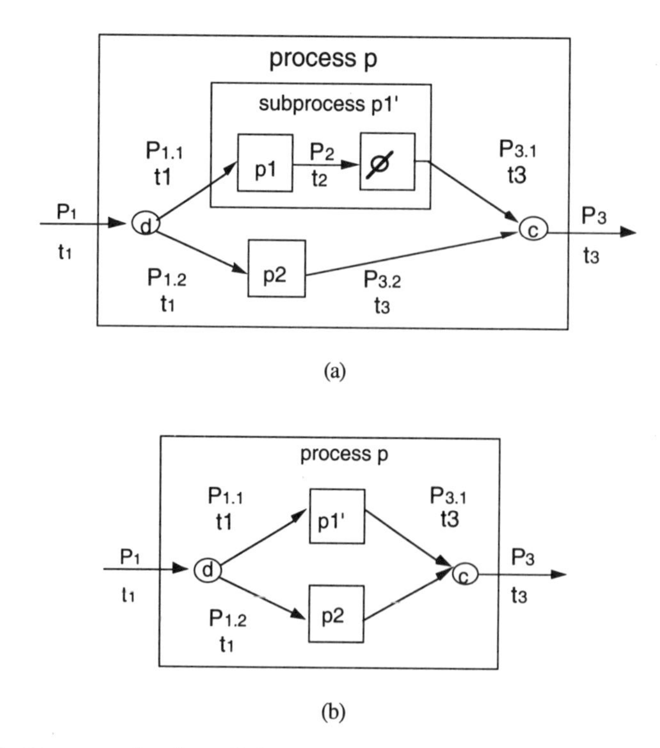

Figure 5.10: P/p network of parallel-composed subprocesses p1', p2, showing nesting (key as in figure 5.4)

P/p networks may contain any number of nested structures, and structures may be nested on any number of levels. The use of nested structures loses no information and, if the internal composition is properly defined, enhances understanding. All networks and subnetworks of the nested structure obey the syntax rules of P/p graphs.

Series, parallel and nesting compositions facilitate analysis: the calculation of the characteristics of the process as a whole from the characteristics of the constituent subprocesses. These compositions also assist in design: the invention of structures to meet the required parameters of the complete process. For these reasons, it is advisable to use these structures wherever possible.

OTHER STRUCTURES

In practice many processes evolve, rather than being designed deliberately, and many process owners manage processes without the benefit of an explicit process representation. The inherent structure of processes can be quite ramified, and, should difficulties arise, their cause is hard to diagnose. Retrospective use of P/p modelling can then reveal the structure. Knowledge of the structure can provide the basis for analyzing the situation and devising a solution for the problem. A case of this, taken from management practice, is given later in this chapter in Example 5.17.

USE OF STRUCTURES

The solution of complex problems requires the judicious use of structures.

- Structures are management aids.

  In course of planning, the complete process will be subdivided into a structure of constituents. The products at the intermediate points of the structure allow the process owner to observe progress, and check the correctness of the sub-outputs along the way. In case of detecting an error or deficiency, the process owner may intervene to take corrective action, instead of discovering the bad news only at the end of the process.

- Structures are the tool of designers and developers.

  The supplier must provide a solution to meet the specification. This usually means inventing a structure of subproblems for which solutions are already available, and assembling these in accord with the structure.

Choosing the right structure is often the key to success. For example:

- If it is paramount that no resource be wasted then the process owner might opt for a serial structure with quality checks after each major stage, seeking to ensure that each partial result is correct. Only if the result is satisfactory will the process owner start up the next subprocess in the sequence.
- If speed is of the essence, the problem owner will opt for a 'maximally parallel' structure, dividing the complete task to independently solvable subtasks, all subtasks to be undertaken simultaneously.
- If the satisfactory operation of a plant depends on the reliability of a particular component, then, in the interest of reliability, the designer may introduce a 'parallel redundant' structure (duplicating or triplicating the critical component).

5.2 Gate rules

As we know, the general purpose of gates is to show explicitly the routing of products through the P/p graphs. The rule of the gate defines the particular way in which products are collected and distributed at a given gate.

Rule definitions may be accomplished at the P/p network stage if enough information is available, but is obligatory at the P/p framework or P/p model stage, along with all the appropriate attribute definitions of products and processes.

Collection gate Assume that the gate opens if at any time instant m out of the n multiple arcs receive an input product, where m is any number between 1 and n. We can group the collection gate rules according to whether m=1, $1< m < n$, or m=n. (When m=0, the gate is closed.)	Distribution gate Assume that when an input arrives, the gate transmits outputs to m out of the n multiple arcs, where m is a number between 1 and n. We can group the distribution gate rules according to whether m=1, $1<m<n$, or m=n, and . (When m=0, the gate is closed.)
The gate opens if and only if m = 1 (on arrival of a single input): The rule of the gate is 'exclusive or'.	The gate sends the output to one of the multiple out-arcs (m=1): Being the mirror image of the 'exclusive or' collection gate, this type of distribution gate is also called 'exclusive or', or 'selective'.
The gate opens if and only if m = n (on the simultaneous arrival of inputs on all in-arcs): The rule of the gate is 'and'.	The gate sends outputs simultaneously to all of the multiple out-arcs (m=n): Being the mirror image of the 'and' collection gate, this type of distribution gate is also called 'and', or 'inclusive'. NOTE that the incoming product must carry the information as to which of the n multiple arcs should receive the product.
The gate opens if one or more inputs are present, i.e. if $1 \le m \le n$. The rule of the gate is 'or'.	The gate sends out outputs to one or more of the multiple out-arcs ($1 \le m \le n$). Being the mirror image of the 'or' collection gate, this type of distribution gate is also called 'or'. NOTE that the incoming product must incorporate the information as to *what part of* the output should be assigned to each of the m multiple arcs.
The gate opens when a specified number ($1<m<n$) of inputs is present simultaneously. The rule of the gate is **'m-out-of-n'**.	The gate sends outputs simultaneously to a specified number of the multiple out-arcs ($1<m<n$): The rule of the gate is **'m-out-of-n'**. NOTE that the incoming product must incorporate the information as to *which* of the m arcs should receive the output, and *how* the output is to be divided among the m multiple arcs.
The gate opens when a distinguished input is present, together with one or more others. The gate rule is **'priority and'**.	The gate sends outputs simultaneously to a priority arc and to one or more of the other multiple out-arcs. The gate rule is **'priority and'**. NOTE that the incoming product must specify *which* the priority arc is, *what* other arcs should receive output, and *how* the output is to be divided among recipient arcs.

Table 5.1: Examples of rules for collection and distribution gates

The gate rules listed in table 5.1 are far from exhaustive: they are merely representative examples. Furthermore, some of the rules listed in the table have several versions, as examples 5.3 and 5.4 show.

Example 5.2

When the input to the 'and' (inclusive) distribution gate is an information product then the full message may either be passed to all outputs, or else potential recipients connected to the various gate outputs may be distinguished, for example on a 'need-to-know' basis. In the former case the gate rule is 'broadcast', in the latter case it is 'discriminated'.

Example 5.3

When the input to the 'and' (inclusive) distribution gate is a material product then each output arc will receive some part of it.

If the input to the gate is subdivided equally among the outputs then the gate rule is 'egalitarian', and no further elaboration is required; otherwise the distribution gate is 'discriminated'.

Example 5.4: Some applications of 'exclusive or' collection gates

- *A phone connection is set up when one of many possible number combinations arrives at the exchange.*
- *A validated password (one of many) initiates access to a database.*
- *A plastic card (one of many) allows the use of a photocopier.*

Example 5.5: Some applications of 'exclusive or' (selective) distribution gates:

- *Delivery of a parcel to one of a store's many customers.*
- *The result of a decision process identifying the product as 'passed' or 'failed'.*
- *The routing of an e-mail message to the correct recipient.*

Example 5.6: Some applications of 'and' collection gates:

- *Assembly of a simple table, there must be all of the five input products, a tabletop and four legs.*
- *Commencement of an identity parade only when all the candidates have assembled.*
- *Reassembly of an internet message only when all the packets have arrived at the destination.*

Example 5.7: Some applications of 'and' (inclusive) distribution gates:

- *Members of an audience listening to a lecture.*
- *Dissemination of e-mail to all on the network.*
- *Junk mail distribution.*
- *Dispatch of message as packets over the internet.*

Example 5.8: Some applications of m-out-of-n collection gates

- *Collection gate with m-out-of-n rule.*
  The ten symbols of the decimal counting system (0 – 9) can be encoded in five combinations of 0's and 1's, where any two 1's indicate, by their position, the value to be represented.
- *The arrival of any two signals from five, at the gate, will cause it to open momentarily.*
- *'Priority and' collection gate with m=k+1 entries*
  At a race course the starter's gate has n number of traps. There will be up to k horses entering the race (1≤k≤n), and each horse must be positioned in a trap for the race to start. Whatever the number of entries, there is an essential requirement: the sound or flag that will signal the start the race. Thus, the collection gate of the P/p graph has m=k+1 entries, but the race will start only if a) the priority input (the starting signal) arrives, and b) k number of entries are present.

5.3 Defining P/p graphs

P/p graphs have been encountered several times already, thus many of their characteristics will be familiar to the reader. The time has come to offer their definition.

P/p graph
collective term designating P/p networks, P/p frameworks and P/p models
Our working definition

P/p networks

Many situations facing the problem solver can be represented as a *P/p network:* the simplest form of P/p graph. P/p networks inherit all the characteristics of networks listed in chapter 4, with some additional features already discussed. To summarize these, we define:

P/p network
acyclic b-type network where each arc is a placeholder for a product or a product cluster and each node is a placeholder for a process or a gate
Our working definition

The P/p network is a useful representation of the layout of the structured process, but it gives little information about the properties of the constituent parts.

P/p frameworks

These are an important elaboration of P/p networks:

> **P/p framework**
> P/p network representing a class of referents where
> – classes of products and processes given as black boxes are characterized by their well defined attributes, variable type and bounds,
> – classes of products and processes given as structures are constructively defined,
> – classes of product clusters are given as sets of product classes,
> and gates are characterized by their rule
> Our working definition

To keep the graphical representation simple, the characteristics of product, process and gates are usually given in separate tables, the graph labels providing the cross-reference. The tables of definitions elevate a P/p network to the status of P/p framework.

Recall the classification of products and processes in chapter 4. For hard products, the table will allocate variables to all the attribute measures, and may, where available, allocate bounds and values to some of them. For P/p networks containing soft products, those with some or all attributes non-measurable, it is not possible to progress beyond network, although parts of the network may be isolated as P/p frameworks by excluding the soft components and including attribute tables for the remainder.

For each product and each process of the framework, the attribute definitions, together with the bounds and dimensions of each attribute, are entered into an *attribute table.* The attribute table may contain specific values, but for a P/p framework this is not mandatory. Since some or all of the attributes are not assigned a measure, and since time stamps are usually given only as variables rather than actual measures, the P/p framework cannot characterize an individual referent. However, it serves to represent the *class* of all those referents whose attributes conform to the definitions, and whose attribute measures fall within the bounds given in the tables.

Compared with the P/p network, the P/p framework is a significant advance in a problem solving context.

P/p models

P/p models are the ultimate elaborations of the P/p framework.

> **P/p model**
> P/p framework representing an *individual referent*, where products and processes are characterized by their attribute values
> Our working definition

In case of P/p models, the attribute definition, together with the bounds, value and dimensions of each attribute, is entered into the appropriate attribute table. For a product, the attribute table of the P/p model thus represents a specific entity at a specific instant, and the characteristics include the value of the time stamp. For a process, the entry in the attribute table shows the duration, given by the difference between the time stamp of the input product and that of the output product.

P/p modelling

P/p graphs offer a comprehensive instrument of operational and quality management.

- Effective *operational* management calls for planning of activities and their results, implementing the plan effectively, monitoring and controlling the operation of the organization, and continually enhancing its performance and the quality of its products. To do this, the manager must know the structure of the process, the timing of the subprocesses and all products, the definition of products and process attributes and the measure of each selected attribute, and the assignment of authorities and responsibilities of personnel.
- Recent developments in quality management point to the need for a "process approach" to quality and a "system approach to management", requiring organizations to "apply suitable methods" for measuring and monitoring products and processes [4]. To satisfy the demands of the standard means the use of systematic, measurement-based information on the products and processes of the organization.

  P/p graphs make all the required characteristics explicit. Compared with the syntax of P/p graphs, usual forms of process documentation are incomplete or ambiguous.

The new quality standard distinguishes five maturity levels that may be attained by an organization. The lowest of these – Level 1 – is characterized by having "no formal approach". At the highest – Level 5 – the organization is "best-in-class", having passed through intermediate stages of a "reactive approach", a "stable formal approach", and a stage of "continual improvement", demonstrated by performance measures. P/p modelling assists the organization in attaining progress, and demonstrates progress internally, and to external assessors and auditors.

Starting from the least developed state when the processes of an organization are undocumented or partially documented, it would be unrealistic to expect that a full P/p model can be reached in one step. Instead, it is usual for the P/p model to be achieved through a sequence of refinements, involving the P/p network and the P/p framework along the way. Chapter 12 is devoted to presenting this progression.

5.4 Keys for P/p graphs

One of the demands on a P/p graph is that a key be present, either locally within the graph, or by reference. The key ensures that the symbols are consistently used and the graph is meaningful.

The basic key set for hard products and processes

The key shown in figure 5.11 is adequate for most P/p graphs with hard processes. Notice the symbol for the 'waiting' process. The inputs and outputs of a waiting process share the same attribute values, but have a different time stamp.

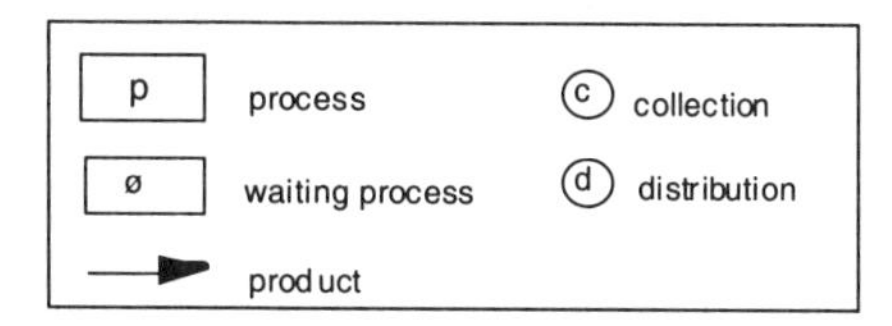

Figure 5.11: General key for P/p graphs comprising hard products and processes

The extended key set

As we move our target towards representation of hard, soft and cognitive (cloud) products and hard, soft and cloud processes, we enlarge the key of figure 5.11 to that of figure 5.12. The basic and extended key sets will be adequate for all further examples in this chapter.

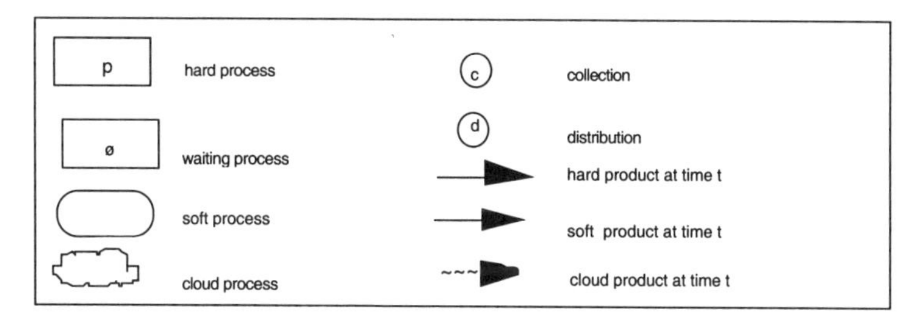

Figure 5.12: Key of P/p graphs, expanded to soft and cloud products and processes

'Shorthand' keys

In practice some subgraphs occur frequently. It is convenient to assign to these a reserved 'shorthand symbol', adopting it as a house standard. The shorthand symbol for a locally stipulated 'house standard' will normally be added to the expanded key set, to assure that it is used consistently throughout the organization.

THE SUBGRAPH OF THE SHORTHAND SYMBOL IS A PROCESS

A house standard symbol may be called for in case of a frequently occurring (single-input, single-output) process. It is sufficient to designate such a process with the appropriately shaped standard symbol (to signify a hard, soft or cloud process), together with a distinguishing label pointing to the definition of the internal structure of the nested process, applying to it the usual rules for P/p graphs.

THE SUBGRAPH OF THE SHORTHAND SYMBOL IS A CACTUS

Much more care is needed in those cases where a house standard symbol designates a frequently used subgraph of the P/p graph which is not a process but a cactus, having more than one input, more than one output, or both. Careless inclusion of a cactus component would reduce the P/p graph to an ordinary b-type network, forfeiting the advantages of P/p modelling. To guard against this, the internal structure of the cactus must always be properly defined as a P/p graph.

Example 5.9: 'If-then-else' cactus

Figure 5.13 shows the most commonly used cactus symbol: a shorthand for designating test and two-way decision making.

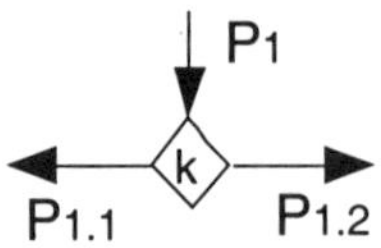

Figure 5.13: The two-way decision (if-then-else) cactus

Example 5.10: The 'test-and-route' cactus

Another familiar shorthand symbol is the 'test-and-route' (or 'case', or 'multiple choice') cactus, shown for the three-way case in figure 5.14, labelled 'v'. A common use of this cactus is in quality tests, one route for 'pass', one for 'reject', and one for 'reject but repairable' (or 'nonconformant in this application but usable in another context').

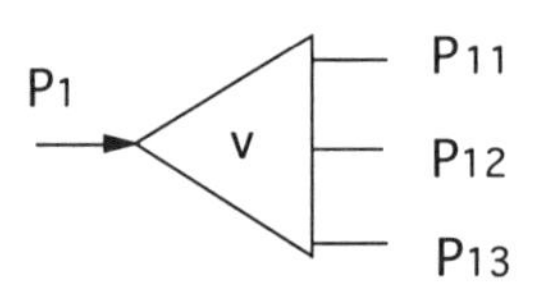

Figure 5.14: Shorthand symbol of a 'test-and-route' subgraph for a three-way choice

Example 5.10 continued

Figure 5.15 shows the P/p network of cactus v in figure 5.14. The network has two nodal elements: the process p and the 'exclusive or' distribution gate d.

Process p performs two functions:

1. *As its name indicates, it tests the incoming product P_d, comparing them with a specification resident in the process.*
2. *It assigns to the product a label showing the conclusion drawn from the comparison.*

The output of process p is the product P_e whose attributes should be the same as those of P_d, enlarged by the label generated in p. The label identifies the product as P_{d1}, P_{d2} or P_{d3}, routing it to the appropriate output of the exclusive or distribution gate d. Since p is the only process in cactus v, the duration of v is the same as that of p.

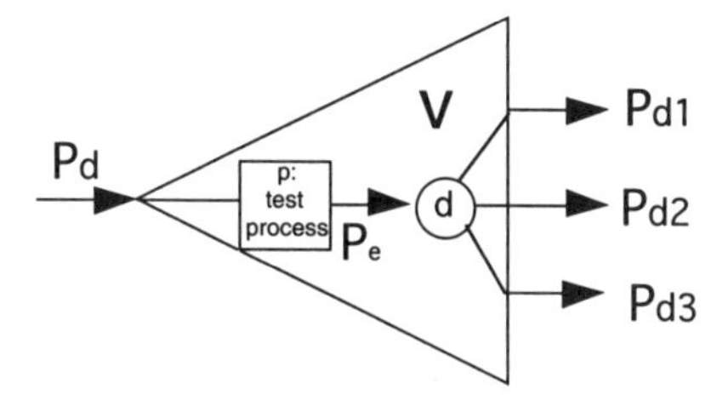

Figure 5.15: P/p graph of the 'test and route' symbol for a three-way choice

A comment on keys for P/p graphs

For ease of drawing and reproduction, the symbols of P/p graphs (rectangles, circles, ellipses, etc.) are simple. It is not practical to reserve these symbols for P/p graphs alone: they are often used in other contexts, such as directed or undirected graphs that are not P/p graphs. Many such examples appear in this book. The multiple use of symbols need not cause confusion if two simple rules are observed:

- the type of graph is stated, and
- the key is provided.

5.5 The route to a P/p model

A P/p graph, be it a network, a framework or a model, is a tool for modelling systems, expressing the ideas of individuals, helping communication between interested parties, analyzing systems, designing and developing them, and reasoning about them. A P/p graph is an aid for identifying entities whose attributes need defining and measuring, or, at its weakest, just describing. The well-defined format of the graph imposes a discipline, and admits to checking and quality assurance. The format serves as a guard against incompleteness, inconsistency, error, internal contradiction and incomprehensibility arising from poor definitions.

Developing a P/p model is a gradual process. The first systematic modelling step may well be the construction of a giant black box cactus as the representation of the operation of a piece of machinery or an organization, together with its inputs and outputs. Refinement of this, and decomposition of the black box representation into a structure of its large scale components, will allow allocation of inputs among the various constituent parts, at this stage usually represented as cacti.

Gradually, as structural refinement and clarification proceeds, more details will be added, single input, single output process-like operational components will emerge, and product-like passive entities will become identified. To achieve this, gates will have to be introduced, and the cactus network will give way to a P/p network.

The next stage is to identify the attributes that are deemed of importance, and define the attributes of products and their attributes. This proceeds in parallel with the definition of gate rules, showing the advance of products through the P/p graph. When this stage is satisfactorily concluded, we have a P/p framework!

Throughout the modelling activity, measured values of some attributes will emerge. These are to be carefully recorded throughout. After achieving the P/p framework, data collection will intensify, leading to a P/p model, ready for validation.

The modelling process is never complete. Validation will call for correction, and reveal scope for refinement. Use of the validated model in practice will lead to identification of attributes of importance that had been previously excluded, or show the need to decompose parts to greater detail to deepen understanding. In this way P/p modelling progresses continuously, in search of excellence.

5.6 A collection of examples

Example 5.11: A simple hard system

Figure 5.16 shows a P/p network for a simple system consisting of four processes that, together, govern the entry into a secure room. One of the inputs is the 'swipe' card containing user and authorization details while the second is the database holding card details and individual access permissions.

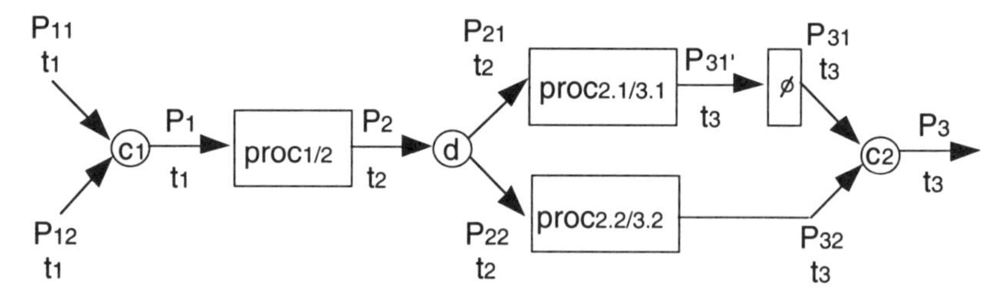

Figure 5.16: Access to a secure room (example by Carol Britton; usual key)

The process will check that the card is still valid and not expired, lost or stolen and that the individual has permission to access the room in question.

The first, collection, gate emphasizes that both the card and the access mechanism must be present at the same time (t_1) for the process to take place, while the process itself compares values and comes to a decision based on the comparison.

The output will contain all the input values but with a later time stamp, plus a binary authorization code either granting or withholding access permission.

The distribution gate functions in 'exclusive or' mode, routing the output according to the value of the binary authorization code: allowing the door to open or giving such warnings as a red light, a buzzer, a message or alerting security.

The second collection gate will respond to one input, and will signal the end of the chain of processes.

The 'waiting' process is there to allow the whole operation to be modelled as a process, and this requires the output products of the two routes to be given the same value t_3.

Informally we may list the attributes of the various entities as below.

The attributes of the security pass P_{11} are deemed to be the following:

- card ID – an integer value between 1001 and 9999
- card holder – a sequence of characters
- status – rank within company chosen from a predefined list
- permissions – rooms to which the holder has access.- from a predefined list of integers or names.

Similarly the room attributes consist of:

- room ID (to match card, permissions entries)
- occupancy – Number of people in room to comply with fire regulations
- state – chosen from open/closed (if open, card not needed).

The P/p graph identifies three processes:

- proc1/2 check card validity
- proc2.1/3.1 card invalid
- proc2.2/3.2 card valid, open door.

A process attribute template might be of the following shape:

- domain of valid input products D
- duration; t units
- owner: name
- agent: machine or person
- function (in the form output = f(input).
- status: free/busy.

The three processes will have values for these attributes. The owner will be the security department and the agents in each case will be mechanism of the door lock. The following are some of the tables that elevate the P/p network to a P/p framework and illustrate the type of information required to develop the framework into a P/p model:

Product type code	Product type name		
P_{11}	Card		
Attribute code	**Attribute name**	**Value**	**Dimension**
$a^1_{1.1}$	card ID	n	n: 0001...9999
$a^2_{1.1}$	card holder	e	e: Employees
$a^3_{1.1}$	status	s	s:{available, allocated, cancelled}
$a^4_{1.1}$	permissions	p	p: PRoom
Relation code	**relation name**	**relation**	
t_1	time-stamp	$r(t_{1.1})$	
$r_{c1.1}$	co-attribute relation	$r_c(a^1_{1.1}, \ldots, a^4_{1.1})$	

Table 5.2 [5]: Card Product

Notes on table 5.2:

1 The dimensions are drawn from conventional representations: in this case discrete mathematics. For the more general practitioner a natural language description may suffice.

2 The two mandatory relations need not be explicitly included.

3 Since the tables define uninstantiated types, no time stamp yet exists; combining each set of attributes in a single table implies the co-attribute relation. The two relations are included here for completeness.

Product type code	Product type name		
$P_{1.2}$	Room		
Attribute code	**Attribute name**	**Value**	**Dimension**
$a^1_{1.2}$	room number	rm	rm:N | rm _Room
$a^2_{1.2}$	occupancy	$E = \{e_1 \ldots e_n\}$	E: PEmployees
$a^3_{1.2}$	state	closed	{open,closed}
Relation code	**relation name**	**relation**	
t_1	co-temporal relation (time-stamp)	$r(t_{1.1})$	
$r_{c1.2}$	co-attribute relation	$r_c(a^1_{1.2}, a^2_{1.2}, a^3_{1.2})$	

Table 5.3: Room Product

process type code	process type name		
proc1/2	Check Card		
Attribute code	Attribute name	Value	Dimension
$a^{1}_{1/2}$	domain	D	Card X Room
$a^{2}_{1/2}$	transfer function	f	function which transforms P1 into P2
$a^{3}_{1/2}$	status	bool	{free, busy}
$a^{4}_{1/2}$	duration	∂t	time difference on ratio scale
$a^{5}_{1/2}$	owner	e	e: Employees (carries responsibility for the process)
$a^{6}_{1/2}$	agent	ag	ag:device or person who implements the process
Input product type: P_1			
Output product type: P_2			

Table 5.4: Check Card process

The product and process tables above are representative. The reader is invited to complete the example.

Example 5.12: Modelling the operation of an organization

In representing the operation of a system in a P/p graph, we assume that all processes have a definite beginning and a definite end. In reality this is not always the case: there are many natural and artificial processes which seem to operate continuously, without a well defined start or finish. One such process is the operation of a business that appears to be continuous, going on day-by-day, month-by-month, from year to year.

Effective management requires, and the quality standard explicitly prescribes [6], that the processes of the business should be *planned,* and the operation of the business should be *observed (measured* and *monitored), controlled* and continuously *improved.* However, an atomic process is, by definition, indivisible: once it starts, it is not controllable, and its results will only be observable when the process terminates. Even if the real life process is continuous, management must model it as a structure of subprocesses, each timed with its specific beginning and end, each started by its own input product and generating its own output product.

As an example, it is the task of top management to record the key parameters of the organization annually, for presentation at the Annual General Meeting, as input to financial audit, as the basis of preparing tax returns, etc. The measures of the output product P_2 and of the process p of figure 5.17 will be the aggregate of the annual record of the measures of parts of the organization: the performance parameters of teams working on individual projects, measures of the effectiveness of individual Divisions, the efficiency with which resources are used in managing the individual sites of the organization, etc. Each of these part-results are again the aggregate derived by middle management from more detailed knowledge of the structure and performance of the processes under their control.

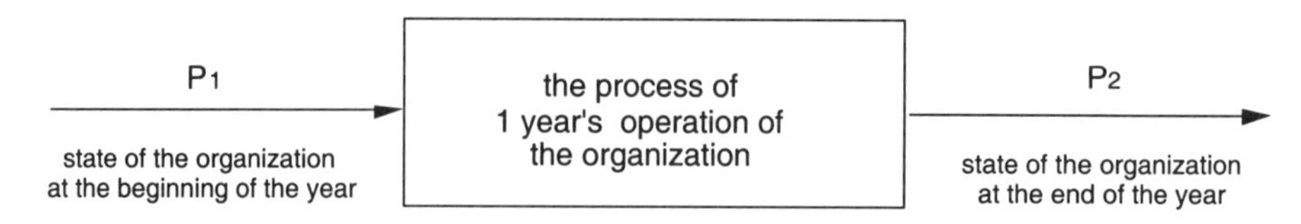

Figure 5.17 P/p model of the financial audit of an organization

Only a structured process can be managed: planned, organized, observed, controlled and systematically improved. Manageability implies that:

- the operation of the organization proceeds according to a *plan* for the next period of operation,
- the plan is characterized such that *conformance* to it could be evaluated on the basis of (qualitative and/or quantitative) measurement,
- the evaluation is based on *observations* of the operation of the business (its products and processes) in reality, and recorded in the form of measures,
- the *measures* defining the characteristics of the plan and of the observation can be compared directly, to establish *conformance* to the plan, or the extent of *nonconformance* ,
- guided by the result, in case of nonconformance (unacceptable deviation) the manager can apply the appropriate kind and degree of *corrective input* product to the problematical part of the structure of the organization,
- in case of nonconformance, the manager can apply the appropriate kind and degree of *corrective input* to the problematical part of the structure of the organization,
- observing the environment and the performance of the organization in a given period, the manager can plan improvements and developments for the period after.

Example 5.13 *An examination routine*

Setting, sitting and grading of examinations is an important part of academic life. Each institution has its own regulatory process which needs to be documented, and the procedures must be observed by all members of faculty.

Figure 5.18 is a P/p graph: a representation of the procedure. Such a graph can serve several purposes: familiarize new staff with the arrangements, facilitate planning of workloads, provide check lists for quality assurance by use of the attribute tables. The product timings – the deadlines associated with the subprocesses – are *prescriptive*, i.e. must be adhered to if the whole examination procedure is to run smoothly and conclude at the appointed time.

Note that the graph is a simplified representation: it does not make it explicit what happens if the internal moderator offers critical comments, or if the external examiner requires modifications. Practice shows the advisability of a department drawing up a comprehensive representation of the examination procedure which shows these eventualities, agreeing the model with the external examiner.

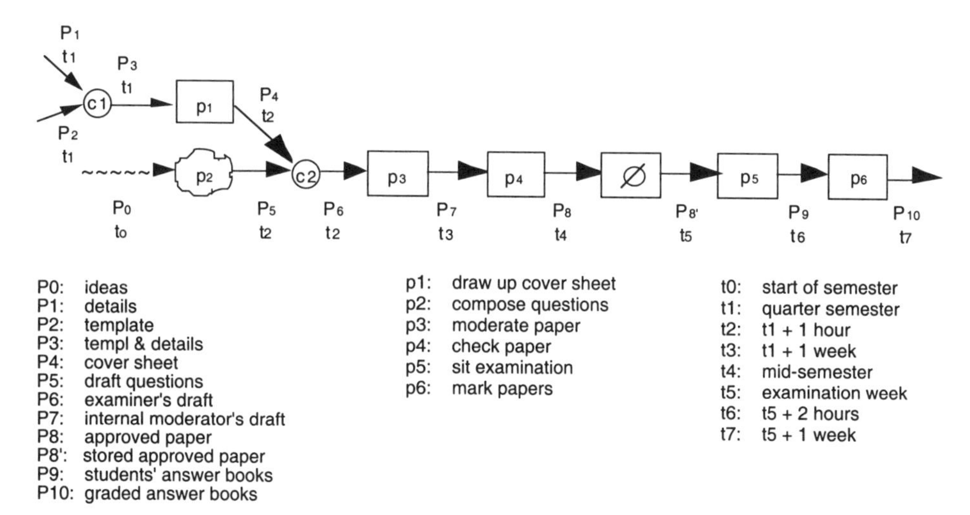

Figure 5.18: P/p graph of an examination sequence

Example 5.14 Introduction to education for business

Management textbooks often introduce their methods by sketching out the progression from idea through theory formation to validated methodology. Unfortunately many of these sketches are obscure and confusing.

In figure 5.19 we show how such a progression could be represented in a P/p graph, making explicit the distinction between cognitive, soft and hard products and processes. This graph can then serve as a basis for education, and for discussion and augmentation in practice. Its advantage over the usual textbook sketches is that it clearly separates what is expressed and what is only an idea, what is measurable and what is not, and suggests which part of the complex process of theory production can be tested, and against what.

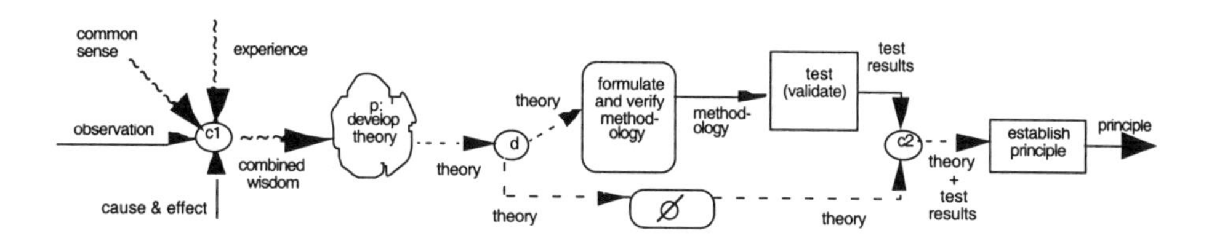

Figure 5.19: Formulation and testing of a theory (usual key)

Notice that the graph does not state whether the principle emerging from the process is valid or not, only that the theory and the test result are *taken into account* when establishing it.

Example 5.15 Operations Management

The graph of figure 5.20 would be familiar to many students of business studies: this is how some textbooks seek to demonstrate the role of operations management.

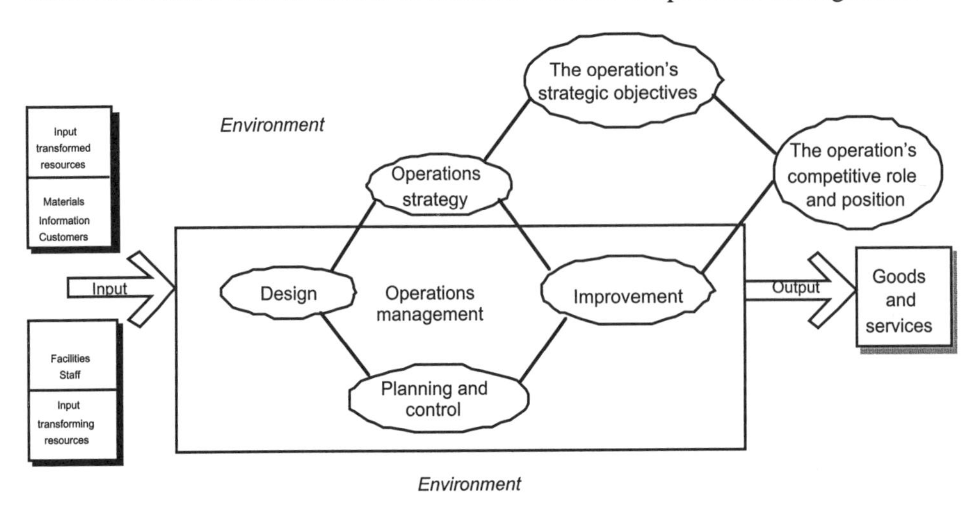

Figure 5.20: A general model of operations management [7]

The picture is not a graph: it is an ambiguous diagram that poses more questions than it answers. The diagram has no key, the input and output arrows imply a flow but the direction of the flow is unclear, and there is no indication as to the contents of the edges.

A great deal may be learned by attempting to transform diagrams like this to a P/p graph. This would involve making *assumptions* about the intended meaning of the diagram. Each assumption has to be validated in discussion with the 'owner' of the diagram: the management expert who wrote the textbook, or the lecturer who decided to adopt it for teaching purposes.

Example 5.16 Top level P/p graph of literature search as part of a project

Any professional task involves gathering information from relevant sources and recording the data in some standard format. Literature search is also part of undergraduate projects, and is one of the standard criteria for grading such projects.

Figure 5.21 shows the top level P/p graph of a literature search process. As an exercise, the reader is invited to select a topic from his/her experience, identify relevant attributes of products P_1, P_2 and P_{11} to P_{16} (such as the id number of some items, the medium, e.g. card index or electronic record or paper, the volume of information, relevance), and suggest a scale for measuring each attribute.

If P_2 is the bibliography / list of references of a final year undergraduate project in the reader's own subject area, what would be a suitable aggregate measure for its quality?

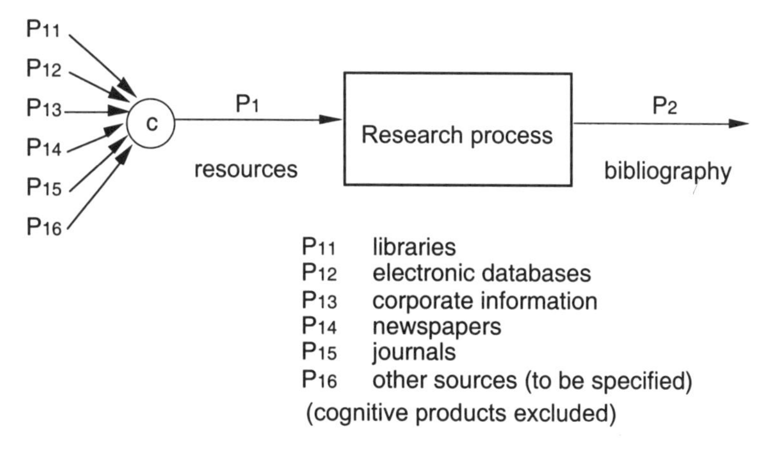

Figure 5.21: Literature search process

Example 5.17 Company reorganization

Figure 5.22(a) is the partially labelled P/p graph of a process structure, arising from the analysis of the design-and-development function of a manufacturing company whose Technical Director is one of our clients. Although the seven 'atomic' process elements (p_1 to p_7) were known to be sound, the process had been troublesome, giving rise to delays, budget overruns, and on one occasion even to the total failure of an important project, causing severe losses to the company.

Three departments were involved in the design-and-development activity. We shall call these Departments A, B and C.

Prior to our involvement, our client had no explicit representation of the design process.

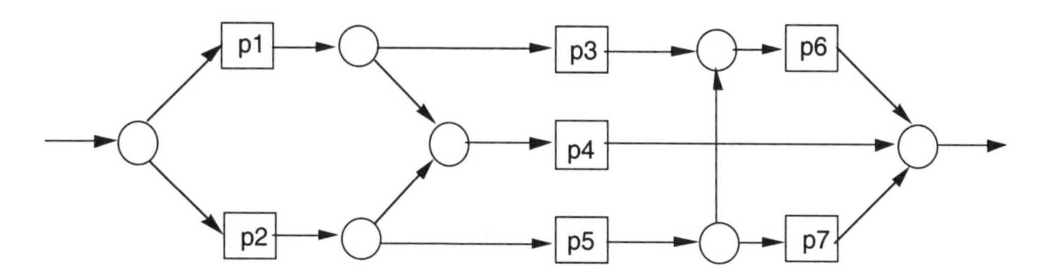

Figure 5.22(a): Partially labelled P/p graph revealing the structure of an industrial process (usual key)

The process of figure 5.22(a) does not admit to simplification: there are no nestable parts. Examination of the 'process owner' parameter of the atomic subprocesses showed that Department A carried out processes p_1 and p_5, Department B did p_2 and p_4, and Department C was in charge of the rest. No department had over-all responsibility. By default, the complete process was in the hands of the person to whom the three Departmental Heads are responsible: the Technical Director himself.

The P/p graph convinced the Technical Director that the process structure was unwieldy, and reorganization was to be considered. Various alternatives were discussed, and the Technical Director finally decided that the design-and-development process was to be restructured in two stages.

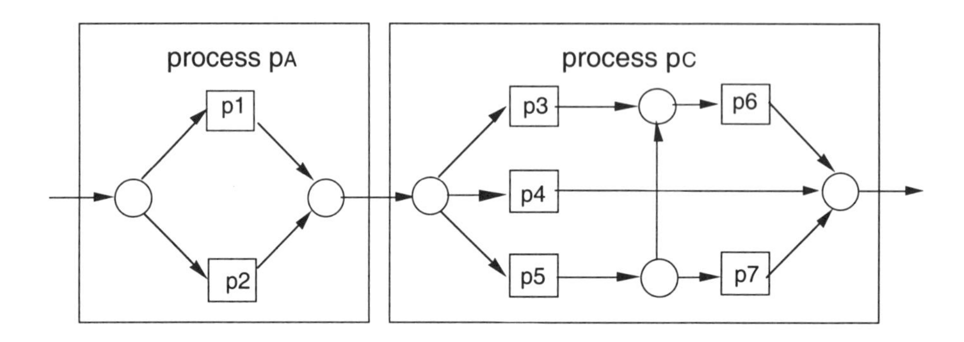

Figure 5.22(b): Partially labelled P/p graph of the modified process at the end of the first stage of reorganization (usual key)

- As first stage, the Technical Director examined the skill profile of each relevant Department, and found that it was easy to transfer the function of process p_2 from Department B to Department A. He affected the transfer, assigned over-all responsibility for the rest of the process to Department C, and adjusted the distribution of resources accordingly. This yielded a structure of two major subprocesses p_A and p_C in series, as in figure 5.22(b).
- Next, the Technical Director charged the Head of Department C with the task of reorganizing process p_C into a series-parallel nested structure, preserving all the atomic subprocesses p_3 to p_7, and maintaining the involvement of the other two Departments in subprocesses p_4 and p_5. This was a more difficult task, involving internally subcontracting some of the work, but the effort proved to be worthwhile.

The resulting structure is shown in figure 5.22(c), where process p_C is decomposed into two subprocesses p_{C1} and p_{C2}, the former in charge of Department B and the latter of Department C. Within p_{C1}, Department C retained responsibility for p_3 and Department A for p_5. We omit here further details of the reorganization, but our client informs us that the design-and-development activity has been working satisfactorily.

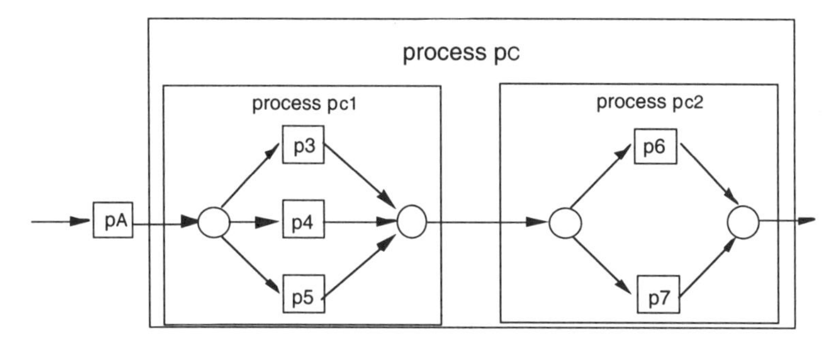

Figure 5.22(c): Partially labelled P/p graph of the modified process at the end of reorganization (usual key)

5.7 Summary

This chapter summarizes the main ideas of producing and using P/p graphs and their accompanying tables. It expands the general notion of graphs introduced in chapter 4, and particularizes these to represent P/p graphs and their three versions: P/p frameworks, P/p networks and P/p models.

The chapter shows that P/p graphs are composed of three types of elements: products, processes and gates. The first two are representations of real-life referents. By contrast, gates are merely modelling aids: virtual processes of zero duration, facilitating explicit expression of paths through P/p graphs. Processes may be composed serially, in parallel, by nesting, or in more elaborate ways. To complement graphical notation, the characteristics of products, processes and gates are tabulated.

The chapter includes some examples to demonstrate the use of P/p models and to help the reader apply the methodology.

5.8 Exercises

Exercise 5.1

Draw a single-process P/p graphs of the 16 example processes of table 4.2.

Exercise 5.2

Represent the manufacture of a pair of shoes on a P/p graph comprising a single process. Make sure that the specification is a component of the input. Now refine the representation to another layer of detail, showing how quality control would compare the final product to the specification and pass or reject the shoes.

Exercise 5.3

A manufacturer supplies goods varying in size from several tons to a few kilograms. The goods are either collected at the factory by the customer's own transport, or are shipped by a distribution company.

Draw a P/p graph which illustrates both possibilities, and includes ordering packing material, moving the goods from final testing to temporary warehousing as traced by the paper trail of documents needed to track the complete process.

Identify the attributes of the products and processes involved, together with example measures.

Exercise 5.4

A class of students is charged with the task of modelling the operation of the departmental office, and you are the lecturer in charge of the class. Figure 5.23 is a diagram presented by one of your students as work in progress towards developing a process representation into a P/p framework.

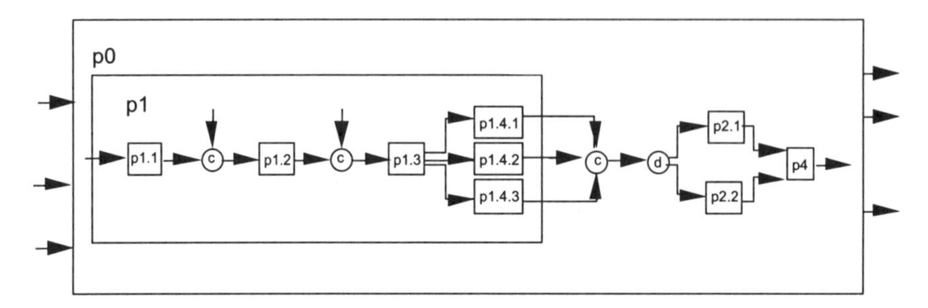

Figure 5.23: Figure representing work in progress towards developing a P/p framework

Explain to your student what is wrong with this diagram.

(i) Is the figure a network? Is it a framework? If not, why not?
(ii) How many cacti are there in the figure?
(iii) How can the figure be converted to a P/p framework?
(iv) What would be needed to expand the P/p framework to a P/p model?

Exercise 5.5

The following, known as the Seven Ages of Man, is an extract from Shakespeare's "As You Like It":

"All the world's a stage,
And all the men and women merely players;
They have their exits and their entrances;
And one man in his time plays many parts,
His acts being seven ages. At first the infant,
Mewling and puking in the nurse's arms;
Then the whining schoolboy, with his satchel
And shining morning face, creeping like snail
Unwillingly to school. An then the lover,
Sighing like furnace, with a woeful ballad
Made to his mistress' eyebrow; Then a soldier,
Full of strange oaths, and bearded like the pard,
Jealous in honour, sudden and quick in quarrel,
Seeking the bubble reputation
Even in the canon's mouth. And then the justice,
In fair round belly with good capon lin'd,

With eyes severe and beard of formal cut,
Full of wise saws and modern instances;
and so he plays his part. The sixth age shifts
Into the lean and slipper'd pantaloon,
With spectacles on nose and pouch on side,
His youthful hose, well sav'd, a world too wide
for his shrunk shank; and his big manly voice,
Turning again toward childish treble, pipes
And whistles in his sound. Last scene of all,
That ends this strange eventful history,
Is second childishness and mere oblivion;
Sans teeth, sans eyes, sans taste, sans everything."

Draw a product/process model to show this sequence of processes. At each stage identify attributes of the product, adding your own to Shakespeare's, and suggest measures for them. Do the same for the processes.

5.9 Footnotes and References

1 To simplify usage, we usually abbreviate 'P/p graph model' to 'P/p model'.

2 Some problem solving situations benefit from the use of 'extended' or 'advanced' P/p graphs which include a type of cycle. These kinds of graphs are beyond the scope of this book.

3 The degree of a node of a graph is the number of arcs at the node. The degree of a node of a directed graph is the sum of its in-degree (the number of incoming arcs) and out-degree (the number of outgoing arcs).

4 "Quality management principles" and "Quality management systems – Requirements". ISO/FDIS 9001:2000.

5 Table format established in L Bahiense L, A Haeberer, O Porto: "Technical Report on frameworks". Labóratorio de Métodos Formais, Departamento de Informática, Pontifícia Universidad Católica do Rio de Janeiro, Brazil, Nov.1997.

6 See clause 8: "Measurement, analysis and improvement", and in particular clause 8.2.3: "Measurement and monitoring of processes", clause 8.2.4: "Measurement and monitoring of products", and clause 8.5: "Continual improvement", Quality management systems – Requirements, ISO/FDIS 9001:2000.

7 Slack, Chambers et al: "Operations Management". Pitman Publishing, 2nd edition.

Chapter 6 Problem solving – process and strategies

We expect simple problems to yield up their solution readily to anyone with commitment, intuition and common sense. Problems of interest to us are not like that. They are inherently complex, and present the kind of challenge for which intuition, common sense and commitment are necessary, but not sufficient.

The purpose of this chapter is to outline the problem solving process and explore various problem solving strategies. The aim is to reduce the risk of problem solving by clarifying ideas, assisting in setting goals, and choosing strategies.

6.1 From problem to solution

The path from complex problem to satisfactory solution is usually tortuous, with many detours, traps and pitfalls. Delays, escalating costs and compromised specifications and failures are not infrequent. Even when the desired solution is achieved in time, it may no longer be fully adequate because in the meantime the situation may have changed, and at the date of completion the solution may already be out of date. Does this mean that the project has failed and there is no progress?

The problem solving spiral

As we know, achieving the satisfactory solution is not the end of the problem solving process. When the personnel of an organization stops recognizing new problems and opportunities, complacency sets in, the organization begins to stagnate, it gradually declines, and finally dies. While the solution for a given problem will represent an improvement, completing one problem solving project is the platform from which to launch the next, each new situation offering new challenges, revealing new tasks. People liken the problem solving process to a spiral without end, leading upwards all the time towards the ultimate goal of excellence. This notion of stage-by-stage enhancement is captured in the 'scientific method'[1], where the solution of each problem is consolidated into the complete body of human knowledge, each project benefiting from the results of its predecessors, and the completion of each project triggering new projects. The same notion appears in the 'quality loop' of ISO 8402: the quality system of an organization must incorporate mechanisms of continuous improvement. A similar idea is embodied in the 'spiral model' of software development [2].

Figure 6.1 is a P/p graph: a simplified representation of the problem solving process p in one cycle of the problem solving spiral. The process contains five subprocesses p1 to p5. On successful completion of process p, the state of the customer's world will have been improved; the customer can start enjoying the benefits of the project. However, in practice the customer will invariably identify shortcomings and opportunities for further improvement ("the outcome of this project is really great, but it would be even better if only …"). The next cycle of the spiral has already started!

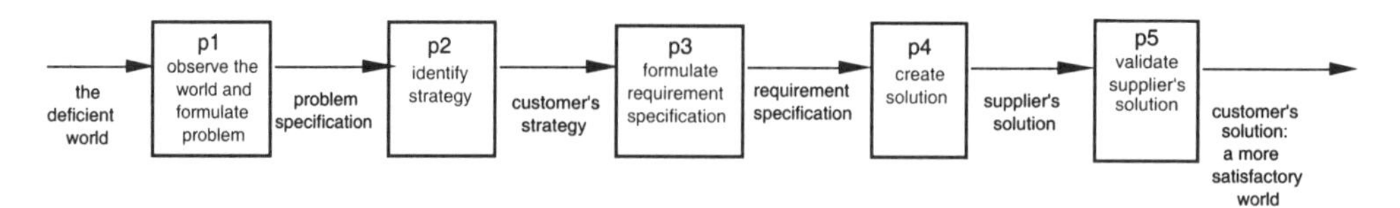

Figure 6.1: The problem solving process – simplified representation of one revolution of the problem solving spiral (b-type key)

Incremental development

An important variant of the problem solving spiral is incremental development: a stage-by-stage solution of problems. This approach may be pre-planned in cases where the problem is well understood and properly defined, and the solution is sought in clearly delineated stages. The stages may be part-solutions, such as the building of a dwelling house where the total contract amounts to a series of part-contracts, and payment is made by the vendor when each planned stage is successfully completed. The stages may also be complete working solutions in themselves, with each stage delivering performance enhancements and/or further facilities.

We must spare thought for those problematic situations where the problem solving process must start without delay, although the problem is poorly understood, the needs are ill defined, and adequate specifications are not available. Among the many examples of solving partially formulated problems are social, health and infrastructure projects in developing countries where the scope of the problem is vast but incompletely understood, and disasters where relief work must start before the extent of the problem is fully assessed. Partial problem formulation might also arise in less dramatic circumstances, such as when a new manager takes charge of the organization, is aware of his/her unfamiliarity with the problems, but perceives that some aspects need urgent attention. In such situations it would be too risky to rush into full-scale projects. Instead, an 'incremental' problem solving strategy is indicated, where some small project is mounted which is expected to yield a solution in a short time. In such projects the goal is three fold:

- deliver a useful solution to an urgent problem,
- gain insight into the problematical situation so as to be able to formulate the next most urgent small project,
- gain further insight into the situation as a whole.

After completing one of the incremental projects – one cycle of the problem solving spiral –, the next project may be directed at a completely different aspect of the problematic situation, or else it may elaborate and enhance an aspect tackled in a previous cycle.

Responsibility

As seen in chapter 2, successful problem solving is the result of cooperation between the customer, the supplier and other interested parties. However, cooperation must not mean divided responsibility. To emphasize this, the process definition in chapter 4 calls for the identification of the 'owner' of each process. The process owner is accountable to the whole constituency for the successful completion of the process: the delivery of the output product in time, within budget, displaying the requisite attribute values. To discharge this responsibility, the process owner must have *authority* to take complete charge of the process.

Responsibility for the complete problem solving process p in figure 6.1 is vested in the problem owner as the representative of the *customer.* Observe that, within process p, all but the penultimate process is the responsibility of the *customer.* The supplier might suggest the specification formulated in p3, but before proceeding to p4 the customer must adopt the specification, and will therefore bear responsibility for it. Only the 'create solution' process p4 is the domain of the *supplier.*

The division of responsibility may be formalized by means of a formal agreement between customer and supplier, known as a *contract*: a voluntary agreement between customer and supplier. In Part 3 of the book we define the notion of 'contract', and discuss the relationships between customer and supplier, and the responsibilities of each. The contracting parties may be two individuals, two different companies, two departments of the same organization, two members of the same group, or whatever.

The customer's risk management activities

Problem solving is a risky undertaking. Risk assessment is a subject of growing importance, and here we can only touch on it briefly.

Risk analysis and risk assessment will be carried out at the outset, and throughout the problem solving process of figure 6.1, involving the identification of the risk factors, and estimation of the potential loss.

RISK ASSESSMENT AT THE START

At the start of the project the problem owner would investigate the risk associated with the undertaking, such as:

- solving the *wrong problem*:

  poor understanding of the problem leading to incomplete or erroneous requirement specification,

  poor timing: circumstances changing in course of the project, and the solution is obsolete before the customer sees the benefits,

- solving the problem *wrongly,* because of:

  unavailability of appropriate human, material and financial resources to allow successful completion of the project,

  unavailability of appropriate technological know-how, supply facilities and services,

  adverse environmental factors arising during the project.

The numerous risks of mounting the project must be set against the risks associated with *not* tackling the problem but allowing the problematic situation to persist, and possibly worsen. As our grandmothers used to say: a stitch in time saves nine.

RISK ASSESSMENT IN COURSE OF PROBLEM SOLVING

At intermediate stages of the process of figure 6.1 further queries arise, regarding:

- the potential loss associated with *carrying on* with the project,
- the potential loss associated with *curtailing* the project prematurely.

At some intermediate stages several options might present themselves, inviting answers to questions about:

- the comparative risk associated with each of the various options,
- the justification of the risk in view of the potential benefits.

Bearing risk in mind will influence the choice of representation of the problem solving process. To illustrate this, consider again the process of figure 6.1. We know that the first three processes of the sequence (p1, p2, p3) all fall within the responsibility of the problem owner. The intermediate products ('problem specification', 'customer's strategy') lend themselves readily to risk assessment, and these are points for possible curtailment of the project. The project may also be aborted at the end of process p3, just before placing the contract with the supplier. Figure 6.2 – a decision tree represented in a P/p graph – enlarges on this part of the problem solving process, making the customer's risk assessment activities explicit.

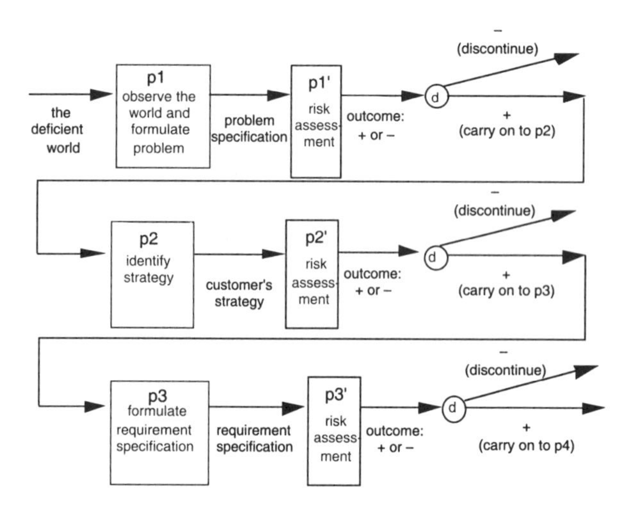

Figure 6.2: The first three activities of the problem solving process of figure 6.1, showing risk assessment and its possible outcomes (b-type key)

The customer's gaining confidence in the requirement specification is also the interest of the supplier: who would wish to work to an erroneous requirement specification, such that even if the design meets the specification perfectly, the customer will be dissatisfied? Thus, requirement elicitation and analysis are *cooperative* activities involving both customer and supplier, under the stewardship of the customer.

Identifying the requirements

We adopt the definition of the quality standard:

> **requirement**
> need or expectation that is stated, customarily implied, or obligatory
> ISO/FDIS 9000:2000

Several methods of requirement analysis and requirement elicitation are in use, and the topic is of much current interest. One method involves 'animation': building some kind of a prototype [3], allowing the customer to try out some selected features of the solution in the working environment. Another method is computer simulation of the problem and of the solution. Yet another method is to construct the P/p model of the current state of the referent as well as of the (direct or indirect) solution, and evaluate the model to see if the solution yields the desired result.

Measures taken in complex, expensive, long term projects include identifying some critical part or critical aspect of the project, and making this the subject of a feasibility study which may be an elaborate project in its own right.

Before entering into the contract to carry out the 'create solution' process p4 of figure 6.1, the potential supplier must also assess the risks. This activity occurs 'off line', forming no part of the problem solving process: the potential supplier who finds the risk excessive will not enter into a contract with the customer, will not undertake the task of process p4. Once committing himself/herself to the project, the supplier will seek to minimize the risks associated with the 'create solution' process p4 (or, putting it positively, maximizing the chance of success). We return to this later in the chapter, when discussing the structure and elements of the problem solving process in more detail.

Although process p4 is the supplier's responsibility, if the project is complex and the process is long, the customer may wish to retain a measure of control. This could take the form of monitoring progress, with the option of curtailing the project if progress is unsatisfactory, or if the risk proves to be excessive. In such cases the contract will prescribe a project plan, dividing process p4 into a sequence of suitably defined segments, the customer carrying out progress review and risk assessment at the end of each segment.

Verification and validation

Verification and validation are tests of the correctness of the actions of the problem solving process of figure 6.1. Verification and validation are important notions, related but quite distinct. Both terms are used extensively in course of problem solving, namely in specification, design, development and quality management, but consistent terminology is yet to emerge. Some sources [4] offer helpful explanations, such as:

> *"Verification is the confirmation that the model does what it was designed to do.*
>
> *Validation is the acceptance of the model objective, architecture, design, and operation as suitable to the needs for the model.*
>
> *Verification should include tests for which the results were known (theoretical cases), qualification tests (tests to explore the model's limits and responses to out-of-bound data), and benchmarking against similar models, if appropriate. Verification should judge the success of the model against the objectives defined early. If not done already, the users of the model must operate it successfully to provide the ultimate acceptance."*

Nevertheless, definitions, even in authoritative sources such as ISO, tend to be vague and uninformative [5]. We must therefore define:

> **verification**
> formal proof of the internal consistency of the specification or the design of the referent, or of the conformity of the design to the specification
>
> Our working definition

and

> **validation**
> convincing demonstration under defined operating conditions of the conformity of:
> – the specification against the requirements, or
> – the implementation against the design, or
> – the implementation against the requirements
>
> Our working definition

Validation involves the real world: either the problematical *referent,* or the *solution,* or both. Validation occurs at the conclusion of several of the subprocesses of figure 6.1. By contrast, in accord with our definition, *verification* is carried out entirely in the world of models: it tests the design of the solution within subprocess p4 of figure 6.1. An alternative representation of the problem solving spiral to demonstrate the distinction between verification and validation, such as that of figure 6.3 below.

The boxes of the figure are numbered for ease of reference. Forward arrows show actions to promote progress of the problem solving process, whereas reverse arrows indicate tests to check results.

- The problematical referent is in the real world, placed in Box 1.
- The specification of Box 2 'lives' in the abstract world of models. Its correctness must be checked against the reality of Box 1. This test is validation: it compares an entity of the model world with an entity of reality.
- The specification of Box 2 must also be tested for internal consistency: freedom from incompleteness and contradictions, as well as correctness of syntax. Since this test takes place entirely in the model world, it is verification.

- The design of Box 3 must be checked against the specification of the solution in Box 2. Since this test takes place entirely in the model world, it too is verification.
- The implementation of the design (Box 4) must be checked against the design in Box 3. This test is validation: it compares a real life entity with an entity of the world of models.
- The real life entity in Box 4 is the original problematical referent modified by the newly acquired solution. As the referent operates in practice, new problems will arise, leading to a new cycle of the problem solving spiral.

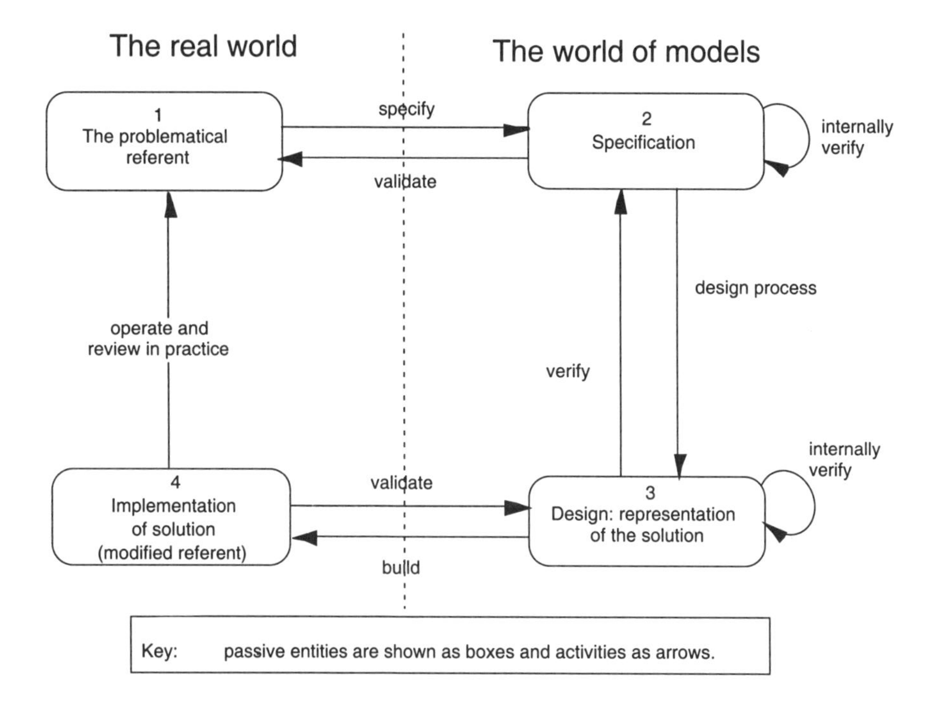

Figure 6.3: Verification and validation in course of one revolution of the problem solving spiral

Supplementary verification and validation activities take place at several places in course of problem solving. For example,

- the customer *validates* the requirement specification against repeated observations of the referent before releasing it to the supplier,
- the supplier *verifies* the design of the solution before committing resources to implementation, *validates* each component before building it into the solution, and *validates* the solution as a whole before releasing it to the customer,
- the customer *validates* the solution before adopting it into service – and before releasing payment to the supplier!

6.2 The customer specifies the problem (process p1)

The rest of this chapter is devoted to the discussion of each component of the problem solving process p of figure 6.1.

Problem formulation

Recall the first few examples of chapter 2, describing adverse situations in a company, a school, the underground transport network of a capital city. If the unsatisfactory circumstances prevail and escape the notice of those responsible, the situation will continue to decline, until finally the organization is put out of its misery by external events. The company will go bankrupt or will be bought out by a competitor, the local authority will close the school or will bring in a team of professional 'trouble shooters', the underground railway will be privatized for better or for worse as far as the travelling public is concerned. On the other hand, if the management is alert and keep an eye on events, then the situation will trigger an investigative process that will converge on a representation of reality as it deviates from the goal. The process is *problem formulation,* and its outcome is the *problem specification.* This is a new concept emerging logically from modelling the problem solving process in detail.

Specification

Specifications are used extensively throughout the problem solving process. The international quality standard defines:

> **specification**
> document stating requirements
>
> ISO/FDIS 9000:2000

For our purposes, this definition is too vague. A specification needs to be specific (!), identifying the relevant attributes of the referent, and characterizing them by their *measures.* The ISO definition does not prescribe the use of measures explicitly, although an appended Note strongly implies this. Another flaw of the ISO definition is that it is *too narrow.* In problem solving one needs a specification not only for defining the required solution but also for defining the problem itself. Thus, in the following we discriminate between *problem specification* and the customer's *requirement specification,* and distinguish further between the customer's and the *supplier's* specification. Meanwhile we offer the generic definition:

> **specification**
> a formal model of the referent, characterizing its relevant attributes by their measures
>
> Our working definition

Problem specification

The problem formulation process filters out the relevant elements of the mass of detail displayed by the referent, distilling them into the *problem specification.* The problem specification refers to no background, offers no excuses for the troubles that have arisen, names no scapegoats, suggests no solutions. It simply provides *facts* in terms of figures, giving a concise, coherent, objective, *descriptive* representation of the unsatisfactory referent at a given time instant.

We define:

> **problem specification**
> specifications whose measures characterize the shortfall between (1) the formal model of the *prescribed, predicted* or desired referent at a specific time instant of the present or the past, and (2) the *descriptive* model of the same referent: its *actual* characteristics at the same time instant.
> NOTE: the problem specification may include observable characteristics as well as attributes defined as trends: rates of change of attributes.
> Our working definition

The problem specification emerging at the end of process p1:

- should give measures of the *present value* of attributes, such as the share price in £ (or $, or whatever),
- will give *comparative* figures: measures of the *distance* between the actual measures of the referent at the present time and the goal which should have been achieved: the planned or expected value of an attribute,
- may include measures of *trends:* the current rate of change of attribute values, and measures which characterize *threats*: predictions based on current data of pending calamity, such as, in our examples, public outcry to sensational newspaper headlines, or imminent bankruptcy as the expected effect of the action of competitors.
- must be validated before moving on to further activities of the problem solving process.

Example 6.1

In chapter 2, Example 2.1 refers to a highstreet retailer, and implies that the company sets itself targets in terms of five key attributes:

- *turnover (period of time unspecified in the example),*
- *monthly net profit (presumably averaged over a longer period, such as a quarter or half a year),*
- *interim dividend (presumably per ordinary share),*
- *share price, (or rate of change of share price over a specified period),*
- *number of members of staff required to deal with customers' complaints.*

Assume that the company reviews the value of the five attribute measures at the end of every six-monthly period. The problem specification could be formulated as the difference between the target values and the actually achieved values.

6.3 The customer chooses a problem solving strategy (process p2)

Let us assume that the problem specification is now to hand, and problem solving proceeds to process p2 in figure 6.1. In the second process in the sequence, the customer must decide what kind of *problem solving strategy* to adopt. As we know, this process is the responsibility of the customer, or the problem owner as the customer's representative.

CUSTOMER'S OPTIONS OF PROBLEM SOLVING STRATEGIES

The customer's aim is to close the gap between target and achievement. For this, the customer can choose between two main problem formulation strategies: –

- The customer's *direct* approach is to initiate a project whose aim is to modify the unsatisfactory referent – the unprofitable company, the unsuccessful school, the unreliable underground system in our examples, or else set some ambitious new goal to take advantage of some new, unexplored opportunity, such as a recent opening in the market, or an emerging technology. In case of the direct approach the aim is that, by the end of the project, the referent's performance should meet the goal.
- The customer's *indirect* approach is not to construct a solution to the specific problem but to seek a *mechanism:* an instrument to be installed into the unsatisfactory referent which can not only deal with the specific problem in hand, but also with similar problems that may arise in future. For example, install new machinery to replace the company's obsolete equipment, enhance the computer system to improve administrative efficiency, acquire new staff skills. The aim of the mechanism is to act as the means of improving the unsatisfactory referent so as to attain the desired performance, and to enhance the capability of the organization to handle problems of a kind. In this case the task of the problem solving process is to *identify a new referent*: specify, generate and install the new mechanism which is expected to alleviate the problem, or exploit the new opportunity.

Example 6.2

The company introduces a new product line whose manufacture generates a new kind of toxic waste product. A decision is required whether to opt for a solution by 'outsourcing' (a direct strategy of engaging a subcontractor to dispose of the waste on a regular basis) or to acquire the means and skills in-house (an indirect strategy of ordering a waste disposal unit from a different subcontractor so that the task could be carried out by the company itself).

Example 6.3

One of the UK's distinguished universities decides to purchase from software developers a software packages for dealing with some administrative tasks, such as accounting, personnel record keeping and payroll. The customer is highly skilled, the supplier has attested reputation, and the task is of routine nature. Nevertheless, the project turns out to be a disappointment: although the packages worked, they failed to satisfy the University's expectations. The inevitable internal 'post mortem' blamed the supplier, but closer investigation showed that the cause of the trouble was the University itself: the University failed to specify the problem, and adopted an indirect strategy without first investigating other strategic options.

6.4 The customer specifies the requirement (process p3)

In the problem solving process p, the third process p3 produces the customer's *requirement specification.* We know that this process too is the responsibility of the problem owner as the customer's representative. The requirement specification is a *prescriptive* representation: an information product stipulating the key attributes and their measures to which the system must conform. The requirement specification might stipulate the improved referent, as represented in the problem specification, or the mechanism to be created to affect the improvement. The time stamp of the requirement specification is the date at which the specification is issued, and the attribute measure set includes the deadline by which the solution must be available.

Requirement specification, direct strategy

If the customer opts for the direct strategy, the task of requirement formulation process p3 is simply to construct a *specification for the desired state of the referent,* together with the *constraints* of the solution: the financial, material and other resources available for the project, and the deadline date by which the solution must be available. The strategy is simple: once the solution is developed and the customer accepts it as valid, the problem solving process is at an end for both the customer and for the supplier (figure 6.1). However, the direct strategy involves other risks, such as not maintaining the skills and other means of coping with the problem, and the solution interfering with the day-by-day operation of the organization.

Requirement specification, indirect strategy

Similarly to the direct case, in the indirect case the requirement formulation process p3 must *specify the desired state of the referent* and the *constraints* of the problem solving project. Additionally the process must identify and specify the *mechanism* which is to affect the improvement of the original referent, and the way in which the mechanism will fit into the organization. The mechanism becomes the *new referent* of the problem solving process, and as far as the supplier is concerned, the specification of this new referent is the output of the requirement specification process.

Note that, in case of the indirect strategy, the referent of the problem specification is different from the referent of the requirement specification. The former is the problematical entity of interest, whereas the latter is the mechanism that will put the problematical entity to rights. The solution is developed off-line: the problem solving project does not interfere with the operation of the organization, the customer remains in sole charge of the organization throughout the project. However, this strategy carries its own risks. When the supplier delivers the valid solution – one which meets the requirements specification, – the supplier's task is complete, but the customer has more work to do. The newly obtained mechanism must be absorbed into the structure of the organization, and its effectiveness in curing the original problem validated (figure 6.4).

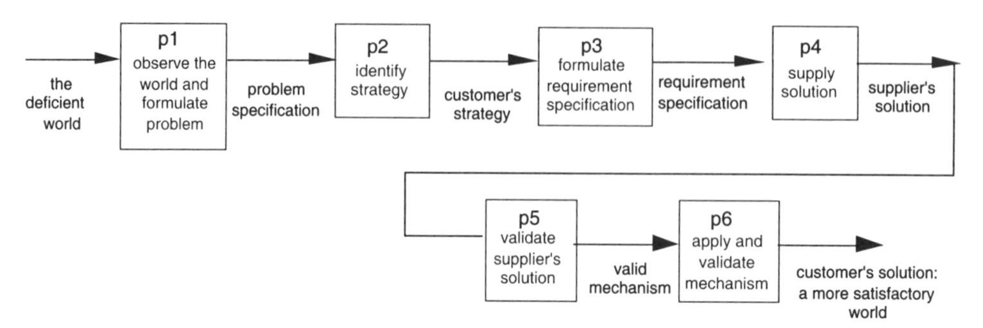

Figure 6.4: From problem to solution, customer's indirect strategy(b-type key)

The risk is that the mechanism may have met the customer's requirement specification, and yet it may still fail to produce the desired improvement as far as the original problem is concerned.

Example 6.4

Ophtalmologists traditionally manage shortsightedness by prescribing glasses or contact lenses for the patient. The strategy is indirect, the implements providing the means of alleviating the sight deficit. In recent years an alternative direct strategy has become available: laser treatment which modifies the lens in the eye of the patient.

Defining 'requirement specification'

It is not sufficient for the successful problem solving project to close the gap between the goal and the performance of the referent: the project should seek to ensure that the gap would not reopen. The requirement specification needs to have a *predictive element*, anticipating the projected *life history* of the referent, making provisions for the solution *remaining* satisfactory in the future, continuing to meet needs.

Consider again the two problem solving strategies available for the customer. We define:

requirement specification – direct problem solving strategy:
specification prescribing the desired characteristics of the problematical referent

Our working definition

and

> **requirement specification – indirect problem solving strategy**
> specification of a mechanism for bringing about the desired characteristics of the problematical referent
>
> Our working definition

Examples 6.5

A hungry person might order meals from the local takeaway (direct strategy), or might buy a cooker as the means of preparing meals (indirect strategy).

A company might send out documents to a firm of printers and binders (direct strategy), or might invest in a binding machine so as to do the job in-house (indirect strategy).

6.5 The supplier develops the solution (process p4)

Supplying the solution is the fourth process (p4) in the sequence of figure 6.1 (or figure 6.4). The process, shown in figure 6.5, is composed of four subprocesses:

p4.1 developing the *supplier's specification*,

p4.2 selecting a *solution strategy*,

p4.3 developing a *candidate solution* in accord with the chosen strategy [6],

p4.4 ascertaining the validity of the candidate solution, thus raising its status to *supplier's solution*.

All four subprocesses, just as the 'create solution' process p4 itself, are the supplier's responsibility.

Figure 6.5 is a simplification in at least three aspects:

- In practice, when the problem is complex, several possible solutions may be pursued simultaneously and independently, and the supplier conducts a 'feasibility study' to evaluate these in competition, selecting the most promising. The winner is then carried to conclusion.
- In reality the 'create solution' process seldom succeeds first time, and it is usual for the supplier to retrace his/her steps several times before reaching the solution.
- The supplier's specification is input not only to the 'select solution strategy' subprocess (p4.2), but also to the 'develop candidate solution' (p4.3) and the 'validate candidate solution' (p4.4) subprocesses. For the sake of clarity of presentation, figure 6.5 omits these; hence the figure is incomplete. The reader is invited to draw up a P/p model of the full process.

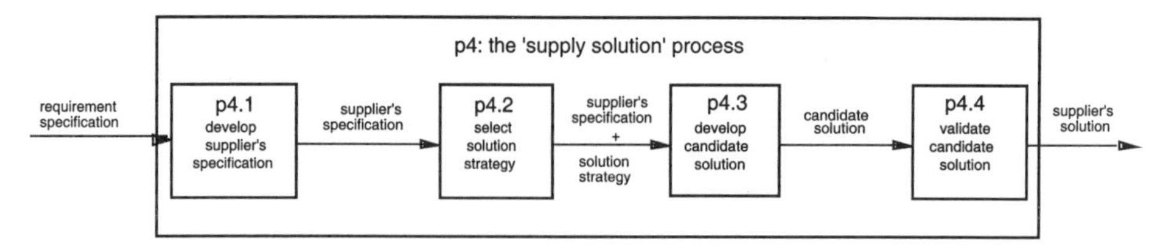

Figure 6.5: Structure of the 'create solution' process

We now proceed to discuss the four elements of the 'create solution' process, at the end of which the solution is ready for the *customer's validation.*

Develop supplier's specification (p4.1)

The solution must satisfy the customer's needs: it must conform to the customer's requirement specification. The future system must also meet further demands, to which we collectively refer as 'quality characteristics'. These:

- prescribe attributes and attribute values constrained by relevant international/ national standards and the supplier's house standards,
- might be stipulated by laws and bylaws,
- might be demanded by environmental or health and safety considerations.

Using the language of logic, we can describe this relationship as *implication*: the supplier's specification *implies* the requirement specification. The prudent supplier will impose further demands and restrictions as contingencies to offer a degree of protection for the eventualities of the supply process, or to provide extra safety and reliability. The customer's requirement specification, tightened and complemented by quality characteristics and by the supplier's own demands, forms the *supplier's specification.* We define:

supplier's specification
a *product* which is the prescriptive representation of the entity to be developed by the supplier, incorporating
– all of the attributes given in the requirement specification,
– attributes representing the supplier's own quality requirements.

NOTE that the supplier's specification must be *at least as* stringent as the customer's requirement specification, ensuring that if an entity meets the supplier's specification, then it will always satisfy the customer's requirement specification

Our working definition

Example 6.6
Novel technologies demand new solutions. In designing the ARPANet – the founding network which later became the Internet –, the issues of reliability and robustness were paramount, driven by the military need to maintain communications in time of war.

> *Among the innovations introduced by the devisers and implementers of ARPANet were the following (quoted freely from source: Hafner K & Lyon M: "Where Wizards stay up late, the Origins of the Internet", Simon & Schuster, 1996):*
>
> 1. *The new concept of distributed networks, based on the theory of Paul Baran with an inbuilt redundancy level of 3-4 in which the network can sustain a large amount of damage without ceasing to function.*
> 2. *The new concept of self-recovery wherein if one of the linking computers fails for some reason, it reboots and copies software from one of its linked neighbours without requiring human intervention.*

Supplier selects solution strategy (p4.2) ***and develops candidate solution*** (p4.3)

Having established the supplier's specification, the next task is to select the supplier's *solution strategy.* This means deciding *how* to provide a candidate solution which not only meets the supplier's specification, but also promises to succeed in validation, is expected to be delivered on time, and will be within the budget of the project.

Assume now that the customer opted for the indirect approach. The supplier must then provide a mechanism that will solve the customer's problem (figure 6.4).

The supplier may adopt several strategies, of which we outline only a few:

- the 'ready made' option,
- the 'structural' option,
- the 'customized' option,
- the 'prototyping' option.

THE 'READY MADE' OPTION

If a problem – or one *similar* to it – had been solved before, there may be no need to invent the solution anew. If the supplier considers that a suitable entity already exists which will meet the specification and is obtainable within the time scale and budget, then it is often a sound strategy to locate such an entity and adopt it as a *candidate ready made solution.* Almost certainly the candidate will not match the supplier's specification precisely. If it falls short of the specification then the supplier must continue to search for an alternative, or resort to another strategy. If the candidate is 'overdesigned' – too good for the purpose, capable of meeting more stringent criteria than those of the supplier's specification – then from the viewpoint of the problem in hand this is irrelevant; what is essential is that the ready made candidate solution should *at least* conform to the supplier's specification.

If the supplier selects the ready made option then the 'develop candidate solution' process, p4.3 in figure 6.5, will degenerate to a single process of 'procure candidate ready made solution'. A simplified, incomplete representation of this process is shown in figure 6.6. (Once again, the reader is asked to draw up a complete P/p graph.) The result of this process is the 'candidate solution' which is the input to the supplier's 'validate candidate solution' process in figure 6.5.

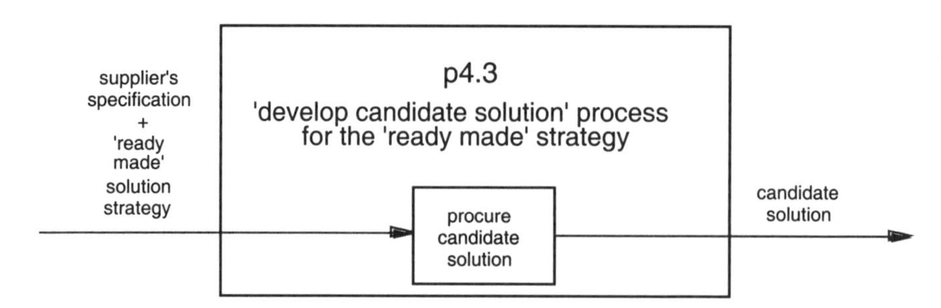

Figure 6.6: 'Develop candidate solution' process, 'ready made' strategy (b-type)

THE 'DESIGN-AND-MAKE' (OR 'STRUCTURAL') OPTION

When there is no ready made solution at hand, the supplier must start afresh. The 'develop candidate solution' process p4.3 of figure 6.7 will now consist of three subprocesses: 'design candidate solution' (p4.3.1), 'verify design' (p4.3.2), and 'build candidate solution' (p4.3.3, also called 'implement design'). Figure 6.7 shows the case when these three subprocesses form a sequence. In practice the 'develop candidate solution' process is seldom accomplished in such a simple sequence: instead, it is frequently the result of several corrections and design modifications.

Industrial experience suggests, and case studies of complex long term projects show, that it is not unusual for design modifications to chase each other, new modification requests arising before the design team had time to respond to the previous ones. This kind of situation leads to delay, confusion, and even chaos. When the time scale is too short, or when design verification methods are too weak, the 'build candidate solution' process starts before the correctness of the design is adequately proven. Therefore, some design faults may come to light very late, when much of the construction is completed and most of the budget had already been exhausted. In such a case the supplier faces the unhappy choice of *either* completing the construction of a system which is known to be inconsistent with the specifications, *or* incurring heavy losses in correcting the design and building the system all over again. One of the main aims of this book is to assist in reducing such risks in the development of complex systems.

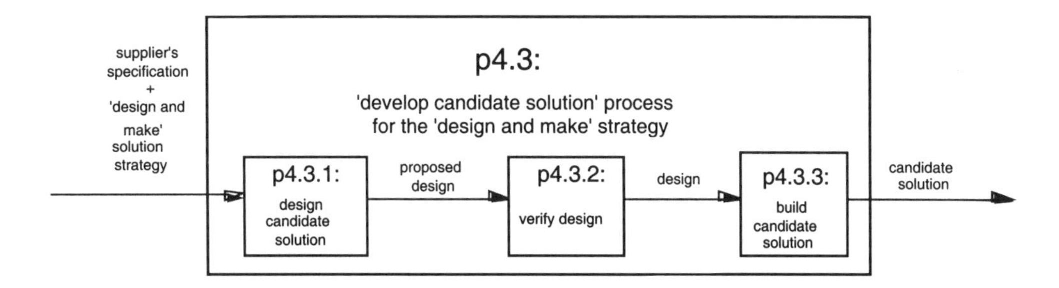

Figure 6.7: 'Develop candidate solution' process for the 'design and make' strategy

The outcome of the 'develop candidate solution' process p4.3 will be the input to the supplier's 'validate candidate solution' process p4.4 of figure 6.5, just as for the 'ready made' strategy.

Hierarchical design

The 'develop candidate solution' process (p4.3) creates a *hierarchical structure*, most conveniently represented as a tree – a graph defined in chapter 4.

Two-level systems

Designing a two-level system (process p4.3.1) is the case of the simplest design hierarchy. The structure is a two level tree, with the supplier's problem – the supplier's specification – at the root, and the supplier's subproblems – the specifications of the 'atomic' components – at the leaves. The atomic components of the hierarchy are bound together by the *structure* that describes the relationship among the specifications.

The structure is shown in figure 6.8: a directed graph (but not a P/p graph!). A component in the figure is regarded as 'atomic' if there is no need for the design to proceed any further because a ready made component is available which is expected to meet the specification.

Verifying the design (p4.3.2) is the next task. Once the proposed design of the two-level structure is completed, the 'verify design' process can begin. This means formally proving, or at least objectively and convincingly demonstrating, that the design will meet the specification, *provided* that:

- all of the component parts of the structure meet their specification, and
- the interrelations among the parts are built in accord with the prescribed structure.

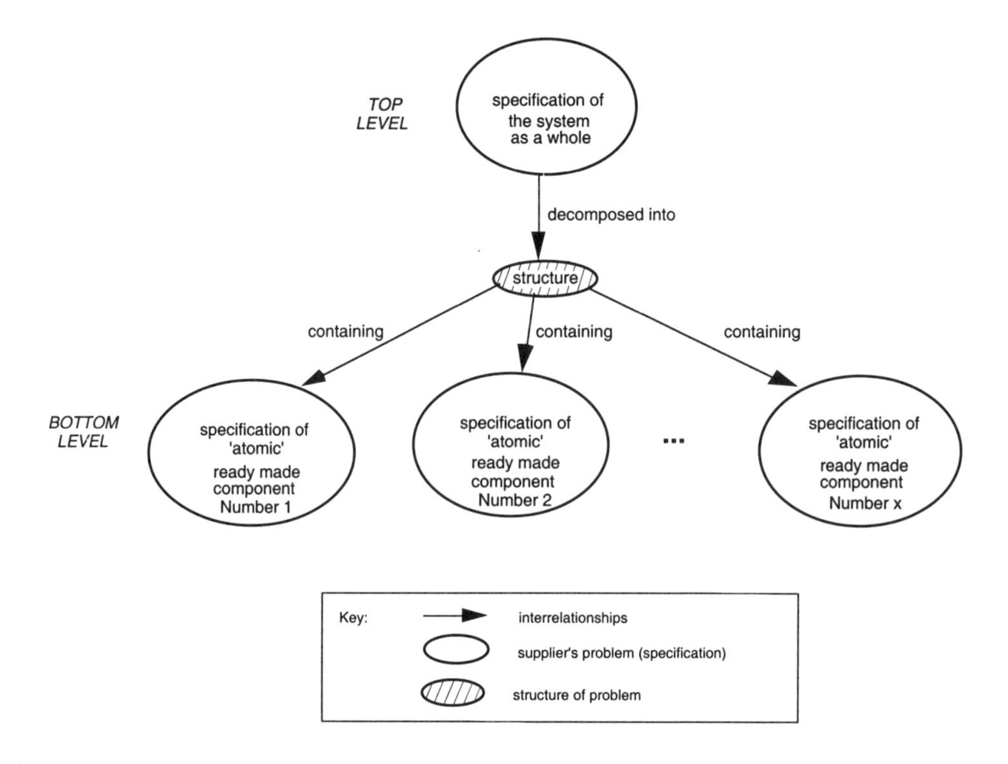

Figure 6.8: Two-level design

Building the two-level system (p4.3.3) follows after the design has been verified. This is when the 'build candidate solution' process starts. The design of figure 6.8, having x number of atomic components, calls for x+1 number of 'build' tasks, namely:

- to procure the x number of ready made atomic components, and validate each one against its specification,
- to construct the structure in accord with the design.

Figure 6.9 shows the finished candidate solution, built according to the design of figure 6.8, ready for the supplier's 'validate candidate solution' process (figure 6.5).

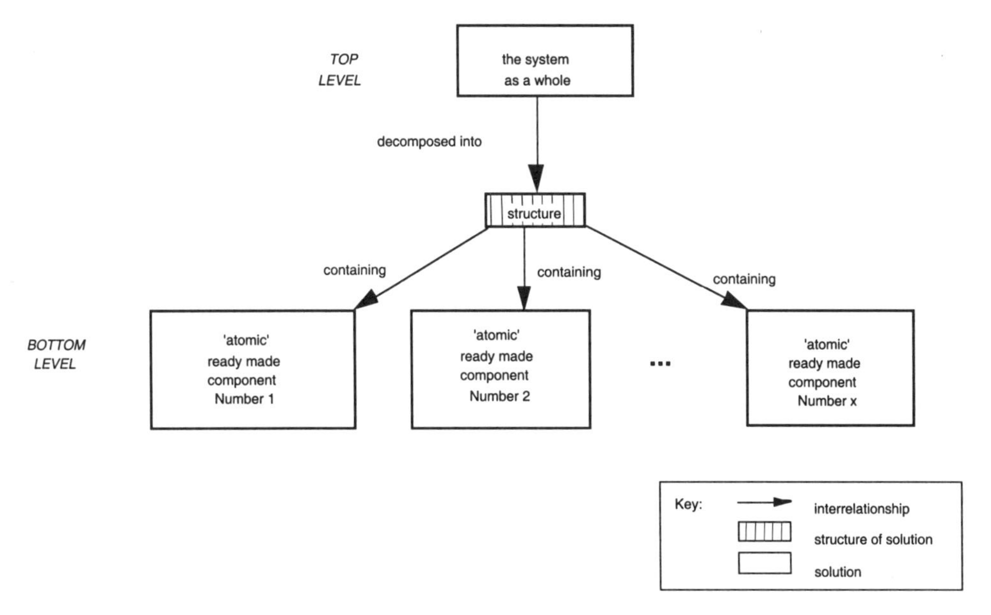

Figure 6.9: Design documentation of a two-level system, to be built to the design of figure 6.8

Multilevel systems

Most solutions are complicated: not accomplished in two levels but being composed as *multilevel hierarchies.*

- ‘Design candidate solution’ (process p4.3.1) proceeds ‘top down’ from the root of the tree, level by level. Candidate ready made solutions are sought for each subproblem, and each subproblem is further decomposed, until a candidate ready made solution is available. Thus, the supplier’s specification – the supplier’s problem – is decomposed into a *structure* of subproblems, each simpler than its parent, each being the specification of a subsystem, characterized by its attribute measures.
- ‘As for the two-level structure, ‘verify design’ (p4.3.2) means formally proving, or at least objectively demonstrating beyond reasonable doubt, level by level, that the system will meet the specification, *provided* that:
    (i) all component parts of the structure meet their specification,
    (ii) all interconnections among the parts are built in accord with the prescribed structure. Verification is interwoven with design: no further decomposition is advised until the design of the level above is verified.
- ‘Build candidate solution’ (p4.3.3) proceeds ‘bottom up’, starting from the leaves of the tree. The verified structures of valid atomic components are assembled, proceeding level by level to verified structures of valid subsystems, until the candidate solution of the problem as a whole is formed. At completion of the ‘develop candidate solution’ process, all component parts and subsystems at all levels have been validated, and structures at all levels verified.

- On completion of the 'develop candidate solution' process p4.3, the 'validate candidate solution' process p4.4 will have a single task: testing the validity of the system as a whole.

Figure 6.10 shows a specific stage of development of the design-and-make process for a particular case. The supplier's specification – the representation of the supplier's problem, shown by a shaded elliptical symbol – is divided into a structure consisting of n number of subproblems (subsupplier's specifications). Each subproblem, marked by a shaded ellipse, is subdivided into sub-subproblems (sub-subsupplier's specifications) which, in this case, are 'atomic'. The complete specification structure would be a hierarchy of shaded ellipses on all levels (in this case three), interspersed with white ellipses indicating the proposed structure, level by level.

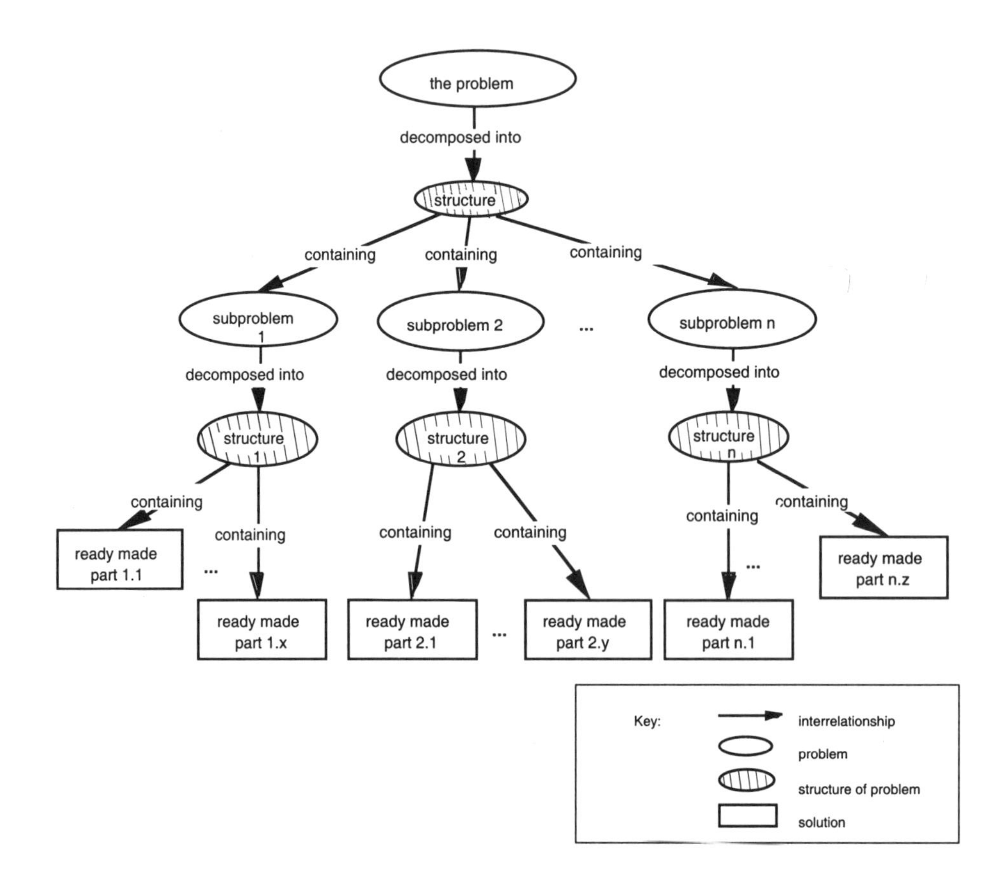

Figure 6.10: A particular stage of implementation of the supplier's design-and-make strategy: solution of atomic problems have been obtained and validated

As we have seen, validation and assembly proceeds from the bottom up. First, the shaded ellipses of the lowermost level are replaced by shaded rectangles, showing that a ready-made solution has been found and validated. Next comes assembly and test, where conceptually the direction of the arrows is reversed. At the end of this, the white ellipses are replaced by white rectangles, showing that the structure has been built and is valid. The process continues upward, and when the solution is built and validated, all ellipses are replaced by rectangles, showing the complete structure of the solution.

Figure 6.10 arrests the development process at the instant when all ready-made solutions of the atomic subsystem have been validated. The next stage would be to validate structures 1 to n, and finally to assemble and validate the structure as a whole.

THE 'CUSTOMIZED' OPTION

When no ready made candidate solution is available, or when the cost of obtaining a ready-made solution is prohibitive, it may still be possible to avoid full scale development. *Customization* identifies and procures an affordable, readily available *programmable 'general purpose' system*, or the ready made solution to a problem *similar* to the one at hand, and adapts this *approximate solution* to the given requirements. To make the strategy successful, the development task should be minimized, preserving as much of the approximate solution as possible.

Development by customization may proceed along the following routes:

- designing and implementing special purpose *software* for the programmable system, leaving the hardware intact,
- *partitioning* the hardware components of the structure into two groups, preserving the parts in the first group and modifying or replacing the parts of the second, and then reassembling the system in accord with the original structure,
- altering the *structure* itself, preserving all the component parts,
- *combining* the above.

All these require complete understanding of the existing system. Otherwise faults hitherto concealed may become apparent, as the following two often-quoted examples demonstrate:

Example 6.7

The first flight of the Ariane 5 rocket failed 40 seconds into the flight. The following extract from the official report pinpoints the cause as the inclusion of a software component controlling the inertial reference system. This had been inherited from Ariane 4 and not tested under the flight conditions relevant to Ariane 5.

"... The specification of the inertial reference system and the tests performed at equipment level did not specifically include the Ariane 5 trajectory data. Consequently the realignment function was not tested under simulated Ariane 5 flight conditions, and the design error was not discovered."

Extract from Official report of the Inquiry Board, July 1996

Example 6.8

The Therac 25 series of accidents has been well documented. The original fault, compounded by the lack of seriousness with which the problem was treated, led to two deaths and several cases of injury caused by a massive X ray overdose in this Linear Accelerator used in the treatment of cancer.

Therac 25 was an updated version of Therac 20 which had operated satisfactorily for some years. The safety system of the earlier version, the software for which had been inherited from Therac 6, was implemented both in software and hardware. The hardware safeguard had masked a fault in the software. The software component was reused in the newer version and assumed to be fault-free and the hardware safeguard was omitted. Under certain operating conditions the software safeguards were bypassed resulting in injury to the patients.

Details from Leveson N: Safeware, Appendix A, Addison Wesley,1995

THE 'PROTOTYPING' OPTION

As we have seen in Section 6.1, a prototype is an initial form of the solution that differs from the final version in some specific way. We also discussed the use of prototyping for clarifying the customer's requirements.

Prototyping may also be used by the supplier as a strategic option of development, or as means of risk reduction. We outline here some of the several possible ways of employing prototypes in course of the 'create solution' process.

- A 'throw away' prototype may be constructed rapidly to test some critical aspect of the specification.
- A reduced version of the design may be built as a prototype when the project involves the use of unfamiliar technology.
- Instead of the 'single shot' process of figure 6.5, the supplier may develop the solution in several cycles of a spiral. This involves designing, building and validating a simplified version of the solution, enhancing this in a series of increments, each increment following a process such as figure 6.5, until the final version meets the supplier's specification in full.
- When the solution requires building many copies of the same article, a prototype of one article may be constructed under laboratory conditions. This 'laboratory prototype' may then be tested in operation in the laboratory or in the field, correcting any flaw before committing investment in the production line. If the solution involves mass production of the article, then the construction of the laboratory prototype might be followed by building production prototypes to test that the design can not only be implemented in the laboratory but be replicated by the manufacturing process. (Such considerations do not apply to software where the cost of production is minimal and design cost is almost equal to the total cost of development.)
- Another use of prototyping occurs when the project involves constructing a complex system which serves many users. Here verification of the design (proving its correctness on paper) may not give

sufficient confidence for going ahead with the 'build candidate solution' process. Instead, a working prototype is constructed for a small number of users, and the effect of the rest of the users is simulated.

SOME CONCLUDING COMMENTS ON SUPPLIERS' SOLUTION STRATEGIES

Comments on the ready made and customized solution strategies

Common sense suggests that the ready made and customized options offer speed, simplicity and low risk. However, in the long term, these advantages might be outweighed by disadvantages, as the examples show.

Example 6.9 – An everyday example

It is easier to buy a suit off the peg than tailoring your own, or have one made to measure. You see what you get, you know how much it costs, there should be no surprises, if you don't like the merchandise in one shop, you can go to another.

However, there are cases to be made for bespoke tailoring. For example:

- *The shape and size of the customer may be so unusual that searching for a ready made suit is a waste of time.*
- *The customer may need protective clothing made of special material.*
- *The customer may wish to impress his colleagues and friends by wearing a handmade, made to measure suit.*
- *The customer may need many suits and frequent replacements, the supplier may inflate the price for urgent consignments, and customer may finally be forced to acquire the capability to make the suits in house, rather than being dependent on the supplier.*

Comments on the 'design and make' strategy

'Design and make' may prove the most powerful strategy for complex problems. While solving the specific problem in hand, the supplier gains valuable skills and technical insights which will pay long term dividends, benefiting future projects, opening up the opportunity for offering new product lines.

A disciplined approach to development by 'design and make' allows each subproblem to be treated independently. The independence of subtasks makes for versatile project management, avoids bottlenecks and undue dependence of the project on individuals, and assists planned quality assurance throughout the development process, instead of relying on *post facto* quality control (the punitive regime of test and rejection at the end of the project, rather than the positive approach of assuring predictable quality). Furthermore, 'design and make' is the *only* approach for an ambitious company who wants to be first in the field.

It must be recognized however that 'design and make' does not allow the supplier to get away from using ready made solutions altogether. The atomic components of the system will always be procured from the outside; the only question is at which level of the hierarchy. The 'design and make' strategy exchanges the procurement task of a single system for the procurement task of many components, with the added job of developing and validating structures.

Supplier validates the candidate solution ($p_{4.4}$)

We return to figure 6.5 again. Regardless of the kind of solution strategy, the 'develop candidate solution' process must always be followed by testing the candidate solution against the supplier's specification. If the 'validate candidate solution' process yields a positive result then the status of the candidate solution changes: it becomes the *solution* as far as the supplier is concerned. At this point the 'create solution' process of figure 6.5 is complete.

6.6 The customer validates the solution (process p5)

When the supplier delivers his/her solution, the final stage of problem solving process can begin. This is yet another validation process, but this time it is the responsibility of the customer (figure 6.1). The customer may be unaware of the supplier's specification: as far as he/she is concerned, what matters is the requirement specification. The finished system must be tested to ascertain that it conforms to the customer's requirement specification. If so, then the supplier has discharged his/her obligations according to the letter of the contract.

Current quality thinking requires more than conformance to the contract. When undertaking a task, the supplier enters into a cooperative relationship with the customer, going beyond the requirements stated in the contract. With this notion in mind, the international standard defines:

quality
degree to which a set of inherent characteristics fulfils requirements
ISO/FDIS 9000:2000

Those who follow the development of the standard will note that the word 'degree' appears for the first time, signifying commitment to *measure* quality. We are pleased to adopt the spirit of this definition. However, we find that in this context the words 'set' and 'inherent' add nothing. We note also that an earlier draft of the standard was more informative, referring explicitly to 'interested parties' whose requirements are to be fulfilled. Thus, we define:

quality
degree to which the characteristics of a system to fulfil requirements of interested parties
Our working definition, based on ISO/FDIS 9000:2000

The requirements of the customer and other interested parties may alter in course of the development process, and the supplier must anticipate this, at least to some extent. The supplier must also recognize obligations to members of the community who may be indirectly affected by the newly created solution, and to the environment in which the solution system exists. When creating a supplier's specification that is more stringent than the customer's requirement specification, the supplier seeks to anticipate these broader demands, such that they should not come as a surprise at the late stage of 'customer's validation'. The gap between the requirement specification and the supplier's specification can act as a buffer, protecting the solution against the customer's unstated needs, and against the community's tacit expectations.

6.7 When resources are inadequate

Assume now that the problem has been correctly identified, the solution has been designed and costed, but the planned solution cannot be implemented because the costs are beyond the available resources. Nevertheless, the project plan could be used in several ways:

- as grounds for a plea / demand for increased resources, and, in case of projects of national significance, as an instrument for mobilizing public opinion via the media,
- as modification of the plan, curtailing the project, implementing those selected parts which could supply useful if limited improvements to the original problematic situation,
- as a basis for identifying part-problems implementable within the resources at hand, with the intention of resuming the project when further resources become available.

In all three cases the structured and deliberate approach discussed in this chapter would be of assistance. In the first case it would provide reasoned justification for increasing the resources; in the second case it would assist in identifying the most useful parts of the complete project for partial implementation; in the third case it would serve in planning which parts of the project to implement and which parts to defer, assure that the work completed would be usable in the interim, and give a sound basis for continuation.

6.8 Summary

This chapter examines the notion of 'problem', and follows the problem solving process from its earliest beginning – the problem owner's vague unease about a situation – to its conclusion, when the solution passes the customer's validation test. The route between recognizing that a problem exists and accepting a solution as valid is complicated, and no matter how useful the solution is, there is always room for improvement. Progress is likened to a spiral, with several cycles and possible detours. Most of this chapter deals with one simplified cycle of the spiral.

A definition of 'specification' is offered which emphasizes the role of measures. Within this generic definition, distinction is made between 'problem specification' and 'requirement specification', and between the customer's and the supplier's specification. The 'supplier's specification' is a more stringent model of the solution than the customer's requirement specification, incorporating local and general standards as well as quality requirements.

In course of problem solving, both the customer and the supplier faces risks, and the discussion extends to some aspects of risk management.

Problem solving also confronts the customer and the supplier with strategic issues.

- The customer must choose between a direct and an indirect approach: using the problem solving project for developing the referent itself, or for providing the *means* of development.
- The supplier can attempt to locate a suitable ready made solution, design and develop a solution anew, opt for a customized solution by adapting an existing system to the supplier's specification, or employ prototyping as a strategic instrument of development.

Having developed a candidate solution, this must first be validated against the supplier's specification, and then against the customer's requirements. In keeping with contemporary principles of quality, the supplier's obligation goes beyond the customer's stated requirements specification: the solution must also meet the customer's implied needs, as well as more general criteria of quality.

We conclude Part 1 of this book with a checklist which has proved useful in many problem solving contexts.

A CHECKLIST FOR PROBLEM SOLVERS

The checklist below is not complete: it is simply a reminder of some points of good practice. We recommend that you always:

- identify your *referent* and its *boundary*,
- check the meaningfulness and ownership of any received *document* and ascertain the correctness of any *diagram* before incorporating the information in your representations,
- ensure that all your key *terms* are defined and the definitions quality-assured,
- construct a *P/p graph* of the problem solving process as soon as possible, incorporate all relevant information, and strive to continually improve the maturity of the representation,
- establish the nature of each *representation* (descriptive, predictive, prescriptive), checking the correctness of descriptive representations, the theoretical basis of predictive representations and the authority of prescriptive representations,
- distinguish between *problem specification* and *requirement specification*,
- assure that your *black box* representations use measurably defined *attributes*, and your specifications are given in terms of *measures* of such attributes,
- *validate* your specification before embarking on design,
- use explicitly defined *components* and *structures* in your *structural* representations,

- complete the characterization of your higher level representation in course of *planning* and *design*, before elaborating it in more detail,
- *verify* your design before embarking on *implementation*,
- use a *bipartite tree* to represent progress with your design and implementation tasks,
- keep your *documentation* up to date, and use the bipartite tree to trace the effect of any modification throughout the structure,
- assure that all your *products* and *processes* are properly defined, and the process definitions include the identification of their owner.

6.9 Exercises

Exercise 6.1

Section 6.1 contains the statements:

(i) within process p_3, "the customer validates the requirement specification ... before releasing it to the supplier",

(ii) within process p_4, "the supplier verifies the design of the solution before committing resources to implementation, validates each component before building it into the solution, and validates the solution as a whole before releasing it to the customer",

(iii) process p_5 is the activity where "the customer validates the solution before adopting it into service – and before releasing payment to the supplier!".

Show that these statements are consistent with our working definitions of 'verification' and 'validation'.

Exercise 6.2

Attempt to compile a problem specification on the basis of the information given in Example 2.1. Comment on the information and on the choice of attributes.

How would you expect the attribute set of the problem specification to vary if the business is:

(i) an estate agency specializing in domestic housing,

(ii) an international chain of clothing shops,

(iii) a chain of opticians?

Exercise 6.3

SSADM is a problem solving methodology backed by the UK government [7]. Draw a P/p graph of the stages involved in this problem solving methodology. (Details of the methodology can be found on the Internet or in any technical library.)

Exercise 6.4

"Sound systems" for domestic use come in many forms, from the very simple to the fiendishly complicated. In deciding which to purchase or build, the problem owner can adopt various strategies. Trace some of the routes which might be followed to satisfy this problem owner's dilemma.

Exercise 6.5

Define the problem of exporting meat. Suggest various strategies to include:

(i) exporting carcasses,

(ii) exporting live animals.

Exercise 6.6

A highly reputable manufacturer of studio quality audio equipment forms a new 'Audio Systems Division' which offers design consultancy services. You are appointed as the new Head of Division, and you immediately come under heavy pressure from the Sales Director to use the company's own products in the designs, although these may not always give best performance and best value for money. You are keen not to antagonize the Sales Director, but you are also anxious to establish your Division's reputation for high quality service and ethical conduct.

How do you decide to resolve the situation, and how is your decision reflected in the 'supplier's specification'?

Exercise 6.7

Many software-based projects inspired by the UK Government have foundered recently, such as computerizing the Passport Office, the National Insurance Recording System, the Benefit Payment Card Scheme and procedures of the Child Support Agency, not to mention the ongoing saga of the proposed Air Traffic Control System [8]. In what way might Product/process modelling have helped to avert or alleviate such difficulties?

6.10 Footnotes and References

1 See e.g. M Bunge: "Scientific research". Springer Verlag, 1967.

2 See e.g. J McDermid, Paul Rook: "Software development process models". Chapter 15 in "Software Engineer's Reference Book", ed. J McDermid, Butterworth, 1991.

3 We define:

prototype:
an exemplar of the solution of a problem
Our working definition

4 Systems Engineering Handbook Release 1, INCOSE, 1998.

5 The definitions are:

verification:
confirmation, through the provision of objective evidence, that specified requirements have been fulfilled

validation:
confirmation, through the provision of objective evidence, that the requirements for a specific intended use or application have been fulfilled

ISO/DIS 9000:2000
(Terms in italics are further defined in the Standard)

6 Here the term 'candidate solution' means that the solution has not been approved as yet. Choosing a suit from the rail in the shop is a candidate until it is tried and approved by the purchaser. Similarly, a suit made to measure by a bespoke tailor is a candidate until the possible flaws are corrected and the customer signifies acceptance.

7 See e.g. "SSADM and application packages". HMSO, October 1994.

8 See various reports issued by the National Audit Office.

Part 2

Chapter 7 Systems

In chapter 4 we discussed systems at length. Here we cover some of the same ground, but this time give greater depth and explain some of our notions in terms of mathematical formality.

7.1 System – a formal representation

Let us recall our definition:

> **system**
> a set of interrelated entities
>
> Our working definition

The entities may be regarded as elements of a set **E**, over which a set of interrelations **R** is defined. Mathematically this is expressed as: with

$$S = (E, R) \qquad \text{(expression 7.1)}$$

where S is the system,
(**E**, **R**) is an ordered pair of sets,
E is set of entities, and
R is a set of interrelations among the entities
(conventionally upper case characters in bold represent sets).

A system may be *infinite* or *finite*. An infinite system may comprise an infinite number of entities (the set **E** may be infinite), and these may be interrelated in an infinite number of ways (the set **R** may be infinite). We write this by showing sets **E** and **R** in expression 7.1 as *unbounded,* using the infinity symbol α:

$$S_\alpha = (\mathbf{E}_\alpha, \mathbf{R}_\alpha) \qquad \text{(expression 7.1a)}$$

where $\mathbf{E}_\alpha = \{e_1, e_2, \ldots\}$ and $\mathbf{R}_\alpha = \{r_1, r_2, \ldots\}$, and
since $\mathbf{E}_\alpha$, $\mathbf{R}_\alpha$ are infinite, there is no indication of the end of the progression of elements in $\mathbf{E}_\alpha$, $\mathbf{R}_\alpha$.

Unbounded sets imply a system of infinite complexity. The human mind would find it impossible to comprehend a system of too many elements and too numerous interrelations, and would boggle at the notion of infinite number of elements, and/or interrelations.

Finite systems

Fortunately most problems can be represented as *finite* systems: systems where both the element set and the interrelation set has a specified upper bound, as in the expression:

$S = (\mathbf{E}, \mathbf{R})$ (expression. 7.2)

where $\mathbf{E} = \{e_1, e_2, ..., e_n\}$ and $\mathbf{R} = \{r_1, r_2, \ldots, r_m\}$,

and m, n are positive integer counters.

Expression 7.2 means that the set **E** has exactly n number of elements, over which exactly m number of interrelations are defined.

The systems of interest to us are *finite*: they have a finite number of elements, and their representation takes the form of expression 7.2. This is a helpful representation of reality, but we must bear in mind that in real life entities will have a boundless number of parts, limitless number of features, and an infinite number of interrelations structuring the whole of its innumerable parts. Of these, the systems professional must select the attributes, parts and interrelations relevant to a given purpose of analyzing, constructing, operating, or otherwise tending the system. Selection is an essential part of modelling. Only by systematic, purposeful simplification can we reduce unsolvable, infinitely complex real-life problems to tractable problems. The selection must be judicious: it must omit characteristics of secondary importance while retaining all essential features of the referent.

In the following we confine our attention to finite systems.

Systems versus sets

We may use expression 7.1 to demonstrate the difference between a set and a system.

- A *set* (such as **E** in expression 7.1) is a collection of individuals: elements which are unconnected, unrelated and unordered.
- A *system* may contain the same set of elements, but it also possesses a collection of interrelations (the set **R** in expression 7.1) over the elements. The interrelations define connections among the elements of the set, indicating how the elements may interact. The interrelations assure that, collectively, the elements of the set can be regarded as a *whole*. Since wholeness is an essential characteristic of a system, the interrelation set **R** must always be attached to the element set **E**, and if the set **E** is not empty then the set **R** must not be empty: it must contain *at least* one interrelation.

System entities

In expression 7.2 we use the symbols $e_1, e_2, \ldots e_n$ to stand for individual entities: the elements forming the set **E**.

- If the system is represented as a black box then the entities may be *attributes, variables* corresponding to attributes, or *attribute measures*.
- In case of structural representation the entities will be the *parts* from which the complete system is composed.

The ancient Greeks argued endlessly over whether matter was discrete, made up of atoms, or continuous. It proved to be discrete, but even the atom was later found to consist of smaller and smaller particles. However, for much of science it is sufficient to regard matter as made up of individual indivisible atoms. In any problem solving situation the depth of hierarchical subdivision is chosen to suit the purpose of the problem solver/modeller. Choose the largest components that can be represented confidently as black boxes with known properties. If the overall attributes of a component are reliably established then there is no need to subdivide the component any further: it is regarded as one of the indivisible black box atoms of the structure. This principle, long established in engineering manufacture, is now also recognized in the software process where previously written modules are stored for reuse.

System interrelations

A system is a cohesive set of entities. As we know, it is the interrelations that supply the cohesion. The nature of the interrelations depends on the nature of the chosen representation. If the entities are structural parts then the interrelations govern *how* those parts fit together.

Example 7.1

The following is a set of natural numbers: ***E*** *={3, 7, 8, 2, 6, 101}.*

To create a system, we add the ordering interrelation 'less_than', thereby creating the system:

S = ({3, 7, 8, 2, 6, 101},{less_than})

where 'less_than' is a two-place (binary) interrelation defining ordered pairs: ***R*** *= {(3,7), (2,3), (6,7), ..., (8,101)}.*

Example 7.2

A pile of bricks is represented as a set of bricks E and a relation R: 'in_random_order'. Adding some window frames or taking away some bricks would change the element set E. Changing the positions of the bricks does not change the element set, but it changes the positional interrelations among the bricks. For example, lifting a brick from the edge of the pile and putting it on top would change the height and the footprint of the pile. Building the pile of bricks into a wall, those same bricks will form another system with relations such as 'on', 'under, 'next_to', at_rightangles_with, and others. Given the bricks and the interrelations, one can build the wall. The wall will be a new entity, having characteristics separate from and additional to those of the bricks, and these 'emergent' characteristics are derivable from the characteristics of the bricks and the pattern in which the wall is built.

Example 7.3

Some of the entities in London's underground railway system are stations, trains, tickets, signals, passengers. There are many and varied interrelations over the entities. One of these interrelations, 'directly_connects_to', designates adjacent stations. Expressed as binary relations, and using the London Underground as the system, individual relations include:

directly_linked_to (Leicester Square, Piccadilly),
directly_linked_to (Hampstead, Belsize Park).

These relations show that Leicester Square station is directly connected to Piccadilly station and Hampstead to Belsize Park. The entire relation 'directly_linked_to' will comprise all possible pairs of adjacent stations taken from the entity set ***E*** *of stations.*

Another relation in this system 'is_accessible_from', pairing all stations which form the entity set of the underground system, including all station pairs which are directly linked, as well those that are two or three stops apart, and many others. Placing some of these into expression 7.2 gives:

$$System_{LondonUnderground} = (\{LeicesterSquare,\ CoventGarden,\ Piccadilly,\ \ldots\},\ \{is\_directly\_linked\_to,\ is\_accessible\_from,\ \ldots\}).$$

*The careful reader will have noted that this representation is incorrect. The London underground may have many stations and they may be interrelated in many ways, but both sets must be finite. The correct expression will take the form of expression 7.2, indicating in some way that the element set **E** has a specific number of elements containing all the stations, and the interrelation set **R** defined over these has a finite number of interrelations. A possible – but clumsy and inconvenient – way to make this explicit is by enumeration: listing in the definition of S all the stations and all the interrelations.*

*Note also that the structural relations in the set **R** need not be physical. A meaningful relation in our underground system is use(passengers, trains), generate(passengers, income), or create(overcrowding, danger).*

7.2 Defining systems

Recall that the systems notation S = (**E**, **R**) is equally suitable for representing referents as wholes or as structures.

Systems as wholes

Where the referent is to be represented as a whole, a unity, then, as we know, the entity set **E** in the systems notation represents the collection of chosen attributes. These are held together by at least two interrelations which affirm that all the attributes belong to *the same referent* and are valid at the *same time instant*. We name these the 'co-attribute' and 'co-temp' (or 'time stamp') interrelations, and give them the symbols r_c and r_t. Using the subscript B to describe this view of a referent, equation 7.2 now becomes

$$S_B = (\mathbf{E}_B, \mathbf{R}_B) \qquad \text{(expression 7.3)}$$

where $\mathbf{E}_B = \{\mu_1, \mu_2, \ldots, \mu_n\}$ is the set of attribute measures,

$\mathbf{R}_B = \{r_c, r_t, r_{B1} \ldots r_{Bm}\}$ is the interrelation set, and

expression 7.3 is the representation of the system as a whole.

Both sets $\mathbf{E}_B$, $\mathbf{R}_B$ are finite, $\mathbf{E}_B$ having n number of elements (the referent being characterized by the measures of n number of its attributes), and $\mathbf{R}_B$ defining m+2 interrelations over these, consisting of the mandatory coattribute and time stamp interrelations, and m further interrelations.

Systems as structures

The structural view of the system is a set of parts, over which a set of interrelations are defined, forming the representation of the system as a whole. The systems notation for a structural representation is shown in expression 7.4, the suffix S indicating structure.

$$S_S = (\mathbf{E}_S, \mathbf{R}_S) \qquad \text{(expression 7.4)}$$

where $\mathbf{E}_S = \{comp_1, comp_2, \ldots comp_p\}$

and $\mathbf{R}_S = \{r_{S1}, \ldots r_{Sq}\}$.

Here again, both sets $\mathbf{E}_S$, $\mathbf{R}_S$ are finite, $\mathbf{E}_S$ having p number of elements (the system being composed of p number of parts), and $\mathbf{R}_S$ defining q number of interrelations over the parts.

Structures may be represented graphically by trees, as in figure 7.1, which is one of the simplest of such graphs.

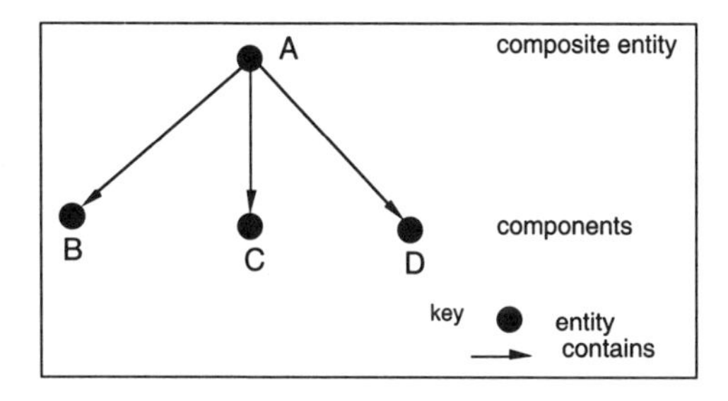

Figure 7.1: An incomplete graphical representation of system A as a structure

The following examples and discussion illustrate the need for making explicit the relation set in structural representations.

Example 7.4

Robbie the Robot has been asked to build an arch (figure 7.2). He is given components A, B, C, and the structural decomposition tree of figure 7.3. The robot is unable to complete the task. Giving Robbie the Robot three blocks, A, B and C, and an instruction to 'build an arch!' is inadequate: the information is missing as to how the three parts are interrelated to form the new entity 'arch'. There is more to the building of arches than supplying the component blocks.

Figure 7.2: Robbie tries to build an arch

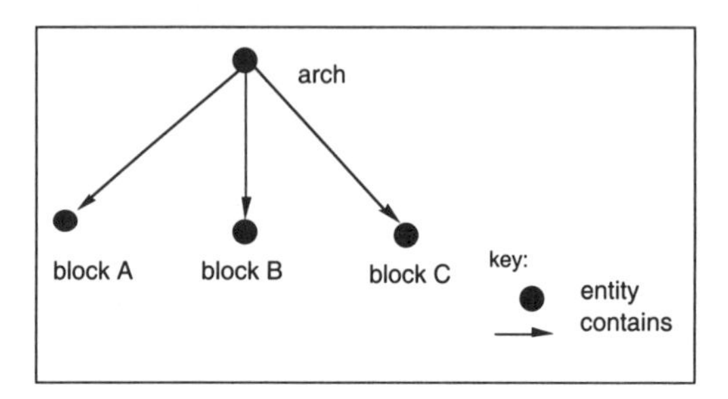

Figure 7.3: Decomposition tree of the arch

Example 7.5

The difficulty in Example 7.4 also arises in universities offering "integrated engineering degree courses". Such courses have become fashionable in Europe and the UK in recent years, covering, for example:

four disciplines:

material science, mechanical engineering, manufacturing engineering and management (engineering course at a well known and respected British technological university),

three disciplines:

software engineering, electronics and music (undergraduate course at a renown European University).

In the last of these cases the 'mission statement' of the University claims that the course provides "unified interdisciplinary education", and on completion of the course the graduate will be competent to manage "multidisciplinary tasks or single disciplinary projects" in any of the three constituent fields. No indication is given in the curriculum, and none in the syllabuses, as to how the parts of study are interrelated to form a whole.

No doubt the students who attend the courses in Example 7.5 gain some insight into each of the constituent disciplines. However, we know that an unrelated set of parts does not amount to a system, and a collection of courses does not amount to a coherent programme of engineering education. To add real value to the variety of subjects included in the course, the curriculum should contain some elements which present explicitly the way in which the parts are linked together form a coherent whole. Instead, this *system forming element* is all but ignored in some of the courses of our example. As a thoughtful writer remarks: "It is the *integration element* of a complex system that completes the engineering aspects!" [1], [2].

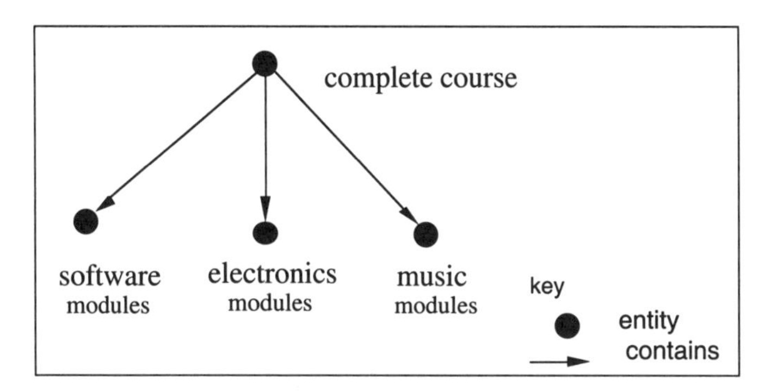

Figure 7.4: A course of disparate parts, or a coherent programme of education?

In Example 7.4, Robbie's dilemma can be solved. Applying systems notation makes this explicit: we need to add a set of relations, thus converting the *set* of entities to a *system*. To do this, Robbie is provided with the following system specification:

$$S_S = (\mathbf{E}_S\,,\, \mathbf{R}_S) \qquad \text{(expression 7.5)}$$

where $\mathbf{E}_S$ = {block(A), block(B), block(C)}

and $\mathbf{R}_S$ = { vertical(B), vertical(C), horizontal(A),on(A,B), on(A,C), not_touching(B,C)}

(Read this as 'A is on B', 'A is on C', 'B does not touch C'.)

Robbie now builds the arch (figure 7.5). Notice that this specification can also be used as a test for an arch, the 'quality' of 'archness' [3].

It is the duty of the those advocating the degree course of figure 7.4 above to show how the three modules are integrated to modify the 'professional skill' attribute of the Freshman to that claimed in the mission statement for the graduate by a relation such as:

integrated(software, electronics, music),

and then to define the relation 'integrated' in practical terms. If this is done correctly, then the attributes of the educational programme as a whole should be accessible from the attributes of the components and the way 'integrated' combines them. An instance of such a course is the Bachelor of Science programme at the American International University in London. That programme comprises two specialist disciplines: computing and business management, and uses the systems methodology exposed in this book as the integrating interrelation.

Figure 7.5: Robbie builds the arch

7.3 Classifying systems

There are many ways of classifying systems: some are historical, some pragmatic, some overlap, and all are strongly influenced by the fields in which the classification is used. We list here some ways in which systems are classified.

- The classification of systems into *infinite* or *finite* systems has already been mentioned; the systems professional will only be interested in finite systems as representations/models of referents.
- Depending on their input and output, systems may also be classified as *continuous* or *discrete* (also referred to as 'analogue' and 'digital'). Discrete systems are 'granular': their resolution is limited, they operate on inputs and generate outputs where there is a finite difference between any two adjacent attribute values. Continuous systems are 'smooth': no matter how close two attribute values are, one can always fit a value in-between. Digital computers work in the domain of discrete signals, and since computers are part of the world of today's systems professional, we shall only be interested in discrete systems.
- The discrete/continuous partition can also be applied to the system structure. Accordingly, engineers discriminate between *discrete component* and *distributed component* systems, the former being built of a finite number of elements, the latter of a continuum of elements. An example of the latter is a cable for the television or the computer: an essential electrical component whose characteristics can best be represented by viewing it as a distributed system. Another example is an oil pipeline, once again an important component in the fuel supply chain, best modelled as a distributed component system.
- *Open* and *closed* systems were the basis of a classification recognized by Bertalanffy [4], who used this to develop the world view of a biologist. A closed system is one which has no interaction with its environment. Originally this had a thermodynamic aspect in that the interaction with the environment was interpreted as a movement of energy across the boundary between the system and its environment, ultimately leading to the attainment of an equilibrium state. A closed system was one in which no such exchange of energy took place, and consequently there could be no interaction with the environment. Today's systems professional is just as much concerned with the transfer of information as of material between the system and its environment. A system in which neither material nor

information transfer is possible is a system of no interest - for the practical purposes of its environment, it may as well not be there.

There are many other viewpoints from which systems may be classified. For instance, an important classification criterion arises from the timing of processing in the system. Accordingly, in one of our examples we shall distinguish between *synchronous* and *asynchronous* systems. We leave it to the reader to identify further classification criteria from experience, and add to the list above.

Example 7.6

A store during stock-taking is a closed system to its customers and suppliers.

7.4 Systems and their environment

We must conclude that open systems operate in interaction with their environment, and are divided from their environment by the boundary. These familiar notions are worth examining in greater detail.

We start by recalling the idea that systems have a boundary, and they interact with the rest of the universe across this boundary. Man-made systems, however complex and powerful, can only interact with a small portion of the universe. To represent this, Figure 7.6 first partitions the universe into 'system' and 'environment', and then further partitions the environment into 'direct environment' and 'rest-of-the-world', the latter having no noticeable effect on the system. An observer in the rest-of-the-world sees the 'system + direct environment' as 'closed'. Place the observer inside the direct environment and the system will appear 'open'.

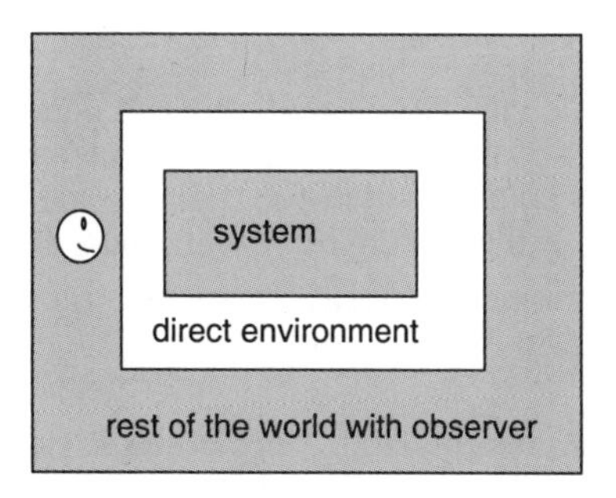

Figure 7.6: A system in the world (explanation of symbols in the text)

Figure 7.7 shows a different view of the same 'system/direct environment/rest of the world' partition. There are two hypothetical observers, one within the system and the other in the environment. Each can perceive changes or measure attributes in the field of the other across their common interface. At the interface, deliberate *messages* may pass from one to the other, and these may be designed to elicit a response. The interface may also allow detection of changes which are not specifically intended for the observer on the other side of the boundary.

Assume now that we modelled the world perfectly (!), such that the system of interest only interacts with its direct environment; the rest of the world does not affect the system, and is not affected by the system. Then the model of the interrelation between system and environment becomes symmetrical: 'system' and 'environment' are only labels, and are interchangeable.

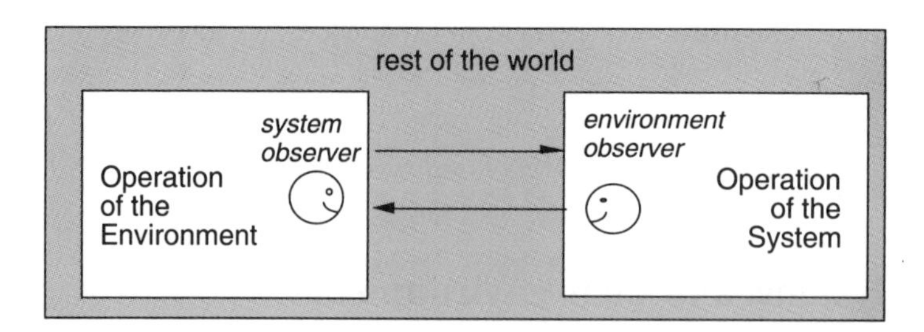

Figure 7.7: Open system interacting with its environment (explanation of symbols in the text)

Before modelling a referent, the modeller must decide what are the boundaries. Failure to draw the boundaries correctly often leads to a failure in the final system implementation, not discovered until delivery of the solution. The advantage of being able to disregard most of the known universe in the model is obvious: the plethora of irrelevant detail would obscure the most relevant and important aspects. The danger is that something vital to the correct operation of a system may be omitted from the environment through the modeller's unfamiliarity with the domain.

7.5 Summary

Any real life entity may be viewed as a system. The generic form for representing a system is as a pair, a set of entities and a set of interrelations among the entities: S=(**E**, **R**). This form is equally suited for defining the system as a whole, or as a structure of parts. For a black box representations, the entity set $\mathbf{E}_B$ comprises representations of the attributes, whereas for a structural representation the entity set $\mathbf{E}_S$ consists of representations of the components.

Among other criteria of classification, we distinguish infinite and finite systems, continuous and discrete systems, distributed component and discrete component systems, and open and closed systems, and, to conclude, the chapter discusses the notion of the system and its environment.

7.6 Exercises

Exercise 7.1

Write the system notation for a set of 4 wooden blocks, a red one, a blue one, a green one and a yellow one, piled up on the table in a specific order. Sketch your result.

Exercise 7.2

For the purpose of informing Freshmen, you have been asked to construct a systems model of a University computer network. Where do you draw the boundary between system and environment? What is included in the environment? If you had to order such a system, what attributes would you choose to represent it?

Exercise 7.3

You are an Estate Agent specializing in hotels. Use the notation of expression 7.3 and 7.4 to describe the hotels on your list.

Exercise 7.4

A company has just taken over a departmental store. You have been asked by a representative of the company to produce a model of the store as a system, in order that they may make improvements. You start by drawing a boundary. Which of the following should be included in the system and which should be relegated to the environment: the store's customers, the suppliers, the credit card system in use, the Board of Directors of the store, the employees, Health and Safety regulations, the buildings, the delivery vans? If you find it difficult to decide about any of the items on the list, prepare a set of questions you would put to the company representative who commissioned you to undertake the task.

7.7 Footnotes and References

1 A G Stoddart: Computing and Control Division Lecture, IEE, 7.12.95

2 A G Stoddart: "Systems Engineering – is it a new discipline?" Computing and Control Engineering Journal, Vol 10, No 3, June 1999

3 Winston P: "Artificial Intelligence", Addison Wesley 1984

4 L V Bertalanffy et al: "Discussion on general systems theory", Human Biology, Vol XXIII, 1951

Chapter 8 Measures

Measurement is one of the cornerstones of civilization, and the foundation of our systems methodology.

In this chapter we look at classical measurement theory. We start by defining 'measure' and 'measurement', and show how to characterize attributes by their measures, and referents by a collection of measures. The chapter introduces a hierarchy of measures which lead to the use of measures in expressing value judgements. The chapter concludes by an example of the use of measurement in process characterization.

8.1 Measure and measurement

Measurement is usually regarded as the characterization of some attribute of a referent by attaching to it a number, and was defined in an earlier version of the quality standard accordingly [1]:

> **measurement**
> set of operations having the object of determining the value of a quantity
>
> Draft BS-EN ISO 9000:2000

We argued in Part 1 that this view is too narrow, and requires revision. For this, we must first observe that 'measurement' is a process and 'measure' is a product. Let us recall that, when constructing our system of definitions, we noted that it was possible to define 'product' without reference to 'process', but when defining 'process', we needed the concept of 'product'. Following the same logic, we now define:

> **measure**
> a symbol of a symbol system designating the value of an attribute of a referent, together with the formal characterization of the variable and scale
>
> Our working definition

and

> **variable**
> alphanumeric symbol designating a well defined attribute of a class of referents, indicating the domain and dimension of possible values
>
> Our working definition

This then allows us to define:

> **measurement**
> the process of assigning a measure to a well defined attribute of the referent
>
> Our working definition

In its wide sense, measurement may be either *quantitative* (requiring the use of a class of numbers to designate values of the scale), or *qualitative* (selecting a symbol from a non-numerical symbol system, such as the collection of road signs given in the Highway Code, or the sequence of letters in the alphabet). Quantitative measurement is a familiar notion for all. Important applications of qualitative measurement include classification and grading.

We use the term 'measurement' to mean the assignment of a numerical or other symbol to a well defined attribute of the referent [2]. The symbol is selected from a symbol system according to a declared and accepted *scale*.

Examples 8.1

The measure of size of an egg may be one of the symbols chosen from the declared set {small, medium, large, extra large}, assuming that the concept 'size' is understood by the section of the population shopping for eggs.

The outcome of a quality audit in a company may be measured on a scale comprising the ordered elements of the set {'pass', 'conditional pass', 'fail'}, relying on a professional (as opposed to the popular) notion of quality.

Metrology – the science of measurement – has devised a system for measuring the attributes of the entities of natural science. Attributes are constructively defined: an attribute is *either* one of a frugal set of 'basic attributes' to which the community assigns an agreed concept and unit of measurement, *or* it is a 'composed attribute', derived by combining basic attributes in accord with the laws of natural science.

In classical metrology eight basic attributes are defined and internationally agreed, among them length, mass, time and electrical current, together with their (SI) units [3], which have been accepted as standard. All other attributes of the physical universe are measured in *derived units:* combinations of the base units in accord with the laws of natural science. Thus, for example, we measure velocity in the derived unit of 1 metre/second, 1 metre and 1 second being the base measures of length and elapsed time, respectively.

The *symbol* representing the value of the measure of an attribute is underpinned by the definition of the *concept* of the attribute, and the *scale* and *domain* of the measure. If the value of the measure is quantitative then the measure must also include the *unit* of measurement and its *dimensions* (such as 1 metre or 1 inch or 1 nautical mile for the unit and dimension of length, 1 second or 1 nanosecond or 1 millennium for elapsed time). The domain is the set of all possible values. For example, the positive integers from 20 to 70 are more than enough to represent the length of a newborn baby in centrimetres, the integers from –20 to +40 is a suitable domain for measuring ambient temperature in the UK in units of °C, and the set {small, medium, large, extra large} is an adequate domain for grading T–shirts.

The general criteria of meaningful measurement are that:

- the referent – the entity of interest – is clearly identified and represented as a *system*,
- the *concept of the attribute* for characterizing the system is well defined,
- the *scale*, *domain* and *unit* of measurement are given, and
- the measure is *valid*: consistent with observations.

Collectively these criteria characterize *model-based measurement* [4], [5].

The theories of the natural sciences, together with the measures of SI, suffice as foundations of model-based measurement in physics and in classical engineering. As an example, car manufacturers might state that a vehicle at maximum throttle would accelerate from a stationary state to reach the velocity of 110 kilometres/hour in 25 seconds. The attribute of interest here is the acceleration of the car, the measure of acceleration being derived, by Newton's theory of mechanics, from the base measures of distance (metres) and elapsed time (seconds), with dimension of metre per second squared. For our example, the average acceleration of the car may be calculated as the ratio of 110 kilometres/hour divided by 25 seconds, that is, 30.56 m/second^2.

The same measurement principles apply in fields other than natural science and engineering, such as in software engineering, industrial psychology and business management. Although measurement of many of the attributes emerging from these fields has not been integrated into SI, it is the professional duty of all practitioners to adhere to the general principles of measurement as far as possible. Bearing them in mind can guard against errors, and can save many projects.

Example 8.2

A company characterizes the rate at which value is added by the execution of processes, seeking to compare the 'financial effectiveness' of various activities. The concept behind the 'financial effectiveness' attribute is not universally agreed [6], and neither does the company stipulate a definition. However, we may assume that 'monetary value' is an accepted notion, and we may define 1 $ (or 1 £ Sterling, or 1 Euro) as its unit of measurement. We can use the established concept of elapsed time, with 1 second (with its multiples and submultiples) as the internationally agreed unit of measurement.

'Financial effectiveness' can now be defined as a process attribute: the difference between the monetary value of the output product and the input product (including the resources utilized) of a process, divided by the duration of the process, with $/second as the unit of measurement.

8.2 Scale types in measurement

At its crudest, measurement allows us to compare attributes of different entities in statements such as:

'this attribute of X has the same value as the attribute of Y',

or 'this attribute of X does not have the same value as the attribute of 'Y'.

A refinement of the process would lead to the more informative statements:

'X has more of this attribute than Y',

'X has the same amount of this attribute as Y',

or 'X has three times as much of this attribute as Y'.

Measurement always involves comparison, and scale types are defined according to the comparison operators which can be used on the values, operators such as 'equals' (=), 'more than' (>), less than (<), and others.

Classification – the nominal scale

As its name suggests, the nominal scale is for naming, labelling, classifying. This is the simplest of the measurement scales: there is only one operator, the equality operator. The scale represents the twin concepts of inclusion and exclusion. For each designated class there is a standard, and the label settles the question: does the chosen attribute of an entity match the standard, in which case the entity is included in the class, or does it not, in which case the entity is excluded. If the attribute matches the standard, its property variable is assigned a symbol signifying its membership of that class. This label is just a *name*: an item of any symbol system. Since, from the measurement point of view, the name is an arbitrarily chosen symbol, it is usual to choose a semantically significant symbol system, assuring ease of distinction by the users of the measure. The scale can be transformed readily by replacing each nominal measure by a symbol of another symbol system.

Examples 8.3

Classification of an item of food as 'fit to eat' or 'not fit to eat' will depend on convention, personal taste and standards set by the appropriate government department. The phrases in string quotes are used as the symbols of the nominal measure for sorting foods into two classes. The scale can be transformed into a single letter code, each item carrying, for example, the letter F for 'fit' or N for 'not fit', indicating class membership.

A two-valued nominal scale is applied to label upholstered furniture as 'flammable' or 'flame resistant'. With safety in mind, the labels are coloured red and green respectively, and also display the message in pictures.

Example 8.4

Players on the football pitch are classified as belonging to one of two clubs, the opposing clubs being 'measured' on a two-valued nominal scale. The team colour is displayed on each player's shirt: an individual belonging to the Arsenal team wears a red shirt, whereas those wearing blue play for Everton, red and blue being the traditional colours of these teams. When Arsenal plays against Manchester United – another team whose colour is red , one or the other team must wear a different colour strip – a scaling transformation.

Example 8.5

Children aged between 2 and 4 at the Cherryfields Nursery are assigned to one of four classes. The classes are measured on a four-valued nominal scale, designating them by symbols of animals (bear, rabbit, penguin and owl), for ease of recognition by children. The choice of symbol system is arbitrary, but the children must be able to recognize the symbols; for example, a scale of fruits (apple, pear, banana, grapes) would do equally well.

The classification scale is very useful, and is widely used. It is a coarse method of measurement, and in borderline cases it can lead to difficulties.

Example 8.6

Cars may be classified and taxed according to their intended use, as being commercial vehicles, saloon cars, sports cars, hatchbacks, four-wheel-drives, person carriers, etc. Classification assumes partition: each car should belong to one and only one class. But what of the situation where the saloon car is used as a commercial vehicle?

Classification as a basis of measurement can also be misused or abused; for example, it may be applied to justify prejudices. Witness the classification of individuals by hair colour, tribe or racial origin as being linked in some way to desirable or undesirable traits.

Less sinister, but still potentially harmful, is the use of apparently value-related symbols for designating nominal measures of classes, thus implying value where none exists. An instance of this is well known in primary education where unstreamed children are randomly distributed between two classes, and classes are designated by the symbol '**a**' and '**b**' – a purely nominal, value-independent scale of measurement. Almost invariably, children in Class **a** *assume* that the symbol implies distinction, and perform better than those in Class **b**. To avoid this, in some schools the two unstreamed classes are designated by the letters '**a**' and 'α'.

A set of entities may be partitioned into named classes according to the values assigned to their matching property variable. If further subdivisions are called for, then a tree structure of classes and subclasses results (figure 8.1). The same classification can be presented as a matrix – as in table 8.1.

	FIXED WING	MOVING WING
ENGINE	PLANE	HELICOPTER
NO ENGINE	GLIDER	BIRD

Table 8.1: A classification matrix

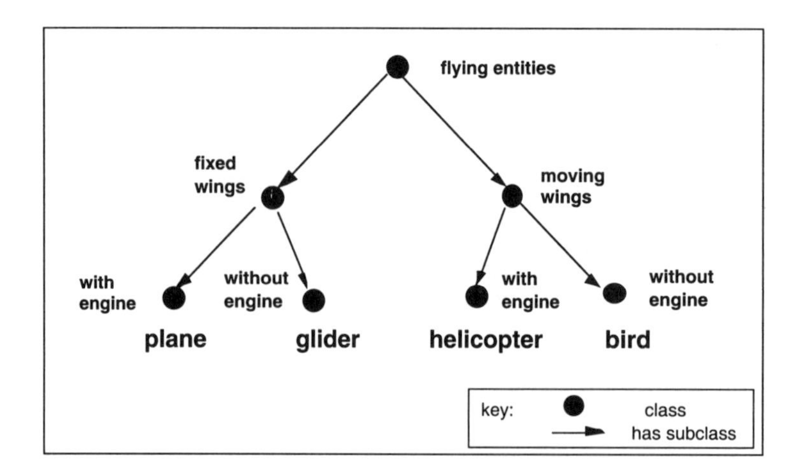

Figure 8.1: A classification tree

Class inclusion matrices displaying class membership are widely used in the search for unrevealed or unrecognised links. Plotting occurrences as points on a two-dimensional graph shows such links as 'clusters' of points.

Example 8.7

Several years ago a market survey of a supermarket chain revealed that the number of avocado pears sold correlates strongly with location in the UK. This provides the basis of management decisions, dividing the country to regions according to consumption level, and differentiating distribution of such items region-by-region.

Sophisticated computer programs can be made to correlate more than two attributes. In methods of machine learning, where a computer is being taught to identify entities by supplied examples, such clustering methods are routinely used. This is also one method of reviewing responses in Expert Systems: computer programs that give advice in some restricted domain. Over time, repeated systematic reviews can improve response time and accuracy.

Example 8.8

Medical Expert Systems use class inclusion matrices of disease against symptoms, expressed as True/False values. Here, each disease is an entity and each symptom is an attribute which is either present or absent.

Example 8.9

One can classify classes of fruit on the basis of sensory perception – colour, odour, touch, or instrument responses – weight, size, sugar content, acidity content. The nominal scale is multivalued, a particular class of fruit being defined by the coincidence of several features, such as 'red, odourless, hard, weighing between 100 and 150 grams', etc. Distinctions are only as good as the power of discrimination of the classifier and the measuring instruments used.

In summary, the nominal scale is characterized by a single relation, the equivalence relation discriminating class membership. The scale uses any convenient symbol system, mapping from attributes to symbols. Classification is useful so long as the attributes are unambiguously defined and the measures are objectively determinable.

The ordinal scale

The ordinal, or ordering, scale introduces two more relations in addition to the identity (≡) relation: greater_than (>) and less_than (<). Using the ordinal scale, we can arrange a set of entities according to our perception of the amount of an attribute they possess. We do this by carrying out a complete series of pairwise comparisons. For example, to order three entities correctly according to 'size', we need three comparisons, calculated as all the possible combinations taken two at a time. The ordinal scale can use any symbol system that imposes ordering, such as the alphabet or the natural numbers, with easy transformation between them.

Example 8.10

To place Tom, Jerry and Fido in correct order of size, it is necessary to make comparisons between Tom and Jerry, then Tom and Fido and then Jerry and Fido – three entities, three comparisons. We leave it to the reader to test the number of comparisons needed to order them when Leo the Lion arrives.

Once the order is established, Tom, Jerry, Fido and Leo can be given a letter each: the bigger the individual, the nearer to A (or further along) the letter in the alphabet.

The scale of letters can readily be transformed into a scale of numbers: the earlier (or further) the letter in the alphabet, the greater the number. The scale can also be positional, standing the smallest at the front and the largest at the back of a queue.

Without the identity relation, the ordinal scale would run into difficulty when two or more items are indistinguishable by the selected attribute. The identity relation allows us to include groups (classes) in the ordering, each class representing entities with indistinguishable values of the compared attribute, consistent with the concept of class in nominal measurement scale. The ordinal scale type thus includes the nominal scale type.

The symbols given for any attribute on an ordinal scale type reflects order, but need not contain the concept magnitude. Thus, values of the ordinal scale do not lend themselves to arithmetic calculations. For this reason that the letters of the alphabet are frequently chosen as the symbol system of the scale. Given the letters {d, a, d, a, b, f, c, a, e, g} to designate the order of 10 items, we would have no difficulty in placing the items in the 'standard' order defined by the alphabet; however, in view of the repeated occurrence of letters 'a' and 'd', the order would be partial.

Examples of ordinal scale are the Beaufort scale for wind speed (table 8.2), the hardness scale for solids (Mho's scale of hardness), the meteorologist's scale designating quality of air (good, average, poor), the supermarket's distinction of vegetables (class A, class B). In each case there is a standard against which an individual item can be tested. The scratch test will show which is the harder of two solids. Even in the absence of air-monitoring equipment, an observation of the distress of those allergic to poor air quality will give a measure of the relative ordering of air quality.

Danger of misuse of the ordinal scale arises where the basis of the comparison is not properly established, and the symbols of the scale are misinterpreted. Where numerical symbols are used to represent order, it is correct to assume that a referent carrying a larger number shows that it displays more of the attribute than another carrying a smaller number, but it would be a mistake to assume that twice the number implies twice the measure. This is well illustrated by the Beaufort scale where the actual wind speed cannot be calculated from the number on the scale. Table 8.2 also shows that a simple observational test supplies the standard against which the number can be assessed.

Summing up, the ordinal scale is characterised by three relations: equivalence, greater_than, and less_than. The sequence of symbols represent partial order, increasing (or decreasing) in value without commitment to the magnitude of the increase (decrease). This type of series is called monotonic. The change in magnitude from one element to the next, while not quantified, is always increasing (decreasing).

Beaufort number	Wind	Effect on land
0	Calm light air	Smoke rises vertically
1	Light air	Direction shown by smoke but not by vanes
2	Light breeze	Wind felt on face, leaves rustle, wind vanes move.
3	Gentle breeze	Leaves and twigs in motion, wind extends light flag
4	Moderate breeze	Raises dust, loose paper and moves small branches
5	Fresh breeze	Small trees in leaf begin to sway.
6	Strong breeze	Large branches in motion, whistling in telegraph wires, difficulty with umbrellas
7	Moderate gale	Whole trees in motion, difficult to walk against the wind.
8	Fresh gale	Twigs break off trees, progress impeded.
9	Strong gale	Slight structural damage occurs, chimney pots and slates blown off.
10	Whole gale	Trees uprooted and considerable structural damage.
11	Storm	Widespread damage, seldom experienced in England
12	Hurricane	Winds of this force only encountered in tropical revolving storms.

Table 8.2: The Beaufort scale of wind force - ordinal measures

The interval scale

Nominal scales can use any symbol set, and ordinal scales can use any ordered set for designating values, such as the letters of the alphabet. The interval scale introduces the idea of distance, and is the simplest measurement scale which must be expressed in numbers. An arbitrary distance between two fixed points is designated by consensus, and this distance is divided into an agreed number of equal parts, and a part becomes the units of measurement. As the name implies, this type of scale allows us to compare intervals. The comparison is indirect, since it is between the attribute value of an entity and the unit held safe to serve as the standard to which all measures must be traceable. The standard is made accessible by a tree structure of certificated calibration stations.

Example 8.11

On the Celsius temperature scale, one fixed point is the temperature at which ice and water coexist at a pressure of 1 standard atmosphere; the other is the temperature at which steam and water coexist at 1 standard atmosphere pressure. If these are marked, for instance, on the length of a column of mercury, then the interval between the two lengths is divided into 100 equal parts and these are called degrees Celsius.

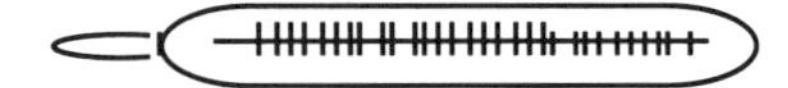

Example 8.12

Calendar time – real time – is measured on the interval scale. An arbitrary zero is chosen. Our current calendar is set by the Christian world, and has now become the de facto secular standard, the zero corresponding to a time instant more than 2000 years ago. Other religions have their own zero. Moslems measure real time from Mohammed's fleeing from Mecca to Medina, and the Islamic Society affirms that their calendar year (until February 2001) is 1421. Jews date their calendar from the time of creation according to Biblical calculations, making the current year (until September 2001) 5761. Hindus have various calendars. One of these sets the current year as 2056, dating from the coronation of the righteous emperor Vikram [7]. Other religions have yet other bases for reckoning the current date. Computer calculations set the zero at midnight, on 1 January 1904, and the number of days since then is used in spreadsheets and word processors to store the current date as the number of days elapsed.

Numbers are the symbols of choice for this scale. But numbers alone are not sufficient, we have to indicate what the units of interval are: degrees Celsius, degrees Fahrenheit, lunar years, solar years. Since the interval scale is numerical, we may make use of some arithmetic operations on numbers. Values in the interval scale may be added and subtracted, and the set of operators is now expanded to $\{=, <, >, +, -\}$. The ordinal scale may also be replaced by another ordinal scale, using the scaling transformation:

$$y = ax + b,$$

where x is the measure on the old scale,
a is a constant scaling factor,
b is the distance between the zero in the new and in the old scale, and
y is the measure on the new scale.

Example 8.13

Temperature on the Celsius scale (°C) can be expressed in degrees Fahrenheit (°F) by the scaling transformation above,

where x is the measure of temperature in °C,
a = 9/5 is the scaling factor from °C to °F,
b = 32°F corresponds to the temperature in °F of 0°C,
and y is the measure of the temperature on the Fahrenheit scale.

Thus, the temperature in °F corresponding to 20°C is

$$y = 9/5 \times 20 + 32 = 68\ °F.$$

The use of numbers implies more than the scale justifies. Although values may be added or subtracted, they may not be multiplied or divided.

Example 8.13 continued

20 degrees Celsius may appear as twice 10 degrees Celsius, but it would be meaningless to say that the object at the first of these temperatures is twice as hot as the one at the second. We are, however, justified in saying that the first object is hotter than the second, and its interval from zero is twice as much.

The ratio scale

The ratio scale incorporates all the previous comparisons and operations, but now the entity is seen as possessing a measurable amount of that attribute, including zero. We thus have an easy test for such a scale type: 'is there a real (absolute) zero?' Measurement is still comparison, but the attribute is expressed as a ratio: a multiple or submultiple of the agreed standard. For example, the standard for the unit of mass is provided by an artifact, such as a bar of gold in a Paris vault; the standard for the unit of length is the wavelength of a specific spectral line emitted by a chemical element.

To define the measure of an attribute of the referent, the attribute must be defined, the unit and dimension of measurement must be given (such as gram, pound, hour, nanosecond, mile, inch, metre/second^2, kilowatt, or whatever), and a numerical symbol must be provided to indicate how many times bigger is the observed attribute of the referent than the unit. The symbols are those of the number system, expressed to the desired degree of accuracy as an integer (5 kg), a decimal fraction (32.6 m^2) or vulgar fraction (2 7/8 in). Where the standard has no dimension, the measure is a scalar, designated by [1], but even this must be made explicit in the definition of the measure. An example is the radian measure of angle, a scalar whose dimension is [1].

Example 8.14

Apart from the usual tasks of measuring mass, length, electrical charge, and attributes whose units derive from them in accord with the laws of physics, we can also measure temperature on a ratio scale: in °Kelvin, the absolute temperature with zero at –273.16°C. This is the 'absolute zero' temperature at which the kinetic energy of molecules is zero. In our universe there can be no temperature lower than this. (Because reaching this temperature depends on a gas being ideal, and no gas is truly ideal, we cannot measure temperatures below about 1 degree K using a gas thermometer, but this does not invalidate absolute zero temperature existing in our universe).

The ratio scale admits to all arithmetic operations on numbers:

$$\{=, <, >, +, -, \times, \div\}.$$

The ratio scale is also open to transformation: it can be replaced by another ratio scale. Since the old and the new scales have a common zero, the scaling transformation is simply:

$$y = ax,$$

where x is the measure on the old scale,
a is a constant scaling factor,
and y is the measure on the new scale.

The reader may care to check from conversion tables that the height of a man may be expressed as 6ft 2in or as 1.88 metre, the velocity of a motorcar as 30 miles/h or 48.27 km/h, the weight of a new baby as 8lb 8ozs, or 3.856kg, etc.

The absolute scale

The absolute scale is the 'counting' scale. Its measures are dimensionless scalars, with [1] as the unit of measurement, and its symbols are the natural numbers, written in numerals (1, 2, 3, ...) or as alphabetic strings (one, two, three, ...). Absolute scales admit to no scaling transformation and map only onto themselves:

one to 1, two to 2, etc.

Other scales

Many other scales are in use. For instance, a logarithmic scale is used for measuring acidity/basicity (pH which is minus the logarithm of the hydrogen ion concentration with range from 0 to 14) and, for power, the decibel as 10 log(P1/P2) where P1 and P2 are power levels. A well known use of the logarithmic scale is the measurement of noise in decibels.

Selecting a scale

As we know from practice, the scale is not unique: for a given problem there may be many options, as the next example demonstrates.

Example 8.15

The task is to select a scale for the end-of-semester examinations of university students.

- *The first option is to classify students, using a two-valued nominal scale, with the symbols 'pass' and 'fail', or simply '+' and '-'.*

- *A more refined grading scheme may employ a ternary (3-way) ordinal scale, with symbols 'pass', 'fail but may repeat', 'fail, without the option to repeat'.*

- *Another grading system may distinguish six grades of students, using an ordinal scale and the symbols of the first 6 letters of the alphabet. The sequence of letters designate decreasing merit, 'A' standing for the top-grade pass, 'B', 'C', 'D' for poorer and poorer grades, 'E' for 'fail but may repeat' and 'F' for 'fail, no repeat'.*

- *The most usual grading system in the UK uses a ratio scale. Expressing merit as a percentage, it assigns 100% for perfect performance, 0% for a performance completely without merit.*

- *A quaint variant of the latter is the interval scale used for awards of degrees in the UK. There are 6 grades, named as follows: '1st Class', 'Upper Second Class', 'Lower Second Class', 'Third Class', 'Pass without Honours)' and 'Fail'. Each grade on this scale represents a performance falling within a set interval of the percentage ratio scale.*

8.3 The 'measurement hierarchy'

We propose four kinds of measures: direct, indirect, object centred and utility measures. These form a hierarchy, each building on the other, with direct measures at the base and utility measures at the top, as shown in figure 8.2.

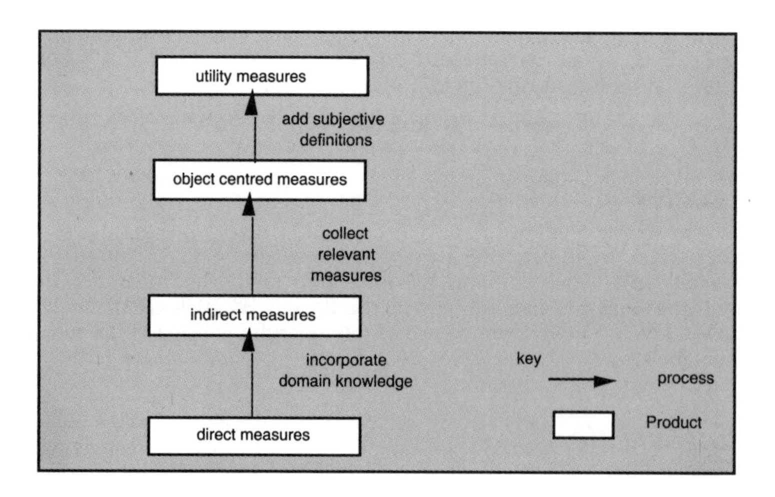

Figure 8.2: The measurement hierarchy

Direct measures

Direct measures can be used for attributes perceived by our senses. Values for individual attributes of an entity may be obtained directly by inspection, by comparison with a standard, or by use of instrumentation. Inspect two children to determine the taller, establish the linear dimensions of a sheet of paper by comparison with a ruler, find the most powerful light bulb by visual inspection.

Example 8.16 – Some examples

- *Temperature of bathwater is measured by the sensation of heat at one's elbow.*
- *Concentration of methane in a coal mine was once measured on the behaviour of a canary in a cage, and later by inspection of a Davey lamp.*
- *Radiation is measured by listening to the clicks on a Geiger counter.*
- *The strength of chilli peppers is measured by the reaction on one's palate.*

Direct measures can also be obtained by using instruments which extend our senses or enhance their accuracy of observation. To measure temperature by a thermometer would involve measurement of length (linear expansion measured in millimetres of a column of liquid under the effect of heat), and then calculating the temperature responsible for the expansion; however, by calibrating the height of the column in units of °C instead of units of millimetre, temperature can be read from the thermometer directly.

Indirect measures

These are used for attributes not readily available for direct measurement. Indirect measures form the second level of the hierarchy of figure 8.2, since they rely on obtaining direct measures of related attributes, from which the attribute value of the desired attribute is deduced by calculation, using a theory of the application domain.

Examples 8.17

- *It is inconvenient to measure surface area by laying down a collage of sheets of known size. Instead, we measure the linear dimensions of the area of interest, and use planar geometry to calculate the area.*
- *Knowledge of solid geometry allows us to measure the volume of a cylinder indirectly, computing it from direct measures of its diameter and height, and measuring the result in the derived unit of metre^3.*
- *Electrical theory enables us to measure power indirectly, deducing it from voltage and current measurements.*
- *Knowing the time stamp of the input and the duration of the process, we can work out the time stamp of the output.*

Whether the value of an attribute is obtained directly or indirectly depends only on the nature of the measure and the instrumentation available. When measuring up for fitted carpets, in principle it is possible to find the area directly by laying out 10 x 10 cm^2 pieces of paper and counting how many are needed to cover the living-room and the staircase, but this is not the preferred method. Archimedes showed how to measure the volume of an irregularly shaped object by measuring the weight of water displaced on immersing it. Temperature is commonly measured indirectly by measuring the expansion of a thin column of alcohol. Each indirect measure draws on domain knowledge: geometry, the theory of thermal expansion, electrical theory, etc.

Object centred measures

Direct and indirect measures aim at finding the value of an individual attribute. By contrast, object centred measures – those at the third hierarchical level of figure 8.2 – characterize an entity not by an individual attribute value but by a whole *set* of measures. The referent – the object of the measurement – is at the focus, and the set of measures, all belonging to the same referent, distinguish the individual from others in the same class. Each of the measures in the set may be obtained by direct or indirect measurement.

Example 8.18 *Two uses of object centred measures*

- *A holiday may be characterized by its cost, location, duration, board and room facilities, transportation service, and the like.*
- *An employee may be characterized by name, address, date of birth, sex, marital status, academic qualifications, professional qualifications, length of relevant experience, status in the company, position filled.*

Direct, indirect and object centred measures – a summary

Let us refer again to the four-level hierarchy of figure 8.2. The measures at the bottom three levels have something in common: they are all *objective* measures, and they can all be checked by an independent observer provided with sound senses and the right equipment. Such objective measures form the basis for all hard scientific theories, and have led to the remarkable achievements of modern science.

Utility measures

Utility measures are at the pinnacle of the measurement hierarchy of figure 8.2. They differ from objective measures: they are used for taking *decisions* and making explicit the *value judgements* about the entity of interest. Where decisions are made or judgements are called for in professional life, accountability demands declaring the factual basis and the value system used. This means defining a scale for measuring the outcome indirectly, and forming a theory called the 'utility function' as to how the outcome is derived from the object centred measures of the referent. The object centred measures provide the factual basis of the decision or evaluation: these measures are objectively verifiable. The utility function combines the object centred measures into a single measure for the attribute, and this utility function represents the subjective contribution of the decision maker.

The resulting 'utility measure' is understandable by the whole constituency. Although the measure contains a subjective element, it is far from haphazard. In open management the decision maker declares the utility function in advance, invites comments and discussion about it, and thereafter, the outcome of the measurement can be verified: checked for correctness.

Example 8.19

Siting a modern airport depends on many attributes and their measures:

a_1: *the market value of the land on which the airport is to be sited, with its measure* μ_1 *in £/km*^{2}*,*

a_2: *the number of dwellings in the designated site (householders to be compensated), with its measure* μ_2*, an absolute measure with dimension [1],*

a_3: *the population density of the area of the planned flight path, with its measure* μ_3 *whose unit is number of persons per square kilometre,*

a_4: *the population which the new airport would serve, with its measure* μ_4*, given as the number of people living within 1 hour's travelling distance by car or train,*

a_5: *estimate of the monetary value (*μ_3 *in £) to the public of environmental features that will be lost,*

a_6: *other features, such as the measure* μ_5 *in kilometres of the distance from extant motorways.*

Example 8.20

To achieve the award of an engineering degree, each candidate must successfully complete a project: a masterwork, demonstrating the student's readiness to graduate, having accomplished a substantial engineering task independently. The minimum project mark is 40%, merit marks being earned for measures of the following attributes:

a_1: *the student's own contribution to initiate the project and define the specification,*

a_2: *the thoroughness of the search of the literature and background of the topic,*

a_3: *the effectiveness of project management, including planning the project, reviewing and documenting progress, obtaining and utilizing resources,*

a_4: *the depth of theoretical underpinning of the project,*

a_5: *the quality of practical implementation,*

a_6: *the quality of presentation of the project report, including the language of presentation and the quality of illustrations,*

a_7: *the quality of verbal presentation, the candidate's ability to justify choices, respond to queries and reason about the work,*

a_8: *the inherent merit of the work, and its potential publishability ('the sting in the tail', setting apart the first class candidate from the remainder).*

COMPOSING UTILITY MEASURES

Let us assume that the object centred measurement of our referent yielded the measure set $\mathbf{M} = \{\mu_1, \mu_2, \ldots, \mu_n\}$. The utility measure u will be a function defined over these:

$$u = f(M) \qquad \text{(expression 8.1)}$$

If all the measures of the set **M** correspond to desirable attributes, as in Example 8.16, then the utility function can be a simple linear combination (a weighted sum) of these:

$$u = k_1 \mu_1 + k_2 \mu_2 + \ldots + k_n \mu_n \qquad \text{(expression 8.2)}$$

where there are n measures in the object-centred measure set,
μ_i is the ith measure in the set,
k_i is the weighting factor for the ith measure,
and u is the utility measure.

The weighting factors of the various measures indicate the relative importance which the measurer assigns to the measure in forming the judgement.

Example 8.20 continued

The university publishes the formula for calculating the project mark. Each feature is marked out of 100. The initial utility function was designed as follows: m_1 and m_2 were deemed to be the least important, carrying weighting factors of 1, m_3 the most decisive, with weighting factor 4, and all others are assumed to be of equal import, with weight 2. Thus, the utility function has the form:

$$u = \mu_1 + \mu_2 + 4\mu_3 + 2\mu_4 + 2\mu_5 + 2\mu_6 + 2\mu_7 + 2\mu_8$$

(expression 8.3)

1600 marks correspond to 100% performance.

The students soon learn to play the system, ignoring some features – for example, not submitting a project report at all (obtaining 0 marks for μ_6), obtaining an overall pass by earning good marks for some of the other attributes (for example, excelling in practical work, and getting 80 marks for μ_6).

For next year, the university modifies the utility function:

$$u' = \mu_1 + \mu_2 + 4\mu_3 + 2\mu_4 + 2\mu_5 + 2\mu_6 + 2\mu_7 + 2\mu_8,$$

provided that $\mu_1, \mu_2, \mu_3, \mu_4, \mu_5, \mu_6, \mu_7, \mu_8 \geq 40$.

This time the results prove satisfactory, the utility function correctly expressing the university's intentions to promote good practice and assure standards.

In expression 8.2, the merit of the project increases monotonically with each factor, the weighting factors simply show what relative importance is attributed by the designer of the utility measure to the various attributes of the object centred measure. In addition, the weighting factors must also ensure that the additive elements in expression 8.2 are dimensionally compatible. Expression 8.3 satisfied this criterion automatically, because all the measures were scalars (with dimension [1]), but in general this is not the case.

Example 8.20 continued further

The university is obliged to contain the cost of the projects of engineering students, and decides to review the utility function in the light of this requirement. Staff also wish to use the revision to induce students to complete their project well within the set deadline. Accordingly, the object centred measure set is complemented by two new measures:

μ_9: *saving on parts and components, within the set budget B, measured in £,*

μ_{10}: *the merit of early submission of a project report, within the set deadline D, measured in calendar days.*

The proposal is that the new utility function should take the form:

$$u'' = \mu_1 + \mu_2 + 4\mu_3 + 2\mu_4 + 2\mu_5 + 2\mu_6 + 2\mu_7 + 2\mu_8 + k_9\mu_9 + k_{10}\mu_{10}.$$

The decision is to make the value of the new weighting factors $k_9 = k_{10} = 1$. *However,* μ_9, μ_{10} *are not scalar, and their dimensions differ. Since* μ_9 *is measured in £,* k_9 *must have the dimension 1/£, such that the product* $k_9\mu_9$ *should be a scalar. Likewise,* $k_{10}\mu_{10}$ *must be scalar, and since* μ_{10} *is elapsed time measured in calendar days, the dimension of* k_{10} *must the reciprocal of this, 1/day.*

With these provisos, the new utility function will be:

$$u'' = \mu_1 + \mu_2 + 4\mu_3 + 2\mu_4 + 2\mu_5 + 2\mu_6 + 2\mu_7 + 2\mu_8 + 1\times\mu_9 + 1\times\mu_{10},$$

provided that $\mu_1, \mu_2, \mu_3, \mu_4, \mu_5, \mu_6, \mu_7, \mu_8 \geq 40$,

and $\mu_9, \mu_{10} \geq 0$.

The attentive reader will note that the new utility measure has a flaw: it does not specify the maximum mark corresponding to 100% performance, the frugal use of funds, and early submission of the work. We leave it to the reader to propose a further modification of the utility function to remedy this.

The utility function is not always a weighted sum. If merit increases with some measures and decreases with others, as in Example 8.15, the function must take another form, such as the ratio of two weighted sums. The utility function may also take a polynomial form, higher powers emphasizing greater importance of the attributes in the object centred measure set. Another well known example, arising from the field of classical communications, defines a utility function – called the *figure of merit* – as a product of two measures, without any weighting factors:

u = $\mu_1 \times \mu_2$, where μ_1, μ_2 have reciprocal dimensions.

8.4 Practicalities of measurement

Measurement takes time, costs money. Measuring well leads to a gain of invaluable information. Measuring badly, resources are wasted, and errors can arise. It would seem obvious, and yet in practice it is often ignored, that, before embarking on a regime of measurement, the measurer must first identify the referent, and select and define each attribute. The definition must either refer to a concept already agreed by consensus among the relevant community of scientists and practitioners, or be composed of such concepts, the composition being made explicit. For direct and indirect measures, the measurer must show how the attribute is to be observed, how the observation is to be recorded, on what scale and in what dimensional units will the measure be expressed, and to what order of accuracy. For utility measures, the measurer must state assumptions, state the utility function explicitly, and justify it wherever possible [4].

Measures should be precise enough for their purpose, but not more so. Measuring the weight of a chicken at the supermarket requires the use of calibrated scales, but it is sufficient to limit the accuracy to the nearest 50 grams. Having limited the accuracy of the measurement, expressing the weight to seven decimal places is not only unnecessary, it may also be misleading. On the other hand, measuring and recording weight to the fraction of a milligram may be vital in a pharmacy or in an analytical laboratory.

In discussing measurement, distinction is to be made between accuracy and precision. Accuracy represents the closeness of the measured value to the 'real' value, whereas precision involves the repeatability of the measurement. The accuracy of a measure depends both on the instrumentation and the ability of the user of the instruments. If the instrument is wrongly calibrated, then consecutive measurements may agree with each other but may be equally wrong; thus, repeatability is no guarantee of accuracy. Where the expertise of the user is questionable, the results may well be inaccurate but will fluctuate around the correct value. Averaging consecutive results will produce a more reliable result.

8.5 An example of measuring process efficiency

The example arises from a textbook on management [8]. The section on "Measures of process performance" distinguishes between the efficiency of *economic systems* and *physical systems*, and defines each as follows:

> **Efficiency of an economic system** relates the value of the output to the value of the input.
>
> **Efficiency of utilization of a physical system** relates the amount of the output created to the amount of the input used.
>
> Source: R F Bruner et al: The portable MBA. John Wiley, 1998

The definition of economic efficiency refers to the input and output of the process, but does not stipulate the kind of 'value'. Furthermore, it states that the value of input and output are 'related', but does not define the relationship.

Similarly, the definition of physical efficiency refers to 'amount' without specifying the attribute, and states that the measure relates input and output, but does not make explicit the relationship.

Clarifying the concept

Efficiency measures are frequently used in engineering, and are defined as ratios. This idea is manifest in the definition of the quality standard:

> **efficiency**
> relationship between the result achieved and the resources used
>
> ISO/FDIS 9000:2000

We too follow this practice in defining more explicitly the relationship between input and output in both efficiency measures.

Let us assume that in case of economic systems we wish to define how the process utilizes *monetary value*. We can now write:

> **efficiency of an economic system**
> the ratio of the monetary value of the output to the monetary value of the input
> Our working definition

Assuming that the physical system processes *energy*, converting the energy input into some specific 'required form', then we can define:

> **efficiency of a physical system**
> the ratio of the value of output energy created in the required form to the value of the total amount of energy input used
> Our working definition

These definitions can be written as formulae, paving the way towards the definition of process efficiency measures:

$$a_{\text{economic efficiency}} = \frac{\text{monetary value of output}}{\text{monetary value of input}}$$ (expression 8.4)

Likewise:

$$a_{\text{physical efficiency}} = \frac{\text{energy output in required form}}{\text{total energy input}}$$ (expression 8.5)

DEVISING A MEASURE OF ECONOMIC EFFICIENCY

In the original definitions of our example, the *dimensions* of the measures are not explicitly defined. If, in our own definition both numerator and denominator are measured in the same units, $, say, then the measure is a dimensionless scalar.

In the original definition the *scale* of the measure is not explicitly defined. It follows from our expression 8.4 that the measure of the numerator and denominator are positive real numbers, thus the efficiency measure will also use the scale of *positive real numbers.*

The original text implies that economic efficiency should be measured as a percentage; thus, 1% would be the *unit* of measurement. The unit can also be expressed as a positive real number: the ratio of two positive real numbers.

The original definition does not specify the *bounds* explicitly, but the text ([5]) comments that the measure "... should exceed 100%", implying that the *lower bound* of the measure is 1." This is wishful thinking, rather than definition.

Common sense dictates that a *lower bound* of 1 (or 100 %) cannot be guaranteed: if the output of the process is a complete reject with 0 monetary value, the measure will also be 0.

The text makes no mention of the *upper bound.* Based on common sense, we suggest that the upper bound is unlimited, but finite. Thus, the measure $\mu_{\text{economic efficiency}}$ is unbounded:

$0 \leq \mu_{\text{economic efficiency}} <$ infinity. (expression 8.6)

The measure we have devised meets expectations: the larger the measure the better the economic efficiency.

DEVISING A MEASURE OF PHYSICAL EFFICIENCY

In the original definition, *dimensions* are not explicitly defined. If both numerator and denominator correspond to the same concept – energy –, and if they are measured in the same units, joules say, then the measure is a dimensionless scalar.

In the original definition, *scale* is not explicitly defined. Since the dimensions of the numerator and denominator are the same, the measure is a dimensionless scalar, and the scale of the measure is the positive real numbers.

The original text indicates that the *units* should be percentages. The units may also be positive real numbers.

Bounds are not explicitly defined, but the author comments that "physical efficiency cannot exceed 100%". This is guaranteed by the *laws of physics* – in case of energy efficiency, thermodynamics. In any energy conversion process, such as turning electrical power to light energy, thermal loss occurs, and this absorbs some or all of the utilized input. The lower bound is not mentioned, but clearly, in the limiting case this can be 0. Thus:

$0 \leq \mu_{\text{physical efficiency}} \leq 1.$ (expression 8.7)

Here too it is appropriate to comment that the larger the measure the better.

Consistency of definitions

Our proposed definition for 'physical efficiency' is consistent with the long established notion used in all domains of classical science and engineering, and has the usual bounds (expression 8.7).

'Economic efficiency' arises from the younger discipline of management. One must query the use of the term 'efficiency' for a concept which leads to a measure whose domain (expression 8.6) is inconsistent with those of the efficiency measures of the older disciplines of engineering and science.

A further comment and conclusion

The original text [5] states: "... it is important to note that all of the costs or benefits of a process may not be realized in one time period...". In view of this, the author recommends: "long-run profitability is a better measure".

Note that the black box P/p model of the process would make explicit the need to define the *time period* for which the measure is valid. In the absence of this, the long-run profitability measure will be just as ambiguous as is the economic efficiency measure.

The example sets out to show the need to take care in defining measures. To make this task easier, wherever possible the new measure should give value to already established concept, or should be based on such a concept. Where the concept is newly defined, its definition should be based on one or more established concepts, and the definition should make clear how the measure is derived from these. Such 'grounding' of the new in the accumulated wisdom of the old enhances confidence and promotes future development.

8.6 Summary

Measurement is comparison.

There are five main measurement scale types: nominal, ordinal, interval, ratio and absolute. For convenience, many other scale types are in use, such as the logarithmic scale. Understanding the scale types and choosing appropriate symbol systems prevents misuse of numerical measurement values.

A measure is either direct or indirect, depending on how it is obtained. Direct measures are the result of observation, with, or without, instrumentation. Indirect measures are derived from direct measures, using theories of the domain.

Object centred measures form a set, each element relating to one entity. Any measure of the set may be direct or indirect.

Utility measures are subjectively defined functions over the object centred measure set, explicitly expressing the value system of the measurer. A boundless variety of utility functions may be defined, depending on the measurer's needs and the measured data available. A weighted linear combination of measures is frequently used, but in this case the value must monotonically increase (or decrease) with all of the measures of the set, and the weighting factors must carry dimensions to achieve dimensional compatibility.

8.7 Exercises

Exercise 8.1

As far as the greengrocer is concerned, the attributes of an apple are given as weight, colour, crispness, maturity, cost. Assign a scale type to each of these and suggest how they could be measured.

Exercise 8.2

You have to choose an institution in which to complete your formal education. What attributes would be important to you and how could you measure them? If you could not decide between rival institutions, suggest how the measures could be combined into a utility measure, and used to rank the institutions according to 'desirability'.

Exercise 8.3

Two laboratory assistants were asked to analyze the same organic samples and give their results as percent carbon and percent hydrogen by a method involving weighing a sample, burning it and weighing the carbon dioxide and water produced. The first assistant, inexperienced but using excellent equipment, obtained the following series of results:

% carbon	% hydrogen
22.10	10.07
22.05	10.43
21.90	9.95

The second assistant, experienced but using less accurate equipment, produced the following results:

% carbon	% hydrogen
22.45	10.10
21.01	11.50
23.00	9.45

Averaging the results in each of the two cases, which would you take as being the nearest to the real value and why?

Exercise 8.4

(i) Suggest a measure for the size of a computer program. To what scale type would your measure belong? What does it measure?

(ii) During a period of intensive testing of a section of programming code, 53 errors were found and corrected. Could this be used as a measure of the 'correctness' of the code?

Exercise 8.5

'Wind chill factor' has recently emerged on weather forecasts as a measure. Use your initiative to find out how it is defined and measured, and identify the scale type and position in the measurement hierarchy.

Exercise 8.6

Devise a utility measure for the airport siting problem (example 8.19). Assume that the order in which the attributes are listed has no significance.

Modify the measures to make the utility function easier to define and more convenient to present to the public, and find a suitable new utility function.

Check whether or not the measures given in the example agree with your own value system regarding the siting of new airports in the UK. If not, propose new measures and define your own utility function.

8.8 Footnotes and References

1 Note that the final draft ISO/FDIS 9000:2000 of the quality standard offers no definition of 'measurement' or 'measure'.

2 Finkelstein L, Leaning M S: "A review of the fundamental concepts of measurement" in Measurement, Vol 2, No. 1 Jan-Mar 1984

3 International Bureau of Weights and Measures (1977) SI, the International System of Units, 3rd Edition, Page, C H and Vigoureux, P (eds.), London H.M.S.O. for the National Physical Laboratory.

4 A Kaposi, M Myers: "Systems, models and measures", Springer Verlag, 1994

5 A Kaposi: "Measurement theory", Chapter 12 in "Software Engineer's Reference Book", Ed. J McDermid, Butterworth, 1991

6 Draft BS-EN ISO 9000:2000 offers the following definition:

effectiveness
measure of the extent to which planned activities are realized and planned results achieved

7 Source: private communication.

8 R F Bruner et al: "The portable MBA", John Wiley, 1998

Chapter 9 Black box systems

This chapter returns to the generic definition of 'system', and shows how this notion is interpreted when the referent is to be represented as a black box. It builds on the four-tier measurement hierarchy introduced in chapter 8, and discusses the black box representation of individual referents as well as classes of referents.

9.1 The black box as a system

Recall the general notion of 'system', given in expression 7.1 as the pair:

$S = (\mathbf{E}, \mathbf{R})$

where $\mathbf{E} = \{e_1, e_2, \ldots, e_n\}$ is the finite set of elements,

$\mathbf{R} = \{r_1, r_2, \ldots, r_m\}$, is the finite set of interrelations among the elements,

and m, n are positive integers.

As we have seen in section 7.2, this expression can be interpreted to represent a particular referent as a whole, defining it as a black box:

$$S_B = (\mathbf{E}_B, \mathbf{R}_B), \quad \text{(expression 9.1a)}$$

where $\mathbf{E}_B = \{\mu_{B1}, \mu_{B2}, \ldots, \mu_{Bn}\}$ is the set of measures characterizing selected attributes $\{a_1, a_2, \ldots, a_n\}$ of the referent,

$\mathbf{R}_B = \{r_C, r_t, r_{B1} \ldots r_{Bm}\}$.is the interrelation set over the elements of $\mathbf{E}_B$,

and B is a suffix indicating that the referent is represented as a black box.

(As we noted before, the suffix B is frequently omitted where the context makes it clear that the representation is black box.)

In this chapter we examine the black box representation of a referent in more detail. Furthermore, we extend our discussion beyond the representation of individual referents to the black box representation of *classes* of referents. For the *generic class* the expression will be:

$$S_B = (\mathbf{V}_B, \mathbf{R}_B), \quad \text{(expression 9.1b)}$$

where $\mathbf{V}_B = \{\beta_{B1}, \beta_{B2}, \ldots, \beta_{Bn}\}$ is the set of *variables* representing the attributes of the referent,

$\mathbf{R}_B = \{r_C, r_t, r_{B1} \ldots r_{Bm}\}$ is the interrelation set over $\mathbf{V}_B$,

and B is a suffix indicating black box representation, as before.

The representation of expression 9.1b also allows us to characterize *subclasses* of the generic class. For this, we must vary the interpretation of the element set $\mathbf{V}_B$. As an example, in expression 9.1c all the attributes are given as measures, with the exception of the first. Expression 9.1c now defines the subclass of the systems of expression 9.1b: here attributes $a_2, \ldots, a_n$ have constant values $\mu_{B2}, \ldots, \mu_{Bn}$, with attribute a_1 still being given as the variable $ß_{B1}$ that can take up any value within bounds. Many different subclasses can be defined of the class definition of expression 9.1b by fixing the value of one or more elements of the measure set $\mathbf{V}_B$.

$S_B = (\mathbf{V}_B, \mathbf{R}_B)$, (expression 9.1c)

where $\mathbf{V}_B = \{ß_{B1}, \mu_{B2}, \ldots, \mu_{Bn}\}$ is the set of *constants* and *variables* representing the attributes of the referent,

$\mathbf{R}_B = \{r_C, r_t, r_{B1}, \ldots, r_{Bm-2}\}$ is the m-element interrelation set over $\mathbf{V}_B$,

and B is a suffix indicating black box representation, as before.

9.2 Modelling a single attribute

As we know, attributes are characteristics of referents. To represent a referent for a given purpose, the modeller selects a set of key attributes. For the representation to be meaningful, each attribute must be well defined, corresponding to a well understood concept. In hard systems each attribute is represented as a variable, with given *type*, *domain* and *name*, to which the measurement process assigns a specific value (figure 9.1). The individual referent or the class of referents, and the attributes belong to the *real world*, whereas the variable and the measure – the representations of the attribute – are in the *world of models*.

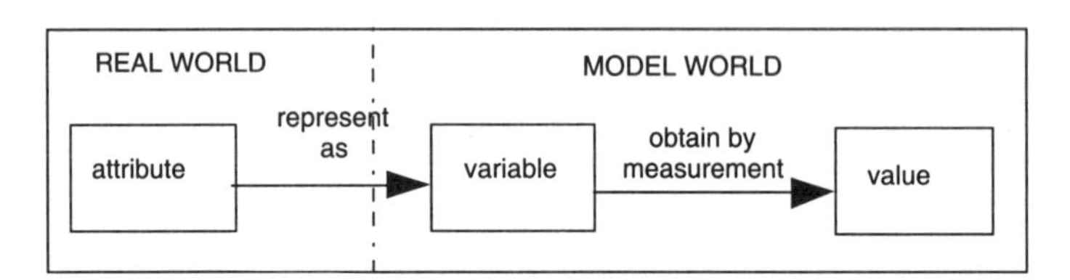

Figure 9.1: From attribute through variable to measure (a-type diagram)

As we have seen earlier, the model of the attribute must meet certain requirements:

- the verbal definition of the attribute must be of adequate quality, and must already be agreed among the community of users, or it must be composed in a specific way from such definitions,
- the variable must adequately represent the attribute for the given purpose, its dimensions capturing the concept of the attribute and carrying the unit of measurement,

- a method must exist for obtaining the value of the variable by measurement, either directly or indirectly,

- where the value of the variable is obtained indirectly, there must be a generally agreed 'domain theory' which allows the value and dimension to be derived as a function of the values of directly measurable constituent variables,

- the permissible domain of values of the variable must be given explicitly, or it must be possible to derive the bounds of the domain indirectly from the domain bounds of constituent variables.

If the attributes are clearly defined, if they exclude emotional, judgmental and prejudicial factors, if each attribute is measurable directly or indirectly, if measures of physical entities are traceable [1] to SI base units, and if the measurement yields repeatable results within set error tolerance, then we have the basis for creating a *hard model* of the referent.

Note that in practice we often need to include in the black box representation of a referent some attributes that have no factual basis, but are subjective impressions of classes of individuals. This does not mean that the attribute is ill defined, nor that the measures are haphazard or measurement is not repeatable. Examples are measures in market research data, opinion polls and exit polls of elections. In each such case the measures are subjective – the opinions of those sampled –, but they relate to a well defined attribute, the method of obtaining them is explicitly stated, the results are testable and repeatable, the referent is clearly identified and a scale is competently devised, the sample is representative, the opinions of a specified population is recorded in the form of attribute values, and conclusions are drawn from the data by means of well established statistical methods. Without due caution, the measures obtained from such surveys would be useless; *with* caution and expertly conducted, the results can be included in *hard models.*

Modelling an attribute as a variable

Consider the first step in the process of figure 9.1, where a selected attribute of a referent is represented in the model world as a variable.

Attributes can take up a range of possible values; for example, a potato may weigh as little as an ounce or almost as much as a pound, the height of a person may be less than 50 cm or more than 2 metres. A given attribute of an individual may change with time, and several individuals possess the same attribute to different degrees. If the referent is an adult human being and the attribute is blood pressure, then this attribute is liable to variation from day to day, or even from minute to minute. If the referent is the climate of the United Kingdom and the attribute is air temperature, then this attribute will show measures varying not only with time but also with location. The experienced modeller will know how to set the domain bounds – the expected minimum and maximum values – of variables so as to capture data on these attributes.

The information needed to model a single attribute as a variable is the triple:

$ß_B$ = <variable_name, variable_symbol, variable_domain> (expression 9.2a)

where the unit of measurement may be attached to the variable symbol or to the domain, and is applicable to all measures of the variable.

We can refer to the triple in an abbreviated form, such as:

$ß_B$ = < name, v, d_v > (expression 9.2b)

In such an expression:

- The mapping between the attribute and the variable name gives the meaning of the model.
- The variable symbol is a convenient, concise representation of the variable name. It would be clumsy to write 'weight', 'blood pressure' or 'air temperature' each time we refer to a variable for an attribute. Where possible, the variable symbol should remind the user of the nature of the attribute. In our example, 'w', 'b' and 'a' would be helpful symbols to designate, respectively, 'weight', 'blood pressure' and 'air temperature'.
- The variable domain definition is needed for several purposes. For example, when measures are to be attached to the attribute, the domain definition allows us to decide what format to provide for the collection and storage of the data, and to conduct quality checks on the data, the simplest being to test that the attribute value is within the set bounds.

Example 9.1

'Population density' is the variable name of a well understood attribute for characterizing a country. We designate the variable name of the attribute by the symbol 'D'. Variable D represents the ratio of P, the number of people living in the country, to A, the size of the land area of the country.

The unit of measurement of P is 1 person. A practical definition for the bounds of the domain of P is the pair of natural numbers:

<N_{min}: the number of inhabitants in the least populous country in the world,
N_{max}: the number of inhabitants in the least most populous country in the world>.

The unit of measurement of A is $1m^2$ (or more practically 1 km^2), with domain defined by the pair of positive real numbers

<A_{min}: the area of the smallest country in the world,
A_{max}: the area of the largest country in the world>.

The unit of measurement for D can be deduced as 1person/km^2, and the domain of D calculated as the positive real numbers <N_{max}/A_{min}, N_{min}/A_{max}>. The population density of any country on the earch will yield a measure within these bounds.

Thus, in this case the variable modelling the attribute would be defined as the triple $ß_B$ = < population_density, D (with 1/km^2 as the unit of measurement), the positive real numbers bounded between N_{max}/A_{min} and N_{min}/A_{max} >.

Table 9.1 gives some examples of defining domains, and table 9.2 has a variety of examples to illustrate the use of such a table in practice, and includes a column for the scale of measurement.

Description of domain	Bounds of domain	Unit of measurement
continuous, infinite	R, which, by convention, defines the complete domain of real numbers	For example, 1 metre
continuous, bounded	(0 … 100), defining the positive real numbers from 0 to 100	For example, 1 mile
discrete, infinite	N , which, by convention, defines the complete domain of integers	For example, 1 Watt
discrete bounded	[1 … 100], which, by convention, defines the set of positive integers between 1 and 100	For example, 1 metre/second
discrete infinite	[-273, …, 0,1, …], which, by convention, the set of integers between 273 and infinity	For example, °C
discrete, enumerated	the set {red, orange, yellow, green, blue, indigo, violet}	[1]
discrete, enumerated	expressed in set notation, for example: {n:ℕ | n≠0 • 2n} which defines the set of positive even numbers	For example, [1]

Table 9.1: Some examples of defining domain bounds

attribute name	variable name	symbol for variable	possible units	domain	scale type
'tallness'	height	h	feet, metres	positive real	ratio
size	weight	w	kg, lbs	positive real	ratio
size	no. of inhabitants	n	[1] (scalar)	positive integer	absolute
cost	value	v	any currency	positive real	ratio
date of manufacture	year	yr	common calendar reference	pos. integer, with upper bound of current year	interval
type of food in store	type	ty	[1]	{meat, fruit, veg, dry goods}	nominal
earthquake severity	strength	s	magnitude on Richter scale	(0, …, 10)	ordinal
duration	duration	∂t	second	positive real	ratio
status	status	f	[1]	binary (free/busy)	nominal

Table 9.2: Some examples of attributes and their representation by variables

Note that, when modelling an attribute as a *variable*, we create the potential for representing not just an individual referent but the whole class of referents that possess that attribute. In our example 9.1 we deliberately set a wide domain for variable D, sufficient for representing the population density of *any* country in the world. A smaller domain might suffice if the class of countries were to be restricted by means of adding a new 'location' attribute and specifying its value to denote a region such as the Baltic or the Balkans. To represent the 'population_density' attribute of an individual country in the class, the variable must take up a particular value within the domain.

Representing an attribute as a measure

Consider now the second step in figure 9.1, where the variable representing an attribute is replaced by a measure within the set domain of the variable. The aim is that the attribute should now characterize an individual, although the measure might also be valid for many other individuals that happen to possess the same attribute with the same value.

In everyday life we often describe attributes by giving values to variables, sometimes without being consciously aware of this. The next example quotes from the manual accompanying a video recorder. The text describes measures of a particular setting of the apparatus:

Example 9.2

"When the unit is set for programmed recording, the PDC light being on indicates that PDC signals are being transmitted."

We can extract the following information from the text: the unit has:
a setting *attribute whose value is* 'programmed recording',
a 'light' *attribute which has the value* 'on', *and*
a 'status' *attribute whose value is* 'transmitting'.

Further examination of the text (not included here) would allow identification of other attributes and attribute values.

Based on expression 9.2 (a or b) – the model of an attribute as a variable –, we can model an attribute by a triple, substituting the variable name by a measure name, and the variable symbol by a measure symbol, retaining the variable domain as the third element of the triple.

$$\mu_B = < \text{measure\_name, measure\_symbol, variable\_domain} > \quad \text{(expression 9.3a)}$$

However, if there is prior knowledge that the measure is certain to fall within the variable domain then the model of a single attribute degenerates to the pair:

$$\mu_B = < \text{measure\_name, measure\_symbol} > \quad \text{(expression 9.3b),}$$

or, in abbreviated form:

$$\mu_B = < \text{name, e} > \quad \text{(expression 9.3c)}$$

The unit of measurement is attached to the measure symbol.

9.3 Modelling attribute sets

Consider now the case where the referent, or the class of referents, is to be characterized not by a single attribute but by a set of n attributes. Then, in accord with expression 9.1b, the attribute set of the class will be modelled as:

$$VB = \{ß_{B1}, ß_{B2}, \ldots, ß_{Bn}\},$$

and, since each element of the set is composed as the triple in accord with expression 9.2b, we can write this as:

$$VB=(<name_1, v_1, d\_v_1>,<name_2, v_2, d\_v_2>,\ldots,<name_n, v_n, d\_v_n>)$$
(expression 9.4a)

Likewise, for the individual referent, where the variables have been replaced by a set of measures (expression 9.1a), the model of the attribute set will be of the form:

$$EB = \{\mu_{B1}, \mu_{B2}, \ldots, \mu_{Bn}\}.$$

If each element is given as a pair, as in expression 9.3b, we have:

$$EB = (<name_1, e_1>, <name_2, e_2>,\ldots,<name_n, e_n>)$$ (expression 9.4b)

Example 9.3

An Estate Agent characterizes the dwelling houses on his books. He selects ten attributes of interest to customers, among them location of the house, frontage, number of bedrooms, number of bathrooms, accessibility to public transport. Each attribute is mapped into a variable whose value is expected to lie within defined bounds (table 9.3). The units of measurement appear in a separate column.

In the table an attribute such as 'convenient for public transport' is characterized by a variable denoting distance from the nearest bus stop or railway station. The attribute 'value' may be obtained in various ways, for example, by consulting a surveyor, and may be distinct from the asking price – an attribute not included in the table.

Table 9.3 can serve as a checklist . With its aid, the characteristics of any individual house may be collected by adding columns for the name and value of measures. Table 9.4 shows such an example.

Although the table 9.4 is clumsy and would benefit from some tidying up for convenience of customers (for example, by omitting variable symbols and measure symbols and showing the unit of measurement against the value of the measures), it contains all the information specified in table 9.3.

attribute name (description)	variable symbol	domain	scale and unit of measurement
address	v1	all valid postal addresses in the UK	nominal, [1]
number of bedrooms	v2	positive integer between 1 and 8	absolute, [1]
frontage	v3	positive real between 8 and 50	ratio, 1 metre
number of bathrooms	v4	positive integer between 1 and 6	absolute, [1]
type of outer wall	v5	binary (cavity or solid)	nominal, [1]
type of finish of facade	v6	binary (facing brick or rendered)	nominal, [1]
method of production of facing bricks	v7	binary (hand-made, mass-produced)	nominal, [1]
kitchen	v8	binary (fitted or traditional)	nominal, [1]
accessibility	v9	positive real (distance from public transport) between 0 and 10	ratio, 1 km
value	v10	positive real, btwn 50 and 2000	ratio, 1k£ Sterling

Table 9.3: Characterizing the attributes of houses on an Estate Agent's list

attribute name (description)	variable symbol	domain	scale and unit of measurement	measure symbol	value and unit of measure
address	v1	all valid postal addresses in the UK	nominal, [1]	e1	10 AnyStreet York
number of bedrooms	v2	positive integer between 1 and 8	absolute, [1]	e2	3
frontage	v3	positive real between 8 and 50	ratio, 1 metre	e3	10
number of bathrooms	v4	positive integer between 1 and 6	absolute, [1]	e4	2
type of outer wall	v5	binary (cavity or solid)	nominal, [1]	e5	cavity
type of finish of facade	v6	binary (facing brick or rendered)	nominal, [1]	e6	facing
method of production of facing bricks	v7	binary (hand-made, mass- produced)	nominal, [1]	e7	hand-made
kitchen	v8	binary (fitted or traditional)	nominal, [1]	e8	fitted
accessibility	v9	positive real (distance from public transport) between 0 and 10	ratio, 1 km	e9	0.58
value	v10	positive real, btwn 50 and 2000	ratio, 1k£ Sterling	e10	115

Table 9.4: Characterizing a particular house on the Estate Agent's list by measures

9.4 The relations of the model

The interrelation set of a black box representation, introduced in chapter 4, contained two mandatory interrelations: the co-attribute interrelation, designated r_C, and the co-temporal interrelation shown by the symbol r_t, or sometimes just t.

- The co-attribute interrelation is defined over the complete set of attributes of the referent. It affirms that all the attributes belong to the *same referent,* guaranteeing the 'referential cohesion' of the model.
- The co-temporal interrelation gives the real time instant at which the attributes of the referent were measured (or are valid), asserting that at that instant the set of measures are simultaneous, thus confirming 'temporal cohesion'.

The minimum interrelation set which a black box representation must have is therefore:

$$RBmin=\{r_c, r_t\} \qquad \text{(expression 9.5a)}$$

Example 9.4

In example 9.3, Table 9.4 intends to represent a specific house. However, without stipulating the co-attribute interrelation r_C to make it explicit that all the attribute measures in the table belong to the same house, the table is but a collection of assorted attribute variables. Moreover, even if we assume that the coattribute interrelation holds, such a house exists only at a single time instant. At any other time the house may have changed its attributes (during the London Blitz perhaps, or by the addition of a patio, or by the renaming of the street, or simply cancelling a bus route).

To assure meaningfulness of representation by the data in the attribute measure table, the measure set $\mathbf{E}_B$ must be turned into a *system of measures* – the black box representation of the referent – by the addition of the interrelation set $\mathbf{R}_B$. $\mathbf{R}_B$ must include both mandatory interrelations: the coattribute interrelation r_C, and the time stamp r_t, and may contain further elements. Such non-mandatory interrelations would be included because the modeller deems them to be relevant to the task in hand. Thus, for an m-element interrelation set:

$$\mathbf{R}_B = \{r_c, r_t, r_1, r_2, \ldots, r_{m-2}\} = \{ \mathbf{R}_{Bmin}, r_1, r_2, \ldots, r_{m-2}\} \qquad \text{(expression 9.5b)}$$

Example 9.4 continued

*In Table 9.4 , the coattribute interrelation r_C, is a 10-place relation, affirming that all ten attribute measures belong to the same house. Since, presumably, the 'value' attribute is obtained by some formula on some or all of the other nine attributes, the interrelation set **R** might have a non-mandatory relation, $r_£$, say, to show this.*

Example 9.5

Consider that the problem is to devise the central heating system for a house, designed as a Georgian box. The house is characterised by its three extreme orthogonal linear dimensions: width (w), depth (d) and height (h). Let the attribute measure set $\mathbf{E}_B$ include these dimensions, together with the cubic capacity of the building. Since volume is computable from the other three *measures in E_B, (v = h x d x w), the property measure set is redundant: any one of the four measures may be omitted without loss of information. The redundancy can be shown by the interrelation set R_B having the extra, 4-place relation, r_v, in addition to the mandatory two: $R_B = \{ \dot{r}_c, r_t, r_{volume} \}$.*

To be a valid representation of the referent, the attribute measures in $\mathbf{E_B}$ in the black box representation should correspond to observable attributes of the referent, and any interrelations between attributes in $\mathbf{R_B}$ must reflect the real relationships between the attributes present in the referent.

Redundancy

Example 9.5 illustrates a case when the set $\mathbf{R_B}$ is redundant: the interrelation r_{volume} is not strictly necessary: its knowledge can be reasonably assumed. The presence of r_{volume} points to redundancy in the measure set $\mathbf{E_B}$. In the example, the measures of three orthogonal linear dimensions (h, d, w), together with elementary spatial geometry, would allow the volume v of the box to be computed. We call such models *representationally redundant.* Carrying redundant information in a model absorbs resources, and hence casual redundancy is wasteful. However, if judiciously applied, representational redundancy is a powerful tool in engineering, frequently used to enhance the reliability.

Engineers also make use of redundancy in real life. Critical components of systems, such as the power supply of hospitals and other essential public buildings, are duplicated, or even triplicated, such that in case of power failure the redundant standby equipment could be brought into service, assuring continuity of operation. Similarly, redundancy is used in communication, where entire messages may be sent repeatedly, or else some parts of the message may be duplicated, allowing detection of, and in some cases protection against, error. Hard engineering methodologies include methods for calculating the degree of protection gained by such *structural redundancy.*

In black box modelling, the irredundant measure set $\mathbf{E_B}$ comprises measures that are independent of each other: none could be computed from the others. Using a geometric analogy, the variables of such a set of independent measures are said to be *orthogonal.* To assure the quality of the black box representation, the modeller must first seek to establish measures based on the principle of orthogonality. Once such a 'minimal' black box representation is established, it can be extended to include redundant elements in the set $\mathbf{E_B}$, in the set $\mathbf{R_B}$, or both, the redundancy offering protection of the integrity of the black box representation.

Note that the presence of the non-mandatory interrelation in $\mathbf{R_B}$ *implies*, but does not *prove,* that the black box representation is redundant. Consider the following.

Example 9.4 continued

In table 9.4 , the magnitude of the 'value' parameter v_{10} presumably depends on some or all of the other 9 attributes. This means that the variables of the model are not orthogonal, and, in principle at least, the measure v_{10} could be obtained by some formula $v_{10} = f(v_1, v_2, v_3, v_4, v_5, v_6, v_7, v_8, v_9)$. A relation capturing this function could be incorporated in the interrelation set

R_B by adding the 10-place non-mandatory interrelation, rvalue. However, unlike the case in Example 9.5 where the non-mandatory relation between height, depth, width and volume is well known and universally applicable, here the r_{value} relation would need to be locally defined, and it will be liable to vary from house to house. The Estate Agent has the option of giving the value of the property indirectly through defining r_{value} in each case, but he and his customers would undoubtedly find it easier to read the information directly from the measure v_{10}.

9.5 Formal definition of black box representations

The definition starts with the general definition of 'system': S = (**E**, **R**), and incorporates the stipulation that the representation will be finite, characterizing the referent by a finite n number of attributes and m interrelations among the attributes.

Black box representation of a class of individuals

The definition uses expression 9.1b to represent the attribute variable set and expression 9.2 to represent any individual variable. The referent is the generic class: all those individuals whose attribute measures fall within the *n-dimensional space* defined by the domain bounds of the variable set $\mathbf{V}_B$. The interrelation set $\mathbf{R}_B$ is given in expression 9.5b. The formal definition is:

> **Black box representation of a generic class of individuals:**
>
> $S_B = (\mathbf{V}_B, \mathbf{R}_B)$
>
> where $\mathbf{V}_B$ is the finite set of attribute variables which characterize the referent,
>
> $\mathbf{R}_B$ is the finite set of interrelations on V_B which includes:
>
> r_c the 'coattribute' interrelation,
>
> r_t the 'time stamp' (or 'time signature'),
>
> and B is a suffix designating black box representation of S_B.

Black box representation of subclasses

The black box representation of a subclass of individuals will be defined in accord with expression 9.1c, replacing one or more of the variables in $\mathbf{V}_B$ by a measured value within the set domain.

Black box representation of an individual referent

As in case of representing a class, this definition also uses expressions 9.1a to represent the attribute measure set and expression 9.2 to represent the set of measures of an individual referent. Adding $\mathbf{R}_B$ of expression 9.5b for representing the interrelation set, we get the definition:

black box representation of an individual referent:		
	$S_B = (\mathbf{E}_B, \mathbf{R}_B)$	
where	$\mathbf{E}_B$	is the finite set of attribute measures which characterize the referent,
	$\mathbf{R}_B$	is the finite set of interrelations on E_B which includes:
	r_c	the 'coattribute' interrelation,
	r_t	the 'time stamp',
	B	is a suffix designating black box representation.

In accord with the definition, an individual referent is represented by a *point in the n–dimensional space* defined by the class. Any individual is a member of the class if it is characterized by the same attributes as the class, and if each attribute measure falls within the bounds set for the attribute variable of the class.

Example 9.4 continued further

For the house characterized in table 9.4, the coattribute interrelation is:

$$r_c = \{\mu_1, \mu_2, \mu_3, \mu_4, \mu_5, \mu_6, \mu_7, \mu_8, \mu_9, \mu_{10}\},$$

where, for example, μ_2 stands for the pair <number of bedrooms, 3>, and the full set can be read off as the pairs of entries in the first and last column of table 9.4 .

If a property developer builds many houses to the same design, then one house will differ from another only in the address, all other measures being invariant. These houses would form a subclass of those in table 9.4, where only the measure of the last column of the first row of table 9.4 is omitted, all other measures are preserved. The coattribute interrelation in this case would take the form:

$$r_c = (\beta_1, \mu_2, \mu_3, \mu_4, \mu_5, \mu_6, \mu_7, \mu_8, \mu_9, \mu_{10}).$$

If such is the lie of the land that the frontage of the houses should vary from address to address then this would be reflected in the model by the measure of variable v_3 being left blank as well as that of v_{10}, and the coattribute interrelation will now be:

$$r_c = (\beta_1, \mu_2, \beta_3, \mu_4, \mu_5, \mu_6, \mu_7, \mu_8, \mu_9, \mu_{10}),$$

where β_3 is 'frontage v3 positive real, between 8 and 50 metre'.

9.6 Black box representations and measurement hierarchy

This section illustrates how the measurement hierarchy of figure 8.2 relates to the black box model. The measurement hierarchy of that figure is incorporated in the left hand frame of figure 9.2.

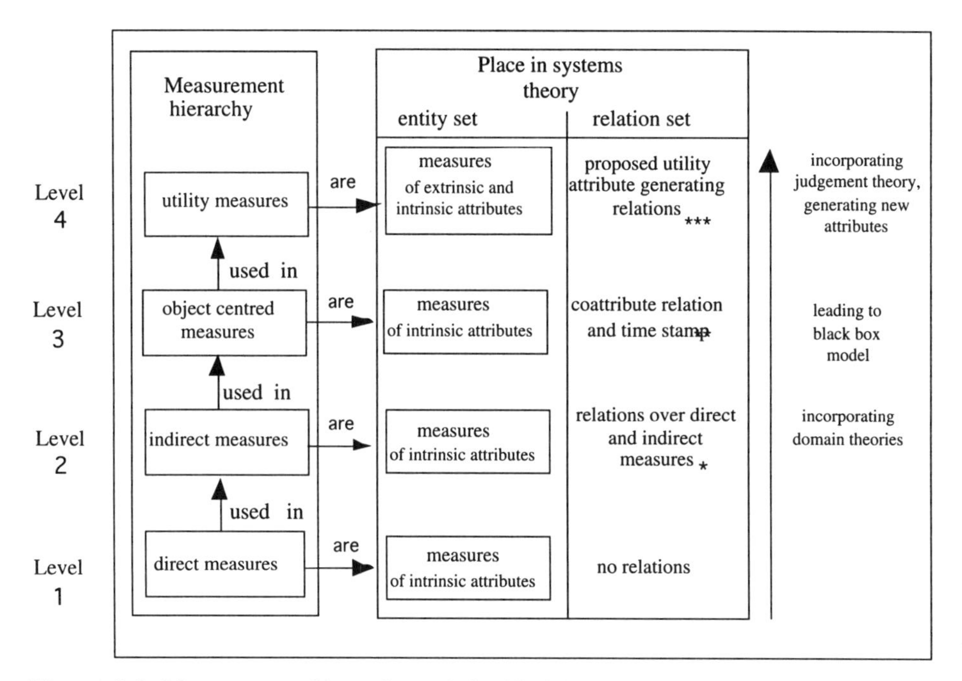

Figure 9.2: Measurement hierarchy and the black box system model (see text for explanation.)

The measures characterize the referent, each measure forming an element of the measure set of expression 9.1b. The measures are collected gradually, starting from the simplest: values of those well defined attributes for which direct measurement is feasible. These are shown as the lowest level in figure 9.2. Each direct measure is the intrinsic characteristic of the individual referent: independent of the observer, and each measure would replace a variable, β_i, in the class model of expression 9.1b by a value μ_i of expression 9.1a.

At Level 2 are those values that are obtained by indirect measurement. This implies the presence of a domain theory of the referent which enables the value of the measures to be calculated from other, directly obtained measures, and derive for them the appropriate units of measurement. The indirect measures are added to the entity set of expression 9.1a, and the relations are shown as present in the emerging relation set and marked with an asterisk (*) in figure 9.2. Again, the values of the measures are intrinsic to the referent. If no indirect measures are used in the model then this level is bypassed.

At the third level, that of the 'object centred' measures, all the relevant attributes of the referent have been modelled and included in the entity set of expression 9.1a. Any relevant domain knowledge had been incorporated. The integrity of the model is affirmed by the coattribute interrelation, whilst the temporal cohesion is assured by the time stamp. At this level, marked with two asterisks (**) in the figure, the representation of the multi-attribute referent becomes a full black box model. The measures still depend only on the nature of the referent and are intrinsic to it.

At the fourth and highest level the intrinsic measures of the referent are complemented by the problem solver's value system. Proposing these 'utility measures' involves introducing a whole new theory, the so-called 'judgement theory', which gives subjective relations over the intrinsic, object centred measures. Judgement theory, detailing how the value judgement is formed, is subjective: it is not provable, and needs justification and validation. Derived from the object centred measures, the utility measures incorporate the *choice* of attributes made by the modeller, and make explicit the *utility functions* applied. The measures no longer depend only on the referent: they are *extrinsic*. This judgemental level of the figure is marked *** in the figure.

Example 9.6

A company issues a general statement of its human resources policy to the effect that there is no discrimination on the basis of age, race, sex, marital status. Regarding professional employment, there is a specific policy declaring the characteristics of applicants to be taken into account when making new appointments. These are:

[1] academic qualifications,

[2] professional qualifications,

[3] number of years of relevant experience,

[4] recent training,

[5] number of patents held,

[6] number of papers/monographs published in the professional press during the past 3 years,

[7] current salary,

[8] position held in current employment.

Based on this, a notional 'utility function' is proposed. For example, the utility function excludes *candidates without a specified minimum level of academic qualification and professional qualification,* favours *candidates with more than 5 years of relevant experience,* disadvantages *candidates without recent training, publications and patents,* favours *candidates with high position and low salary. Note that there is no general or specific policy regarding employment of women of childbearing age!*

Figure 9.2 allows us to trace the evolution of the black box model over the measurement hierarchy, the vertical arrow on the right showing the direction of increasing information about the referent. The figure demonstrates the use of measurement for characterizing a referent objectively, and makes explicit the subjective basis on which informed value judgements are made. When the appointment panel selects one candidate rather than another, the basis of the choice should be clear to all concerned. If this is not done, then the decision may be impulsive rather than rational, and the panel may subsequently be charged with incompetence, bias or prejudice. When the Estate Agent assigns the attribute 'desirable' to a house, he should define it in terms of other measurable attributes. If this is not done, then the attribute 'desirable' is meaningless, a conclusion with which most prospective house buyers would agree.

9.7 Summary

This chapter formalizes notions of attributes and explains their role in black box modelling. It discusses modelling of an individual referent as well as the model classes and subclasses, and states requirements for a valid black box representation.

The measurement hierarchy is applied to the systems model and a method given for devising measures for representing decisions and value judgements.

9.8 Exercises

Exercise 9.1

Consider the following attributes which may be applied to a series of referents: beauty, wholesomeness, health, roundness, greatness, sweetness, user-friendliness, portability, convenience, shininess, heartiness, trustworthiness. Could these serve as modelling attributes? If so, what name would you give the corresponding properties, how would you define a property variable, and how would you assign a value?

Exercise 9.2

Consider a home computer system as your referent. Name the attributes which a computer salesman might consider important, and then those which would be significant to a first time user. How could these attributes be measured?

Exercise 9.3

(i) Name as many attributes of a kettle as you can (a well-known text identifies 21 of these [2]).
(ii) Suggest measures for these attributes.
(iii) Suggest subsets of the attributes of interest to users, the manufacturer, the safety inspectorate. Which of your suggested attributes would be relevant to each of these groups?

Exercise 9.4

You are taking Minutes at an official meeting, and you will issue the Minutes in a document. What are the general attributes that such a document should possess? How would you measure them?

Exercise 9.5

For Exercises 9.2 to 9.4, create a black box definition of the referent by adding a relation set to the set of attributes you have created.

Exercise 9.6

Obtain a company's Annual Report. From the Chairman's statement, identify attributes of the company. Are they measurable? List six measurable attributes to be found elsewhere in the Report. What are their values? Complete a systems definition of the Company using the attribute values you have discovered.

Exercise 9.7

Suggest measurable attributes for your country of birth and represent it as a black box.

9.9 Footnotes and References

1 Note the definition of the quality standard:

traceability
ability to trace the history, application or location of that which is under consideration

ISO/FDIS 9000:2000

An earlier version of the draft offered a more informative definition:

traceability – metrology
property of the result of a measurement or the value of a standard whereby it can be related to stated references, usually national or international standards, through an unbroken chain of comparisons, all having stated uncertainties

Draft BS-EN ISO 9000:2000

2 Alexander C, Notes on the synthesis of form, Harvard University Press, 1964.

Chapter 10 Structural systems

Structural representations are useful tools for the problem solver. Properly formed, the structural representation facilitates the derivation of the black box representation of the referent indirectly when it is not feasible to obtain it directly. In this 'analytical' context, the structural representation is an auxiliary: the means to the end of gaining the black box representation. In addition, structural representations play an essential role in design, where they assist in defining the way of constructing the system of its parts so as to meet the required black box specification.

This chapter is the companion of the previous one. It shows how to interpret the generic definition of 'system' to achieve a structural representation of the referent. It revisits and extends the notion of the bipartite tree, and shows its flexibility in analyzing, designing and implementing system structures, and identifies the key attributes of structural systems of good quality.

The chapter concludes with introducing the universal bipartite tree as a template for complexity management.

10.1 The structure as system

Recall once again the general notion of 'system', given in expression 7.2 and repeated below:

$$S = (E, R) \qquad \text{(expression 10.1)}$$

where $\mathbf{E} = \{e_1, e_2, \ldots, e_n\}$ is the finite set of elements,

$\mathbf{R} = \{r_1, r_2, \ldots, r_m\}$, is the finite set of interrelations among the elements,

and m, n are positive integers.

We showed in chapter 7 that this expression can be interpreted to represent a referent as a structure, given in expression 7.4, and repeated here:

$$S_S = (\mathbf{E}_S, \mathbf{R}_S), \qquad \text{(expression 10.2)}$$

where $\mathbf{E}_S = \{comp_1, comp_2, \ldots, comp_n\}$ is the representation of the set of components of which the system is constructed,

$\mathbf{R}_S = \{r_C, r_t, r_{S1} \ldots, r_{Sm-2}\}$ is the interrelation set over the elements of $\mathbf{E}_S$,

and S is a suffix indicating that the referent is represented as a structure. (As we noted before, the suffix S is frequently omitted where the context makes it clear that the representation is structural.)

Components of a system may be, for example, movements in a symphony, parts of a computer, items of equipment in the Intensive Care Unit of a hospital, cells of a plant, members of a classification system.

We may now state the fundamental principle of structural representation, which, regrettably, is often breached in practice, many structural diagrams showing the components of the system without adequately to specifying the links between them.

> The structural representation of system S_S in expression $S_S = (\mathbf{E}_S, \mathbf{R}_S)$ refers to each component of $\mathbf{E}_S$ by *name*. If any component is unnamed, or if the name of a component is missing from the list then the system is *incompletely specified.*
>
> *Characterizing the components of the structure*
>
> The structural representation must be complemented by the characterization of the attributes of *each named item* of the set $\mathbf{E}_S$. The characterization may either be *direct* or *indirect*. In direct characterization the component of the referent represented by an element of $\mathbf{E}_S$ is given as a black box. In indirect characterization the component is given as a *hierarchical structure*, ultimately resolved into its 'atomic' components, each such component being characterized as a black box. If the complementary information characterizing the named components is missing, the structural representation is an empty shell.
>
> *Characterizing the interrelations*
>
> $\mathbf{R}_S$ stipulates how the named components *interrelate* to form system S_S. If the structural interrelations are missing or are inadequately specified then the referent of the representation is merely a *set* rather than a *system.*

To model the system as a structure (as opposed to just describing it as a sundry collection of components), we need to define $\mathbf{R}_S$: the *interrelation set*, binding the components in a specific manner to form the whole.

- Each interrelation set $\mathbf{R}_S$ contains two mandatory interrelations r_c and r_t (or t), both defined over the complete set of components in $\mathbf{E}_S$, collectively called $\mathbf{R}_{Sman}$. The *co-structural* interrelation r_c assures *structural cohesion*: it asserts that all the components of $\mathbf{E}_S$ belong to the *same system*. In the first case cited above, r_c is a four place relation over the movements forming the symphony, in the second case it stipulates the number of pieces of electronic equipment collectively forming the computer, etc.
- The time stamp or co-temporal interrelation r_t (or t) has the same role as in the black box representation: it guarantees temporal cohesion, giving

the real time instant when the component representations and the interconnections are valid.

The two mandatory interrelations (r_C and t) are insufficient for creating a structural representation of adequate quality. Although they establish *what* the components are and *when* the representation is valid, they do not state *how* the system is constructed.

- For the structural representation to be of adequate, the interrelation set $\mathbf{R}_S$ must possess another formal characteristic. If the component set $\mathbf{E}_S$ has n elements then $\mathbf{R}_S$ needs to have at least one n-place interrelation in addition to r_C and t which defines the place of all n elements in the structure. Alternatively, the task of specifying the structure forming interrelation may be shared among several interrelations, but in any case, each element of $\mathbf{E}_S$ must be the argument of at least one structure forming interrelation; otherwise the element remains disjoint, and the structure falls apart.

In the general case, the interrelation set will have m elements (m≥3), where further elements define structure forming links among some or all of the component of $\mathbf{E}_S$, so that the complete structural interrelation set may take the form:

$$\mathbf{R}_S = \{ r_c, r_t, r_{S1}, \ldots, r_{Sm-2} \}$$
$$= \{ \mathbf{R}_{Sman}, r_{S1}, \ldots, r_{Sm-2} \}. \qquad \text{(expression 10.3)}$$

In case of our example of the symphony, the interrelation r_{S1} might stipulate that the four movements of the symphony should be played one after the other rather than simultaneously, and would also give the order, whereas a further two-place interrelation might state that the second and third movement are to be played without a break. In case of the computer, a structure forming interrelation may take the form of a block diagram which indicates the way in which the components are to be interconnected. The n-place structure forming interrelation may be given indirectly, for example by defining two interrelations over a pair of overlapping sets of elements, between them covering all of the structure, ensuring structural cohesion.

10.2 The structural representation

'Primitive' graphical representation of structure

Chapter 7 illustrated how to draw up graphical representations of structure as a tree: a specific type of directed graph. Figure 10.1 is an example of such a tree, where the root (node A, uppermost in the figure) represents the system as a whole, and the leaves (B, C, D, F) [1] are the components: elementary parts of the structure.

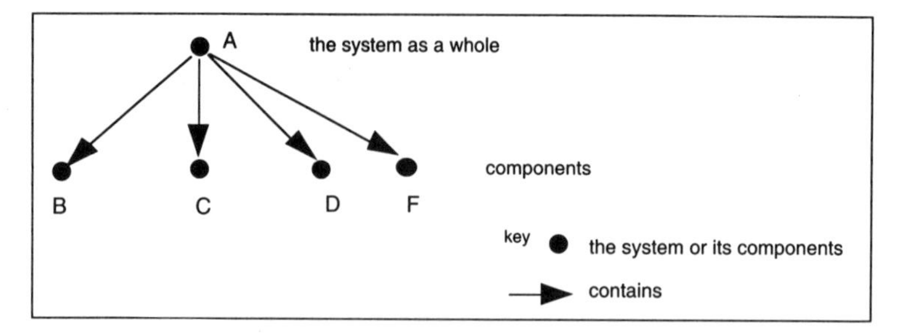

Figure 10.1: An incomplete (primitive) graphical representation of system A and its components B, C, D, F

This 'primitive' representation, using just two kinds of symbols (one sort of arc and one sort of node), distinguishes the whole from its parts, but does not indicate explicitly the interrelations among the parts. (To test this, the reader might try to represent a cheese and tomato sandwich by such a figure. There are four components: two for the slices of bread, one for cheese and one for tomato, but someone who has never seen a sandwich would not know how these components are to be assembled; and what would be the meaning of the arrows?)

To indicate explicitly the structure of a system as an element of the graph, we need a representation of the interrelation among the components, in addition to the two symbols of figure 10.1.

Developing the bipartite graph

Figure 10.2 is a more comprehensive representation of a four-component system. Here a white node represents a four-place structure forming interrelation, call it r_x, and the black nodes show the arguments of r_x: B, C, D and F. If once again we assume that B, C, D, F are movements of a symphony, then r_x might stand for the interrelation 'sequence'. If B, C, D, F are the components of the sandwich, then r_x will be the instruction of how to assemble them.

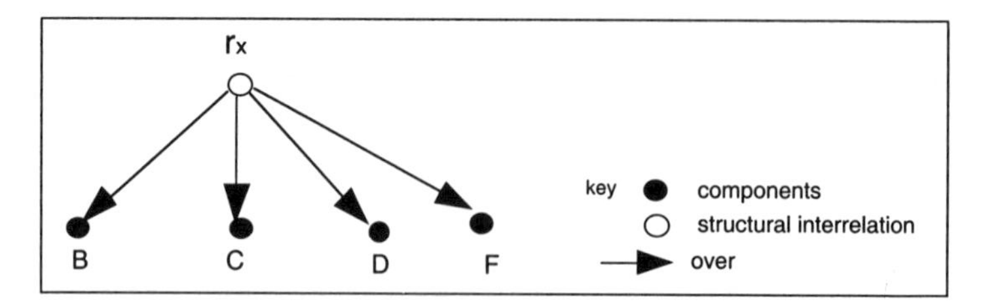

Figure 10.2: The four-place interrelation r_x with its arguments B, C, D, F

The five nodes of figure 10.2 have distinct meanings, and all five are necessary to represent the structure. This graph contains two types of node, hence is called 'bipartite', and is defined as:

bipartite graph
a graph whose vertex set can be partitioned into two sets in such a way that each edge joins a vertex of the first set to the vertex of the second set.
Attenborough, M: "Engineering Mathematics, McGraw Hill, 1994

In accord with the key, the graph of figure 10.2 can be read as:

'a four-place structural relation r_x defined *over* components B, C, B, F ', where 'r_x', 'over' and 'B', 'C', 'D', 'F' are labels'.

Interpreting the bipartite graph

Bipartite graphs are versatile enough to incorporate further systems ideas.

- We denote the system as A, designate the black box representation of A as A_B, and the structural representation as A_S. Since A_S and A_B have the same referent, from the viewpoint of the external observer they describe the same system behaviour: they are indistinguishable. We say that A_S is 'referentially equivalent' to A_B. Adopting the symbol '≅' to denote referential equivalence, we write: $A_B \cong A_S$.

- To convey this information graphically, we add a new node to the tree of figure 10.2, using a new symbol, the dotted arrow ‑‑►, and reinterpret the meaning of the white node. This new graph is introduced in figure 10.3.

- The node labels of figure 10.3 also make it explicit that the components B, C, D, F are characterized as black boxes. All black nodes in bipartite graphs stand for black box representations of their referent; thus, A_B, the topmost node of figure 10.3, is the black box representation of the referent A.

- Referential equivalence demands more than the *existence* of the structural link r_x among the parts of the system. It also requires that the manner of the interrelation should be specified explicitly, and that, collectively, the components be temporally coherent. This is indicated by R_S, the label of the white node, which incorporates the structural interrelation r_x, as well as the time stamp t, the co-structural interrelation r_c of the representation, and any other structure forming interrelation that may have been specified.

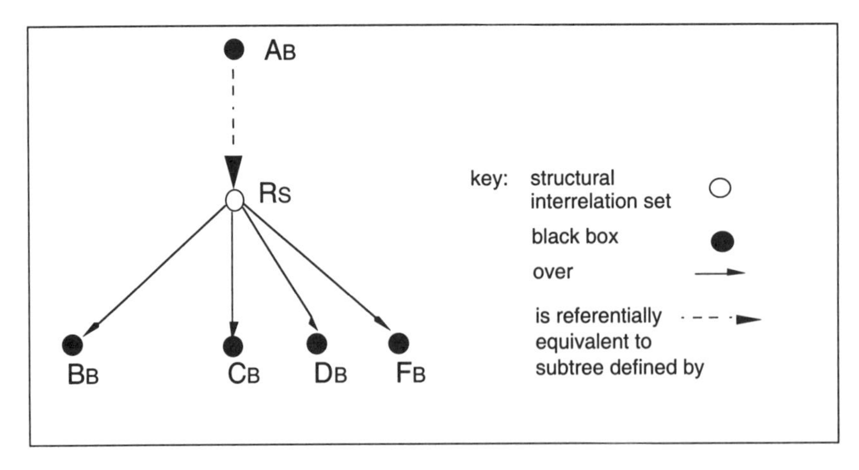

Figure 10.3: Representation of structure $A_S = \mathbf{R}_S(B_B, C_B, D_B, F_B)$ of system A with black box representation A_B

In accord with the key of figure 10.3, the graph can be read as follows:

'The black box representation A_B of A is referentially equivalent to the structural representation (A_S): a subtree defined by the structural relation set $\mathbf{R}_S$ over the black box models B_B, C_B, D_B, F_B of four components B, C, D, F:

$$A_S = \mathbf{R}_S(B_B, C_B, D_B, F_B) \qquad \text{(expression 10.4)}$$

or, assuming referential equivalence:

$$A_B \cong \mathbf{R}_S(B_B, C_B, D_B, F_B) \qquad \text{(expression 10.5)}$$

In these expressions the components B, C, D, F are modelled in the known manner: by their attribute measure set and the interrelation set including the coattribute and cotemporal interrelations. Since the whole structure must be temporally cohesive, the black box representation of all the components must have identical time stamp, which is also the time stamp of the structural representation A_S and the black box representation A_B of A.

Figure 10.3 is an example of a single level structural graph: the system A is resolved directly into atomic components. Figure 10.4 is a more elaborate example, taking the definition of the hierarchical structure a stage further, interposing substructures between the complete system and some of its atomic components. The figure shows the structural graph expanded to two levels of detail.

To represent a referent in a structure, all the paths in the tree must start from a black box, and must terminate in a black box. The root of the tree is the black box representation of the complete referent, each intermediate black node is the black box representation of a substructure, and each leaf of the tree is a black box representation of an atomic component of the structure.

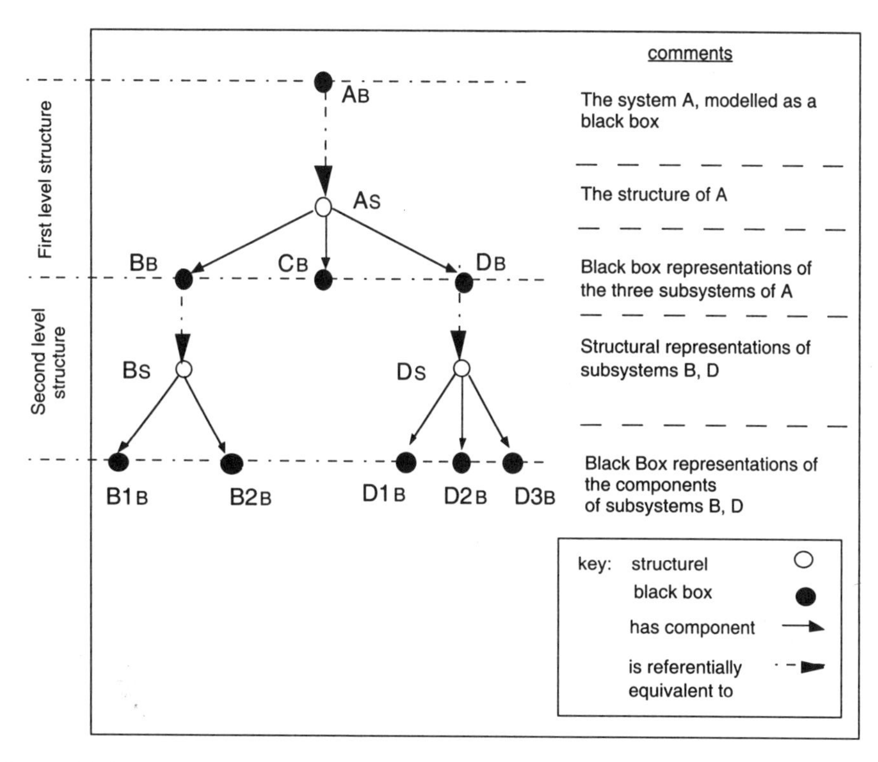

Figure 10.4: Bipartite graph of a system, structured on two levels

Flexibility of the bipartite graph

Consider again the simple one-level structure in figure 10.3, showing the system A and its related parts, B, C, D, F. This graph may be interpreted as:

> "System A, whose black box representation is A_B, is *decomposed into* (or *is designed as*) a structure A_S, defined by the interrelation set $\mathbf{R}_S$ over components B, C, D, F, where the black box representations of the components are B_B, C_B, D_B, F_B."

System construction, or system integration, is the reverse of this. It is a process of combining individual components in some specific way to form the system as a whole. We can represent the *system integration* process by reversing the arrows of a bipartite tree such as figure 10.3, starting from the bottom and moving upwards:

> "Elements B, C, D, F whose black box representations B_B, C_B, D_B, F_B, are *composed* by the structural interrelation set $\mathbf{R}_S$ into a structural system A_S, whose black box representation is A_B."

Upward flow also occurs in case of engineering analysis of a structure when conclusions are drawn from the structural representation about the system as a whole. Starting from the bottom and moving upwards again, we can read a bipartite tree such as that in figure 10.3 as follows:

> "Elements B, C, D, F have black box representations B_B, C_B, D_B, F_B. These are *composed* by the structural interrelation set $\mathbf{R}_S$ into a structural system A_S so as to yield the black box representation A_B. A_S and A_B are *referentially equivalent*: both are representations of the referent system A."

Taking advantage of its flexibility to represent design as well as system integration, the bipartite representation is frequently shown as a generic tree: a directed graph whose root and leaves are identified, but without making the direction of the graph explicit. Figure 10.5 shows such a 'generalized' bipartite tree. Directing the arrows from root A_B to leaves B_B, C_B, D_B, F_B, the generalized bipartite tree reverts to the design tree figure 10.3. Reversing the arrows, the generalized bipartite tree becomes a system integration tree (figure 10.6).

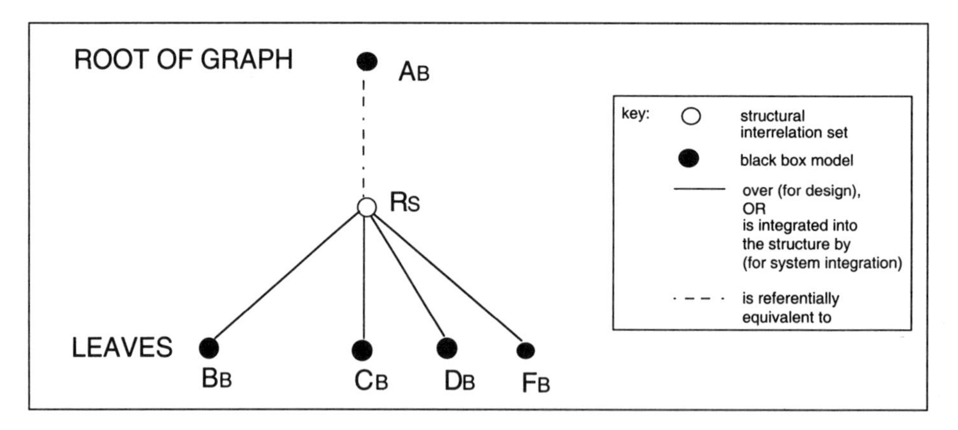

Figure 10.5: Generalized bipartite tree for the design tree of figure 10.3

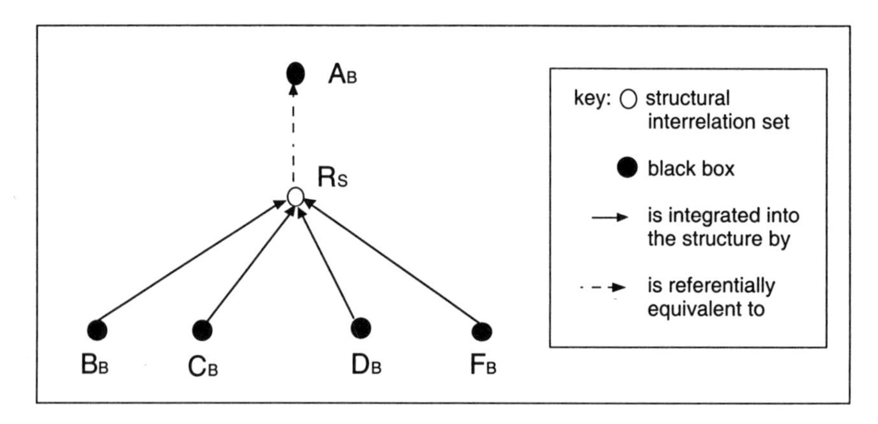

Figure 10.6: The generalized bipartite tree of figure 10.5, adopted for analysis

The definition of 'generalized bipartite tree' builds in two steps on the definitions of 'tree' and 'bipartite graph'. As intermediary, we define:

bipartite tree
tree whose vertex set can be partitioned into two sets in such a way that each arc joins a vertex of the first set to the vertex of the second set
Our working definition

We may now define:

generalized bipartite tree
bipartite tree in which (directed) arcs are replaced by (undirected) edges, two kinds of arcs alternating along each path between root and leaf
Our working definition

The root of the generalized bipartite tree is unambiguously identifiable: both the root and the leaves have valency 1 (only one arc attached), the two distinguished by the root being connected to the rest of the graph by a dashed arc. The tree admits to only two directions:

- in the 'design' tree the flow is directed from the root towards the leaves,
- in the 'engineering analysis' or (or 'system integration') tree the flow is from the leaves towards the root.
- $\mathbf{R}_S$ is a common feature of the design tree and the system integration tree, but it must be realized that the task associated with $\mathbf{R}_S$ differs in the two cases. In design, $\mathbf{R}_S$ is to be *invented* as a set of structural interrelations over a suitable number of elements to be specified, so as to fit the specification handed down from A_B. In case of system integration, $\mathbf{R}_S$ is *given*, and is to be used to derive A_B from the black box models of the components.

10.3 The bipartite tree in analyzing systems

Constructivity

The structure of some referent A is properly defined if analysis of the structural representation A_S can yield the referentially equivalent black box representation A_B of A. Such a structural representation displays *constructivity,* a key characteristic in engineering analysis as well as design, defined in section 4.4.

Constructivity presupposes that the structural system is 'hard', defined in terms of its attribute measures, and that there are well developed domain theories to link the measures together. Many important problems arise from fields where these conditions don't obtain. In such cases the problem solver has dual obligations, and should discharge these in the interest of quality and cost effectiveness: (i) use hard systems models and methods wherever possible, and (ii) engage in research, contributing to the development of the scientific/methodological foundations of the domain, promoting movement towards hard systems methodologies.

Making use of constructivity

Figure 10.6 is the bipartite tree of figure 10.5, adopted for analysis, indicating that, given the black box representation of referents B, C, D, F, and given the constructive definition of the interrelation $\mathbf{R}_S$, the structural representation A_S of referent A can be derived, such that :

$$A_B \cong \mathbf{R}_S \{B_B, C_B, D_B, F_B\}.$$

Before examining the process of deriving A_B from A_S, an introductory note may be in order.

It has already been stated that the time stamps of A_B and A_S are identical. We may therefore use the common denotation r_t or t. However, the coattribute and co-structural interrelations are not equivalent; we therefore refer to r_{cs} and r_{cb} for A_S and A_B, respectively.

- In figure 10.6, all elements are known, with the exception of A_B. However, even at the outset, we have quite a lot of useful information about A_B. Recall that modelling must always be purposeful, hence we can assume that the required attributes of the referent A are given by the problem itself, only their *value* is to be determined from the structural representation.

  Let us assume that there are q number of attributes whose value is sought. Then, from expression 9.1a, we know that the black box representation A_B will take the form:

  $$A_B = \mathbf{R}_B (\mathbf{E}_B) = \mathbf{R}_B (\{\mu_1, \mu_2, ..., \mu_q\}),$$

  where $\mathbf{R}_B$ will have two q–place mandatory interrelations: the coattribute interrelation stating that all of the q attribute measures belong to A, and the cotemporal interrelation.

- We also know from expression 10.2 that A_S takes the form:

  $$A_S = \mathbf{R}_S (B_B, C_B, D_B, F_B),$$

  where $\mathbf{R}_S$ is given as $\mathbf{R}_S = \{ r_{cs}, r_t, r_{S1}, ..., r_{sm-2}\}$:
  m number of interrelations, of which two (r_{cs}, r_t) are mandatory.

- We know further that cotemporal interrelations are common to all black box representations within the structure. Therefore r_t in $\mathbf{R}_S$ gives the cotemporal interrelation of A_B, completing the mandatory set $\mathbf{R}_B$ of A.

We can now turn our attention to A_B's attribute measure set.

- At the outset, the definition of A_B has q number of variables as 'placeholders' for the measures to be computed. We must now find for $\mathbf{E}_B = \{\mu_1, \mu_2, ..., \mu_q\}$, each attribute measure in turn.
- Assume for the moment that $\mathbf{R}_B$ comprises only the two mandatory elements r_{cb}, r_t. In this case we must calculate each attribute measure of $\mathbf{E}_B$ as a function, using the structure forming elements r_{S1}, ..., r_{Sm-2} of $\mathbf{R}_S$. If the constructive definition is explicit then we shall need q number of interrelations to give us the q number of functions, each returning one of the attribute values.

Example 10.1

This simple example does not call for representation as a structural system, but its very simplicity allows the reader to concentrate on the formalism which would then come useful in dealing with complicated situations.

Let the structure of figure 10.6 represent a bag of 4 items of shopping.

- *entity B: 1 kg medium size Coxes apples,*
  (weight: μ_{B1} = 1 kg, purchase price / kg: μ_{B2} = £0.78,
  type: μ_{B3} = Coxes Orange Pippin, size: μ_{B4} = medium),
- *entity C: 3 kg King Edward potatoes,*
  (weight: μ_{C1} = 3 kg, purchase price / kg: μ_{C2} = £0.32,
  type: μ_{C3} = King Edward),
- *the Sunday paper comprising 5 sections, costing 90 pence*
  (weight: μ_{D1} = 0.18 kg, purchase price: μ_{D2} = 90 pence,
  date: μ_{D3} = Sunday),
- *a £5 BT telephone card*
  (purchase price: μ_{F1} = £5, issuing company: μ_{F2} = BT).

If we are interested in two attributes only – the weight of the bag (μ_1,) and the cost of the complete shopping (μ_2) –, some of the attributes listed in the black box model of the component items are irrelevant, but we need two interrelations:

$$r_{S1}(\mu_{B1}, \mu_{C1}, \mu_{D1}): \text{sum}(\mu_{B1}, \mu_{C1}, \mu_{D1}),$$

defining the function f_1 which returns the value

$$\mu_1 = f_1(\mu_{B1}, \mu_{C1}, \mu_{D1}) = \mu_{B1} + \mu_{C1} + \mu_{D1} = 4.18 \text{ kg},$$

and

$$r_{S2}(\mu_{B1}, \mu_{B2}, \mu_{C1}, \mu_{C2}, \mu_{D1}, \mu_{D2}, \mu_{F1}):$$
$$\text{sum}(\mu_{B1}\mu_{B2}, \mu_{C1}\mu_{C1}, \mu_{D1}\mu_{D1}, \mu_{F1}),$$

giving the function f_2 which returns the value

$$\mu_2 = f_2(\mu_{B1}, \mu_{C1}, \mu_{D1}, \mu_{F1}, \mu_{B2}, \mu_{C2,} \mu_{D1}, \mu_{D2}, \mu_{F1}) =$$
$$\mu_{B1}\mu_{B2} + \mu_{C1}\mu_{C1} + \mu_{D1}\mu_{D1} + \mu_{F1} = £7.64.$$

Let us return now to the procedure of deriving the black box representation from the structure of our figure 10.6.

- In some simple cases, such as the purchase price in Example 10.1, an attribute measure for A_B may be derived from a small subset of the attribute measures of the components, and even the weight attribute calls for a subset only. However, in the general case we have, for the ith attribute measure of A_B:

$$\mu_i = f_i\,(\mathbf{E}_{BB}, \mathbf{E}_{CB}, \mathbf{E}_{DB}, \mathbf{E}_{FB}),$$

  where $\mathbf{E}_{BB}, \mathbf{E}_{CB}, \mathbf{E}_{DB}, \mathbf{E}_{FB}$ are attribute measure sets of the black box representations of components B, C, D, F in figure 10.6.
- Since the black box representation of A has q number of attributes, and since we assumed that $\mathbf{R}_B$ comprised only the two mandatory elements r_{cb} and r_t, the constructive definition must give (or allow the derivation from the structure forming interrelations of $\mathbf{R}_S$) q number of functions, one for each attribute of the black box representation.
- Consider now the case when $\mathbf{R}_B$ has some explicit or implicit structure forming elements, derivable from domain theory or general knowledge. In such cases it is possible to obtain the black box representation of the whole system even if the number of structure forming interrelations is less than the number of required black box parameters.

Example 10.2

A cold store has three rooms B, C, D, linked together by doors. The rooms have identical height $\mu_h = 3.5m$, *and the floor areas of the rooms are, respectively,* $\mu_B = 15\,m^2$, $\mu_C = 32\,m^2$, $\mu_D = 25\,m^2$.

To order a new cooling system, the owners of the cold store require two parameters: μ_1, *the floor area, and* μ_2, *the volume. However, the structural representation given by the above description gives only one structure forming interrelation, and even that is not very informative (namely, that the rooms are interlinked by doors). Nevertheless, it is common knowledge that the floor area is computable as the sum of the three black box measures, thus ,*

$$\mu_1 = f_1\,(\mu_B, \mu_C, \mu_D) = 72\,m^2,$$

and the volume is the function of all parameters, computable as the product of the floor area and the height:

$$\mu_1 = f_1\,(\mu_B, \mu_C, \mu_D, \mu_h) = 252\,m^3.$$

Clearly, the procedure just described can be generalized to structures containing more than four components.

We conclude this section with yet another example of the use of constructivity.

Example 10.3

Figure 10.7 shows a simple assembly Z: part of a larger electrical circuit. Z comprises six atomic elements: resistors, labelled Z_{11} *to* Z_{33}, *interconnected as shown. Relevant attribute measures of the six atomic components are given in table 10.1.*

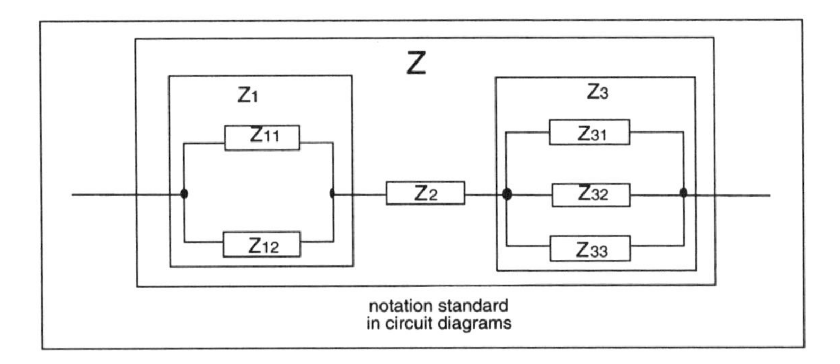

Figure 10.7: Representation of an electrical circuit containing resistances

Name of atomic component	Name, scale, value and unit of measurement of attribute μr	Name, scale, value and unit of measurement of attribute μc	Name, scale, value and unit of measurement of attribute μn	Comment
Z_{11}	Resistance, ratio scale, 3.30 kΩ	catalogue price, ratio scale, 1.00 pence	Supplier, nominal scale, Tom & Co.	purchase price = catalogue price
Z_{12}	Resistance, ratio scale, 2.20 kΩ	catalogue price, ratio scale, 1.00 pence	Supplier, nominal scale, Dick & Co.	catalogue price compounded by 15% delivery charge
Z_2	Resistance, ratio scale, 680 Ω	catalogue price, ratio scale, 1.00 pence	Supplier, nominal scale, Tom & Co.	purchase price = catalogue price
Z_{31}	Resistance, ratio scale, 1.00 kΩ	catalogue price, ratio scale, 1.00 pence	Supplier, nominal scale, Tom & Co.	purchase price = catalogue price
Z_{32}	Resistance, ratio scale, 4.70 kΩ	catalogue price, ratio scale, 1.00 pence	Supplier, nominal scale, Harry & Co.	purchase price compounded by 20% delivery charge
Z_{33}	Resistance, ratio scale, 2.20 kΩ	catalogue price, ratio scale, 1.00 pence	Supplier, nominal scale, Dick & Co.	purchase price compounded by 15% delivery charge

Table 10.1: Attribute measures of atomic elements of the assembly of figure 10.6

The black box model Z_B of the whole assembly is to be characterized in terms of just two attributes: resistance, designated μ_r, to be given in kiloOhms to an accuracy of two decimal places, and purchase price of components, designated μ_p, to be given in pence, once again to two decimal places. The black box model Z_B of Z is to be computed from the referentially equivalent and temporally coherent structural representation Z_S, whose generalized bipartite tree is shown in figure 10.7. The attribute measures of the two subassemblies Z_1, and Z_3, and of the complete assembly Z, are in table 10.2.

Name of entity	Name, scale, value and unit of measurement of attribute μr	Name, scale, value and unit of measurement of attribute μc
Z_1	Resistance, ratio scale, 1.32 kΩ	Purchase price, ratio scale, 2.15 pence
Z_3	Resistance, ratio scale, 480 Ω	Purchase price, ratio scale, 3.35 pence
Z	Resistance, ratio scale, 2.48 kΩ	Purchase price, ratio scale, 6.50 pence

Table 10.2: Attribute measures of the subassemblies and assembly of figure 10.6

Note that all three examples relate to simple problems that do not warrant a sophisticated apparatus of systems modelling. Nevertheless, the examples provide a useful vehicle for demonstrating the use of structural representations in deriving black box characteristics. In spite of their simplicity, the examples display several interesting features of system modelling. In particular, the reader is urged to work through Example 10.3. The footnote offers a lead for those unfamiliar with elementary circuit theory [2].

Constructivity in the soft sciences

We have just seen how, in the hard sciences, constructivity makes use of mathematically formulated domain theory and the black box attributes of leaf components to deduce the black box attributes of the system at the root.

In the soft sciences the attributes of the leaves and of the root may be given by variables and their values, but in many cases a mathematically formulated domain theory is lacking. The concept of constructivity might stimulate research and in due course may lead to the emergence of new and testable domain theories.

10.4 The bipartite tree in system design

Design is the elaboration of the specification of the required system into instructions for its implementation. The specification is a concise representation of the system. Design contains far more information, defining the *structure* of the system and the *specification of all atomic components.*

As we have seen in chapter 6, the specification of a required system can be met in a virtually countless number of ways. The task of the designer is to decide on a strategy for meeting the specification, to propose one *particular* design in accord with the strategy, and to verify the design before embarking on implementing it in practice. Level-by-level elaboration of design detail, and step-by-step verification, are the twin hallmarks of good design. A prudent designer verifies the correctness of each substructure before engaging in more detailed elaboration. Without such a disciplined approach, the designer might waste time and resources, would soon be lost in the detail, and would not be able to detect, let alone diagnose and correct, design errors.

We may now examine the design process with the aid of the example system of figure 10.4.

First level design

- The designer starts from the top of the structure: the specification of the system A, given by the black box representation A_B at the root of the bipartite tree of figure 10.4.
- Proceeding *top down*, the designer proposes one of the possible ways of meeting the specification. The designer *specifies* the required components B, C, D, and *invents* the interrelation set $\mathbf{R}_S$ over the specified components, *assuming* that such a structure will meet the black box specification A_B of referent A.
- The designer *documents* the invented structure as $\mathbf{R}_S$ over the components B_B, C_B, D_B, where $\mathbf{R}_S$ is the complete interrelation set shown by the topmost white node in figure 10.4, and B_B, C_B, D_B are the black box representations of the components B, C, D.
- At this stage the structure is nothing more than a hypothesis. For it to be adopted as the structural representation A_S of the required system A, the structure must pass the verification test of referential equivalence to the black box representation A_B.
- To perform the verification test, the designer must proceed *bottom up* within the first level, *analyzing* the structure $\mathbf{R}_S$ over B_B, C_B, D_B, seeking to deduce from it the attribute measures of a black box with this internal structure.
- If the attribute measures calculated from the structure are consistent with the attribute measures of the specification A_B, then verification has succeeded, and the design is adopted as the structural representation A_S of the required system A. If verification fails, the designer must return to the design invented at step 2 above, modify the structure, the component specifications, or both, and repeat the procedure of steps 3, 4, 5, 6.

Note that the black box characteristics of the required system relate to a prescriptive model, giving *limit values* for the attributes, or defining the nominal values of attributes within specified *tolerances*. To pass the verification test, the attribute values of the proposed structure need not be *equal* to the limit value: they need only to be *within* the set limits.

Successful verification marks the end of the first stage of structural design. What remains now is to decide how to create component subsystems whose black box characteristics meet the requirements set out in B_B, C_B, D_B.

Second level and multilevel design

The procedure illustrated for first level design can be followed at any depth. In figure 10.4, the process is shown only to the next level, but if the design of any component demands, the process might continue to any level of detail.

Consider this process in case of the second level design of figure 10.4, shown in the two-level structure of figure 10.8. The complete system system named A is at the root, and the components B, C, D are labelled 1, 2, 3.

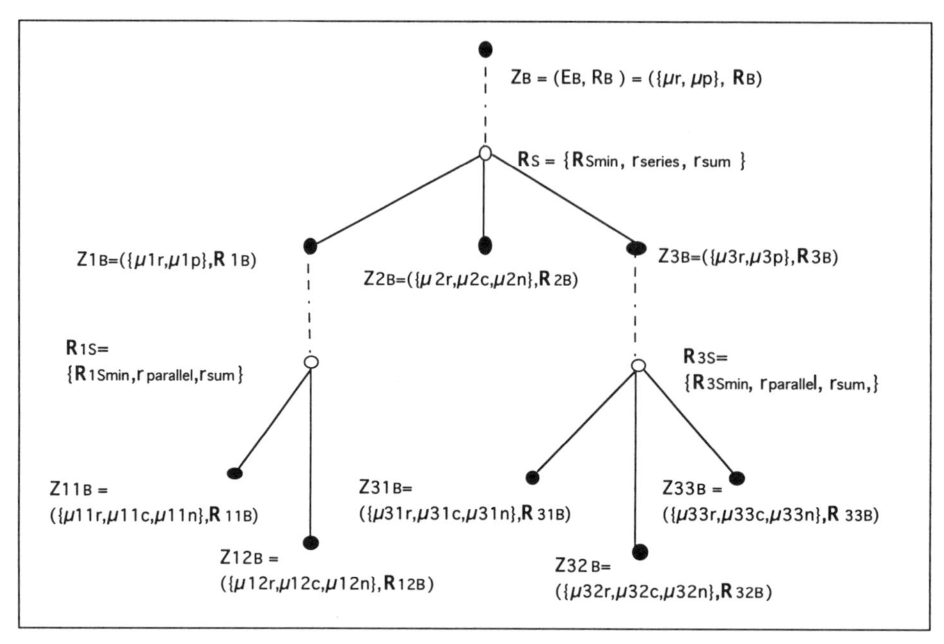

Figure 10.8: Generalized bipartite tree of assembly of figure 10.4 (key as in fig. 10.5)

Let us examine the figure.

- Taking the referents B, C, D of black nodes B_B, C_B, D_B as individual systems (independent starting points), the designer of each proceeds once again from the top down, inventing substructures. In the design in figure 10.8, further elaboration is proposed for subsystems B (labelled 1) and D (labelled 3). A ready made component is adopted for C (labelled 2). The re-labelling indicates the independence of the component design tasks.
- The subsystem designs are hypothetical. Verification proceeds once again *bottom up*, just as for the single stage design, proving referential equivalence of the structures proposed for B and D with their black box specifications. If the attribute measures obtained from a proposed structure is consistent with those stipulated in the specifications, then verification has succeeded. The proposed sub-structures of B and D must both pass such a verification test. In addition, the proposed ready-made component for C must pass validation. If these tests yield positive results then the second level design is complete.

Assume that, in case of the example system of figure 10.8, a two-level structure suffices, no further detailed design is required. Should this not be the case, the process would continue on another level of decomposition. As an example, consider component D (labelled 3), shown to be made up of three components D_1 (31), D_2 (32), D_3 (33). Should 32 require decomposition at a further level, then a new subtree would be suspended from black box node at 32, specifying the new structural interrelation and its black box arguments, etc.

Verification and validation

We must dwell for a moment on the difference between verification and validation in the context of design. We have just seen how *verification* confirms that the design is correct: it is internally consistent and meets the specification. Verification assures us that, built to a verified design, the system will meet the specification, *provided* that the structure is correctly implemented. To check that this supposition is correct, verification of the design must be followed by *validation* of the implementation: –

- Carrying out validation tests on each atomic *component*, ascertaining that each one meets its black box specification.
- Conducting a validation test on the *structure* to ascertain that the components are interlinked in the manner given by the design.
- In principle, correctly constructed systems built of validated components to verified designs, should yield a solution whose validity is guaranteed. In practice, this kind of assurance of validity is not sufficient. Although a correct design, correctly implemented, would *conform* to the requirement specifications, it may still fail to meet the expectations of the customer. According to currently adopted principles of quality, conformance is necessary but not sufficient: the supplier must go beyond conformance, seeking to assure customer satisfaction. This necessitates *validation* of the complete system.

Some comments on the use of the bipartite tree in design

TOP DOWN DESIGN?

As we have just seen, the main flow of action in course of design is top down: starting from the specification – a single node at the root of the tree –, the design process yields a tree such as that in figure 10.8. However, it would be an oversimplification to regard design as an entirely top-down process.

In course of design, top down actions of invention are interspersed with bottom up actions of *verification* along each path from root to leaf. Only in this way can the designer prevent wasting resources on implementing systems to flawed designs. Moreover, as we have just seen, the design process requires stage-by-stage *validation* of (i) the implementation of each component, (ii) the method of construction, and (iii) the completed solution at the given stage of design. Should it prove too lengthy or too costly to obtain any of the deemed ready-made components, the designer must continue resolving the structure to further levels of detail, until successful validation of all leaf components and of the structure built of them.

COMPLEXITY MANAGEMENT

The design process just described is an effective instrument of managing complexity by *separation of concerns:* a notion well established in software engineering.

Observe that, in the process just described, the structural design of an entity on any level of the hierarchy is independent of the structural design of any other entity. For example:

- When proposing the structure for the first level system A, the designer need only to deal with the black box model of A's subsystems B, C, D, not with their structural design in detail.
- Similarly, the design of subsystem B could be considered independently of the context of B. The designer did not need to take account of the characteristics of system A within which B was to function, nor of the features of peer subsystems C and D, nor even of the detailed design of the components of B at the next level of detail.

It is widely recognized that "accidents are caused by human failures in management, design or operation" [3]. A disciplined approach to hierarchical design is the means of reducing the source of human error by keeping the complexity of tasks under control. We return to some issues of complexity management later in this chapter.

10.5 Characteristics of structural systems

Checking the syntax of the structural representation

The syntax of the bipartite tree is sufficiently well defined to allow the problem solver to follow simple guidelines in composing bipartite trees, and to check their syntactical correctness. Early identification of syntax errors can save much time, money and effort in system specification, analysis and design.

- The root and all the leaves of the tree must be black nodes, designating black box representations.
- For analysis (checking, deducing from the structure characteristics of the whole), composition, system integration, the flow is from leaves to root, each of the leaf components being specified as black boxes.
- The root node must be connected to the structure by a dashed line, and to the leaves by a solid line.
- Black and white nodes must alternate on every path between root and any leaf.
- For design, the flow is from root to leaves, specifying the complete system at the root as a black box.
- The structure must be coherent as given by the mandatory interrelation, with at least one structure forming interrelation linking each of the structural elements.
- The representation must be temporally coherent, all components, all subsystems and the complete system carrying the same time signature.

- The structure must be constructively defined: a domain theory must exist for deriving the black box representation of the system from the structural definition and the black box representation of the components.
- It is advisable for the constructive definition to be explicit, with a specific structure forming interrelation for each attribute measure of the system.

Preserved, absorbed and emergent attributes

As we know, a system may be composed as a structure over subsystems, but it must form a coherent whole. When the structural system is modelled as a black box, its attributes will derive from the attributes of its atomic elements and the way they are combined in the structure.

- Some attribute measures of the complete system may be *preserved* in the structure, reflecting the attribute measures of one or more of the components directly, such as the fat content of a cup of tea which is equal to the fat content of its milk ingredient, the other components (tea, water, sugar) containing negligible fat. Similarly, in many cases the attributes of components may be preserved, although the *value* of the attribute of the whole will differ from that of the parts, such as the weight of the whole shopping being the sum of the weights of the parts.
- Other component attributes might be *absorbed* in the structure and disappear altogether, such as the acidity of an ingredient, the vulnerability of individuals in a mutually supportive group, or the arguments of a function.
- Yet other attributes may be *emergent:* arising indirectly, as the result of the characteristics of the components *together* with the interconnection among the components, or interaction among the attributes themselves.

  As an example of an emergent attribute, an electronic oscillator may be composed of an inductor and a capacitor, neither of which manifests oscillatory behaviour on its own, and yet, as a result of the interlinking of these components, the structure acts as an oscillator and has 'resonant frequency' as its characteristic emergent attribute. Example 10.2 contained another instance: the rooms of the cold store had the attribute of volume, but this was not stated explicitly. However, elementary spatial geometry allowed us to calculate the volume of the complete system as an 'emergent attribute' from attribute measures given in the black box components and their structural interrelations.

Reducibility

As we have seen, in a constructively defined structure the interrelations in $\mathbf{R}_S$ are mathematical formulae over the attribute measures of the black box models in $\mathbf{E}_S$. In case of complex problems the formulae can be quite elaborate, and this will have several adverse effects:

- the complicated modelling procedures and calculations may lead to error,

- the problem solver's confidence in the methods may be undermined,
- having spent time and effort on using 'hard' methods without getting satisfactory results, the problem solver may revert to the use of casual representations and informal methods, with their known limitations and shortcomings.

Structural representations become simplified and the black box parameters of the complete system are computed quite easily if, instead of treating the structural system as a monolith [4] (a single-level structure composed directly of its atomic elements), one reveals the inherent internal organization as a multilevel hierarchy of substructures. The experienced problem solver uses this technique quite naturally, and this is what happened in case of the circuit assembly of figure 10.7, repeated in its monolithic form in figure 10.9. This structure, directed for analysis, is shown in figure 10.10. Here, in the expression of $\mathbf{R_S}$, the interrelation for deriving component cost is r_{sum}, as before. However, the interrelation regarding the resistance of the circuit is difficult to describe concisely, since (domain theory tells us) calculating it would now yield the clumsy long expression:

$$z_Z = \frac{z_{11} \cdot z_{12}}{z_{11}+z_{12}} + z_2 + \frac{z_{31} \cdot z_{32} \cdot z_{33}}{z_{31}\, z_{32} + z_{31}\, z_{33} + z_{32}\, z_{33}} .$$

(expression 10.6)

In Example 10.3, the nuisance of handling expression 10.6 does not arise: recognizing the implicit internal structure of the circuit, we interposed boundaries around two subassemblies, naming them Z_1 and Z_2. Transforming the monolithic circuit into the two-level structure of figure 10.8, *reduced* the first level structure to three items in series, of which two were parallel second level substructures. This allowed analysis to be carried out in three easy stages: first computing the resistance of Z_1 and Z_2, and then computing Z as the sum of three items.

Reducibility – the possibility of decomposing a monolithic structure into a hierarchy of simpler structures – is a characteristic of structural systems which the problem solver can exploit. Because of its importance in problem solving, this characteristic of structures is pointed out in different contexts in several chapters of this book. Conversely, *irreducibility* is the property of structures that cannot be decomposed any further. Irreducibility of complicated structures leads to unmanageable systems, and hence it is the source of many project failures.

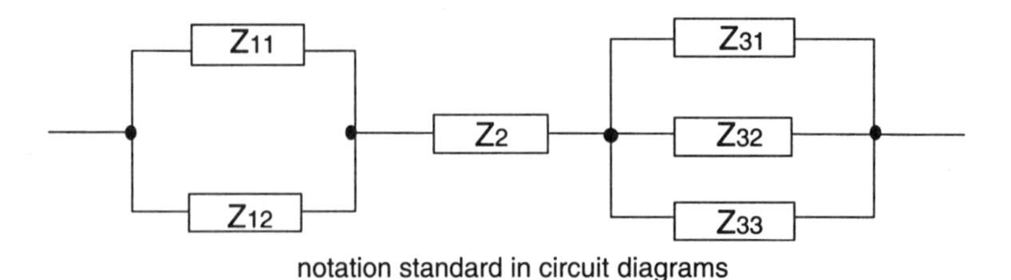

Figure 10.9: The electrical circuit of figure 10.7 as a monolithic structure

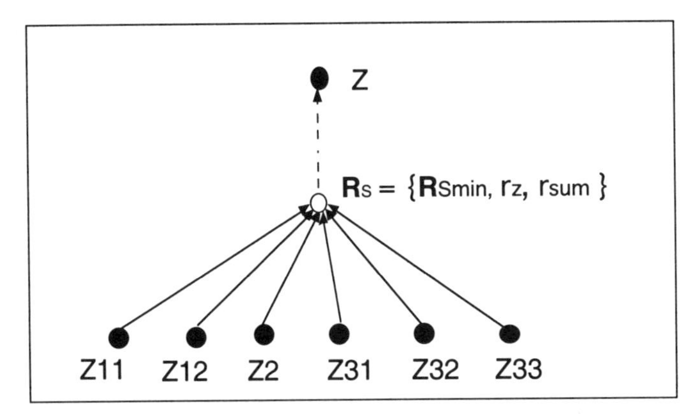

Figure 10.10: Generalized bipartite tree of the circuit of figure 10.9, adapted for analysis (key as in figure 10.6)

The reducibility of the assembly of figure 10.9 is evident to the naked eye, as is the reducibility of expression 10.6. Similarly, the irreducibility of a structure of components connected in series, or else components connected in parallel, is obvious. However, recognizing reducibility in an elaborate structure is not always easy, as the next example will show. Decomposing structures into their irreducible atomic elements presupposes the existence of a domain theory (in case of figure 10.9, circuit theory which maps the circuit assembly into the algebraic expression 10.6). The domain theory defines a collection of simple, irreducible structural interrelations (in figure 10.9, serial and parallel connections) which can be used singly or in combination. Armed with a comprehensive battery of irreducibles and methods for recognizing them, the problem solver can subject any existing structural system to *structural analysis* to reveal its skeleton. The skeleton may take several forms, one of which is a bipartite graph representing the structural system where the structural interrelations at the nodes correspond to irreducibles, and the arcs show the way in which they are interrelated.

Reducibility has played an important part in the development of software engineering. The use of flowcharts – a structural representation of programs – preceded the formulation of the domain theory of flowgraph structures. Huge programs were written without a discipline of design, they were documented in flowcharts (if at all). The resulting programmes were full of mistakes, but too complicated even for their authors to understand, let alone for others to debug, maintain and modify. This led to the well documented 'software crisis' of the 1970s. Research into the theory of software structure has a vast literature (for example, [5], [6], [7]), finally leading to a comprehensive theory of structural decomposition.

Example 10.4

Figure 10.11a is a simple flowchart: a directed graph comprising one sort of arc and five kinds of nodal elements: START, STOP, numbered square ASSIGNMENT nodes, diamond-shaped CHOICE nodes, and small circles signifying COLLECTION. Figure 10.11b shows the same flowchart as a multilevel structure, with its irreducible substructures identified:

- *the top level structure is a sequence of the black box node 1, followed by node A,*
- *the second levels tructure, nested in node A, is 'while-do, anchored on the choice node b, with the single assignment node B,*
- *the third level structure, nested in B, is 'if-then-else', based on the choice node a, with node C and the black box node 2 in the arms,*
- *the fourth level is a sequence of black box nodes 3 and 4.*

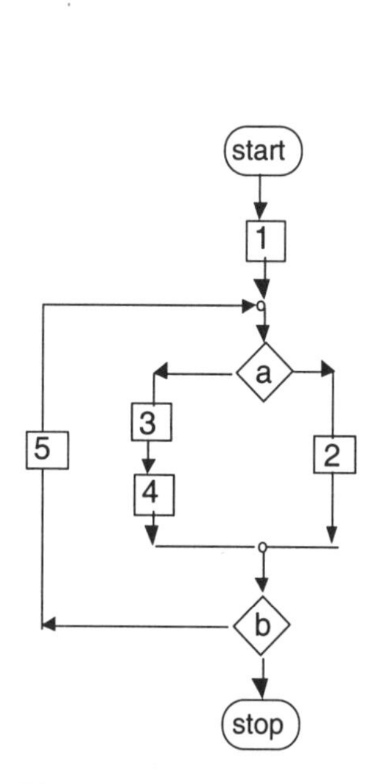

Figure 10.11a:
The flowchart of Example 10.4 as a monolith (key in text)

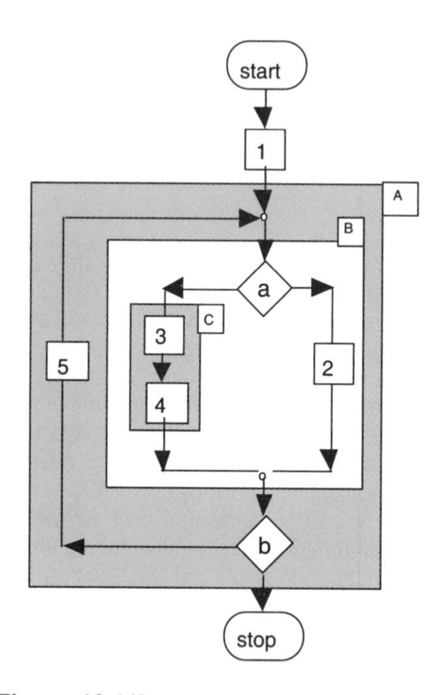

Figure 10.11b:
The flowchart of Example 10.4 as a hierarchy of 'if-then-else', 'while-do' and 'sequence' irreducibles (key in text)

10.6 Universal bipartite tree – a template for complexity management

Introducing the template

Figure 10.12 is the universal version of the generic bipartite tree, used as a template in problem solving. We define:

universal bipartite tree
single level generalized bipartite tree with finite number of leaf nodes

Our working definition

Reducibility can be exploited to transform an elaborate structure into a multilevel hierarchy of simple (or at least simpl*er*) substructures, and separation of concerns enables the problem solver to operate on one structure at a time without reference to the context, making the documentation stereotyped and simple.

Since the tree is universal, the template shows no direction, and even the root and the leaves are not explicitly identified. Nevertheless, the tree is not ambiguous, nor is the meaning of the black nodes dependent on the orientation of the tree: the root is recognizable as the only black node connected to the white node via a dashed arc.

The template in figure 10.12 shows the black nodes marked to represent any referent S. S_B is the usual black box representation of S, defined as a set of attribute measures $\mathbf{E}_B$ and a set of interrelations $\mathbf{R}_B$:

$$S_B = (\mathbf{E}_B, \mathbf{R}_B) \qquad \text{(expression 10.7)}$$

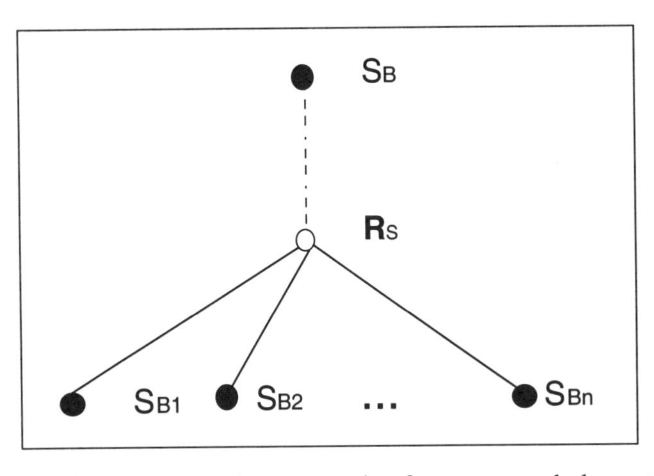

Figure 10.12: Generic structural representation for n structural elements (key as in figure 10.5)

The black node of S_B is joined by a dotted (referential equivalence) arc to the only white node of the figure. This node is labelled $\mathbf{R}_S$, defining a set of structural interrelations over n elements. The black nodes attached to $\mathbf{R}_S$ by solid ('over') arcs are labelled $S1_B$, $S2_B$, …, Sn_B, being the black box representations of components S1, S2, …, Sn. The set of black box representations, together with $\mathbf{R}_S$, define the structural representation of S, in accord with expression 10.2:

$$S_S = (\mathbf{E}_S, \mathbf{R}_S) = (\{S1_B, S2_B, \ldots, Sn_B\}, \mathbf{R}_S) \qquad \text{(expression 10.8)}$$
where $\mathbf{S}_B \cong \mathbf{S}_S$

The template corresponds to the generic case, where $\mathbf{R}_S$ is given as the pair of mandatory elements r_c and r_t, together with a very general structural relation r_x, meaning 'has component' (for design), or 'is component of' (for analysis). To adopt the template for analysis, flow must be directed *towards the root.* Referential equivalence implies that the structure is constructively defined, and the attribute values of S_B are calculated from S_S. To adopt the template for design, flow must be directed *away from the root.* Referential equivalence now prescribes that the attributes of $S1_B$, $S2_B$, ..., Sn_B are so chosen that, combined in accord with $\mathbf{R}_S$, they yield values that satisfy S_B.

Using the template

The importance of the template of figure 10.12 cannot be overstated. The template and the underlying complexity-controlled bipartite model have a variety of uses in industry and business, as well as in education and research.

- The calculation of attribute measures requires a domain theory to exist, and requires the measures to be used, all the way from the leaves to the root, and this is a demanding analytical task. However, the template eases this analytical task, and makes it unnecessary for the theories to be mathematically coherent. As work progresses from one level of the structure to the next, only the measures themselves propagate, not the mathematical expressions. Separation of concerns, together with proper definitions of attributes and measures, enables the user of the bipartite tree to transfer parameters from one type of mathematical structure to another. Thus, a different mathematical formulation may be adopted for the various attributes within a given level, and also for the various substructures within the structure.

- It is helpful in documenting *existing* systems, analyzing them, deducing their attribute measures, drawing conclusions from the analysis, and making reasoned decisions on the basis of the conclusions.

- It may be used in describing *potential* systems, first as a specification and then as a design.

- It aids communication between customer and supplier, as well as other members of the project's constituency.

- It can be adapted to the needs of each task of the project: creativity, analysis, construction and quality checking.

- It assists the creative process by formalizing the separation of concerns, thus freeing the designer from peripheral issues.

- It makes tractable the analysis of complex systems composed of many and varying subsystems, building up attribute values layer by layer, from the attribute values of atomic components to the attribute values for the system as a whole.

- It assists the project manager and members of project teams, including large multidisciplinary teams, in communicating with each other in the universal language of the template.

- It provides uniform documentation for the whole project from its initial conception through specification and design to implementation and completion.

- It is an effective instrument of 'archiving' projects, showing how the specification is developed step-by-step into the verified design, implemented by a validated structure of validated atomic components.

- Should the customer require modification of the specification of the system in course of the project, or should practical considerations in course of design or implementation call for modification of any component or subsystem, the template-based documentation makes it easy (or at least easier!) to trace the effects of the change through the whole structure.

- The template enforces syntax rules, and resolves the structure to black box models of the system, all subsystems and all atomic components, thus facilitating independent testing of parts.

10.7 Formal definition of structural representations

As we have seen at the start of this chapter, the definition of structure stems from the general definition of 'system': S = (**E**, **R**). The definition incorporates the requirement that the model will be finite: the referent will be characterized by a finite number of elements and a finite number of interrelations among the elements.

We may now summarize the discussion of structure in a formal definition:

structure (or structural representation)

The structural representation of a referent S is a system:

$S_S = (\mathbf{E}_S, \mathbf{R}_S)$,

where $\mathbf{E}_S$ is the set of n componenets of S, defined by black box models $S_{1B}, S_{2B}, \ldots, S_{nB}$,

$\mathbf{R}_S$ is the finite set of interrelations on $\mathbf{E}_S$ which includes

r_c, the 'corporate' or co-structural interrelation,

r_t, the time stamp t, common to S_S and all components in $\mathbf{E}_S$,

$r_{S1}, \ldots, r_{Sm}$, the m structural interrelations defined over the components in $\mathbf{E}_S$,

and S is a suffix showing structural representation of S.

The structural representation S_S of S is referentially equivalent to (has the same referent S as) the black box model

$S_B = (\mathbf{E}_B, \mathbf{R}_B)$,

where $\mathbf{E}_B = \{\mu_1, \mu_2, \ldots, \mu_q\}$ is the set of q attribute measures of S,

$\mathbf{R}_B$ includes the coattribute interrelation and the time stamp t,

and B is a suffix showing black box representation of S.

The interrelations of the structural representation represent the domain theories which allow calculation of the attribute measures of the whole system from the attribute measures of its components.

10.8 Comments on structural representations

Structural representations of a referent are not unique. Systems designed to implement a black box with a large set of attribute values would usually have a great variety of structures, depending on the attribute of interest and the time instant at which the design is considered. As a simple case of this, Example 10.3 showed that the structure of the assembly with respect to the resistance attribute is given in figure 10.7 and also in expression 10.6, whereas the structure with respect to the component cost attribute of the assembly is simply the sum of the cost of the individual components.

Depending on the attribute of interest, there are many valid ways to represent the internal structure of a company, a human being or a football team, and the structure of the same entity might differ from one week, one day, or even one minute to the next: the company may have been reorganized, relocated or sold, the person may have lost his job or suffered a stroke, the star striker of the football team may have been injured or sent off.

Example 10.5

Figure 10.13 demonstrates why it is important for structural representations to carry a time stamp. The figure shows a multilevel structure over field units, partitioned into 'occupied' and 'unoccupied' sectors. A train, moving from an occupied sector, leaves it unoccupied, while the unoccupied sector into which it moves now becomes occupied. Should the signal box use a model with the wrong time stamp, an occupied sector may appear to be unoccupied, and the situation becomes dangerous.

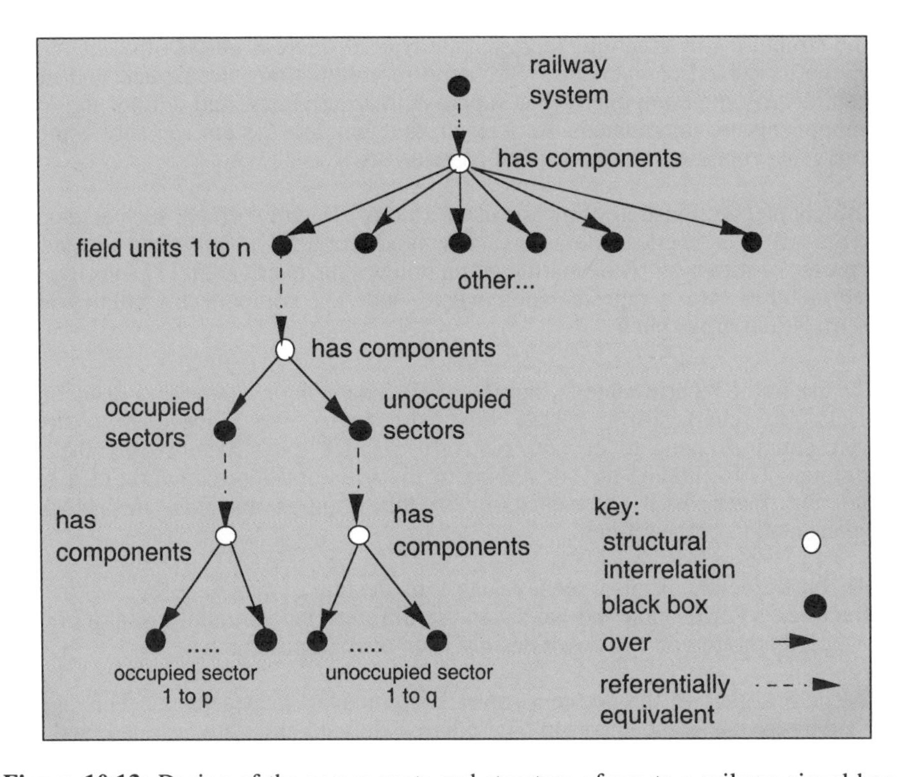

Figure 10.13: Design of the components and structure of use to a railway signal box

Although the structure may vary with time, and although the set of the structural interrelations may be different with respect to each attribute, the interrelations must be consistent: it is not possible for the components of a system simultaneously to satisfy contradictory structural requirements. Contradictions may be apparent, or may be buried deep inside the structure of the system. The template of the bipartite model brings each interrelation into focus, and is an aid to guarding against structural contradictions. As a matter of principle, an inconsistency in the structural relation set negates the whole model, since there is no referent that could satisfy contradictory specifications.

Example 10.6

Contradiction can occur in design, as a result of error. To meet the requirement for two system attributes, the designer of a telephone network proposed two interrelations r_{x1}*: sequence, and* r_{x2}*: parallel, for wiring up the same two peripheral components* X_1, X_2*. Clearly these structural interrelations cannot both obtain at the same time; the design of the structural* *system is internally inconsistent, and a system that satisfies both requirements cannot exist.*

10.9 Summary

The structure (or structural representation) of a referent defines the interrelations among its named components. Structural representations are explicit and concise: they identify the components but suppress their attributes, and defines the way the components are interrelated. As a result, the complete system can show surprising emergent properties, absent from all constituents.

This chapter demonstrates how the usual kind of structural graph, such as the one in figure 10.1, is overloaded, and cannot hold enough information adequately to represent a structure. The bipartite graph relieves the overload: it expands the simple tree notation into a representation where both the component identities and the interrelations are explicit.

The use of the bipartite tree is introduced for analyzing systems and deducing their black box characteristics from their structure. To achieve this, structural representations need to be constructively defined, the structure over the named components facilitating the conversion of the structural representation of a referent and the black box representation of the components into the black box representation of the referent.

The bipartite tree is also seen valuable in design of single level and multilevel structures. Verification and validation are different but essential tasks in course of design; the notion of 'top down design' is an oversimplification.

The hardest task of the problem solver is complexity management. This is greatly aided by the use of the universal bipartite tree, defined and demonstrated, and by the use of reducible structures.

The chapter offers a formal definition of 'structure' as a system.

10.10 Exercises

Exercise 10.1

Why is the tree of figure 10.1 inadequate to represent a system?

Exercise 10.2

A chain of record stores has, as one of its attributes, the value of the stock. Individual stock items are held at the various stores: Store1, Store2, ..., Store6. Show, by a structural tree, how the value of the stock may be aggregated over each individual store to give the stock value for the whole chain. Assuming Stores 1 and 2 are in a sparsely populated area where the prices have to be reduced, how would this modify your structure?

If all the Stores only sell videos, compact disks and vinyl gramophone records, show how stock taking would aggregate the number of units of each.

Exercise 10.3

(i) In the railway example of figure 10.13, suggest what (black box) attributes of field unit 1 could be calculated from attributes of the sectors of the field unit.

(ii) Suggest some attributes of field unit 1 which cannot be calculated from the attributes of its sectors.

Exercise 10.4.

Label figure 10.14 completely, showing black box and structural system models of each of the nodes, and adding a key.

Find an example from your own experience which could be described by a similar structural representation. Is your example constructively defined? If not, what steps would you take to obtain, or at least move towards, a constructive definition?

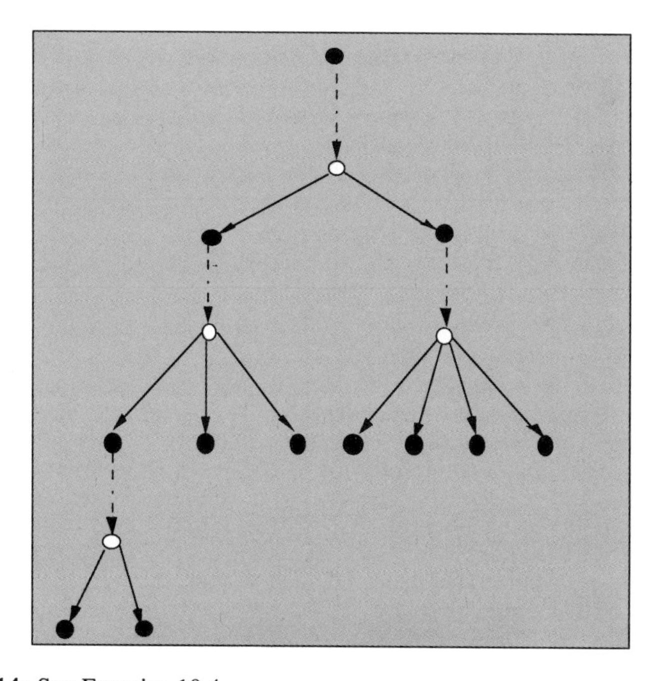

Figure 10.14: See Exercise 10.4

Exercise 10.5.

Write syntax rules for bipartite models of systems, and identify the rule(s) broken by the diagram of figure 10.15.

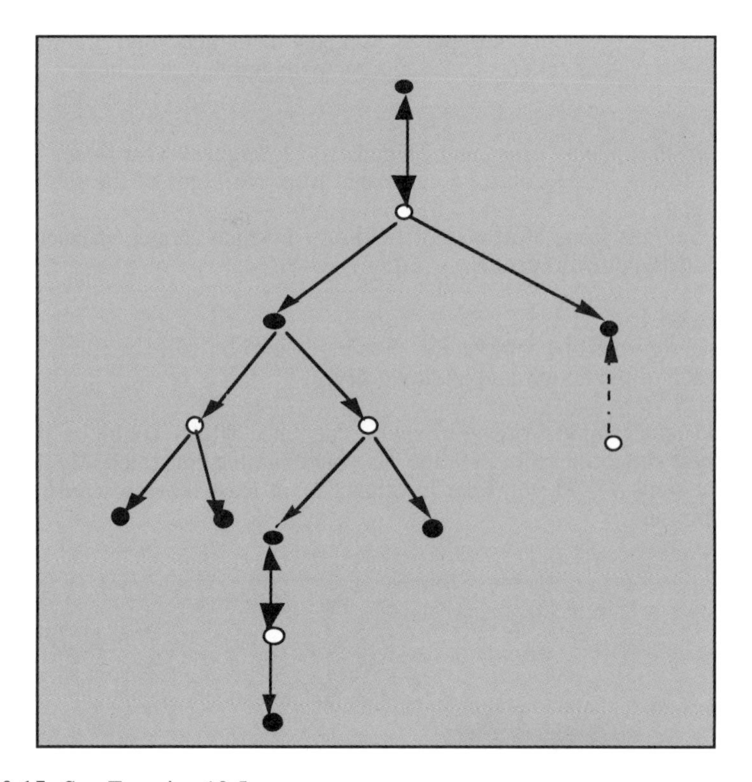

Figure 10.15: See Exercise 10.5

Exercise 10.6

Figure 10.16 is a simplified version of the flowchart of a program named ROOTS (based on Whitty and Fenton: "The axiomatic approach to system complexity", in "Designing for system maturity", State of the Art Report, Editor L Evans, Pergamon Infotech, 1985). The program computes the roots of a certain type of polynomial. The text of the program, written in FORTRAN IV, fits comfortably on an A4 page.

The example demonstrates that even such a small and simple program can lead to excessively complex structure.

Attempt to reveal the inherent structure of the flowchart.

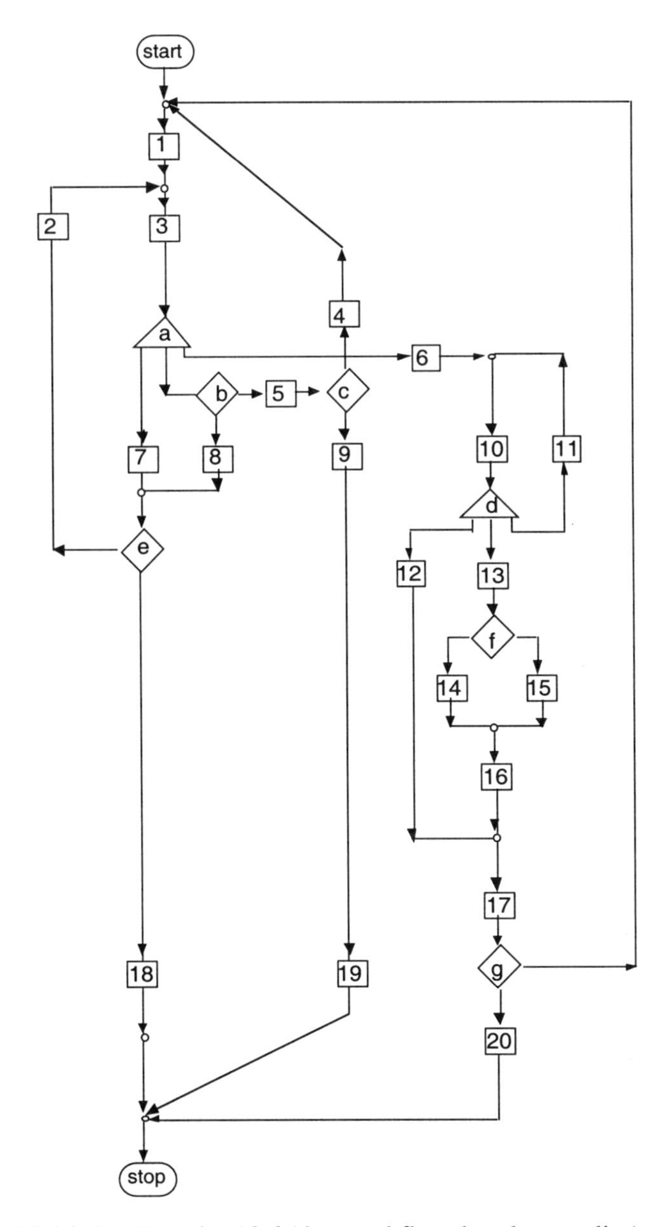

Figure 10.16: See Exercise 10.6 (the usual flowchart key applies)

Exercise 10.7

ISO 8402:1994 has been a very important document for many years, and is still the valid standard at the time of writing, but is soon to be superseded by ISO 9000:2000, of which the final draft has already been issued. In chapter 3 (Exercise 3.10) we quoted the definitions of 'product' and 'process' given in ISO 8402, and repeat them here (in bold). Comments are added in normal type.

product: *The result of activities or processes.*

The ISO definition is indirect and ungrounded: it uses the terms 'result', 'activity' and 'process', some of which requires definition. Of these, only 'process' is defined in the standard.

process: *Set of interrelated resources and activities which transform inputs into outputs.*

This definition is also indirect and ungrounded: it uses the terms 'resource', 'activity', 'input' and 'output', all of which would require definition. None of these is defined in the ISO 8402 standard.

Figure 10.17 shows the ISO 8402 definitions of 'product' and 'process' in a bipartite graph, demonstrating that the definitions are circular: they are mutually interrelated.

(i) Check that the figure represents the definitions correctly, and comment on the figure. Then look up the undefined terms in any general purpose dictionary, redraw the graph if necessary, and evaluate the result.

(ii) In Exercise 3.10 find the definition of 'product' and 'process' given in ISO/FDIS 9000:2000, the final draft of the ISO 9000 quality standard. Construct the graph of these definitions and comment on the result.

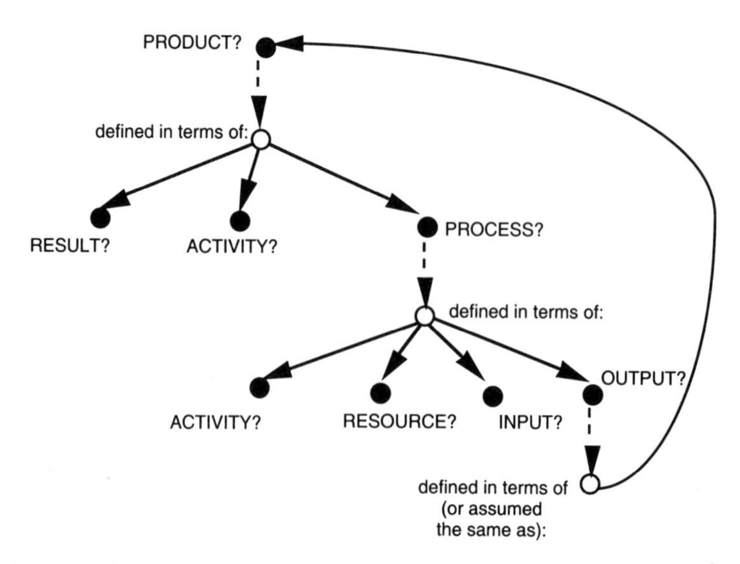

Figure 10.17: See exercise 10.7): Dependency graph of the definition of 'product' and 'process' in ISO 9000's Dictionary ISO 8402 (usual key)

10.11 Footnotes and References

1 The symbol '**E**' is used to represent the element set in expression 10.1. To avoid any possible confusion, we miss out E from the alphabetic progression when naming the elements of the structural system of this example.

2 The resistance of two resistors in series equals the sum of their resistances. The resistance of two resistors in parallel equals the product of their resistances, divided by the sum of the resistances. The value of structure of three or more resistors is calculated by combining them pairwise.

3 Leveson, N.G: "Safeware, system safety and computers". Addison Wesley, 1995

4 The term 'monolithic' is used in the sense of 'unfolded into a single level', or 'with internal boundaries omitted'.

5 Fenton, Whitty, Kaposi: "A generalized mathematical theory of structured programming". Theor Comp Sci, 36, 1985

6 Fenton, Kaposi: "An engineering theory of structure and measurement" in"Measurement for Software Quality Assurance and Control", Ed Littlewood, Elsevier, 1989

7 Fenton, N E: "Software metrics", Brooks/Cole, 1998

Chapter 11 Products, processes and gates

Part 1 of this book discussed the versatility of P/p graphs: their ability to represent referents of many kinds. It identified three kinds of P/p graphs – P/p networks, P/p frameworks and P/p model–, and showed how P/p graphs are built up of just three kinds of elements – products, processes and gates. It offered definition for all three sorts of elements and all three types of P/p graphs.

To gain deeper insight into the properties of P/p graphs, chapter examines more closely the black box characteristics of products, processes and gates., together with the structures which may be built of them, and formalize their definitions. For this, we summarize our earlier discussions, drawing on the universal notion of 'system' as a pair of sets: the element set **E** and the interrelation set **R**.

11.1 Preliminaries

System, black box and structure

We are now familiar with the systems world view. In Chapter 4 of Part 1 we defined the notion of system informally, and explained that the notion was generic: any entity of the real world may be represented as a system. Chapter 7 of Part 2 defined the notion of system formally as a pair of sets, and expression 7.2 gave the generic equation for finite systems, repeated here for easy reference:

$$S = (E, R) \qquad \text{(expression 11.1)}$$

where **E** is a finite set of elements and **R** is a finite set of interrelations.

In chapter 7 we also saw that the system equation could be interpreted in two ways. Viewing the system S as a whole, we represented it as a black box $S_B = (\mathbf{E}_B, \mathbf{R}_B)$ where in a hard system $\mathbf{E}_B$ was a set of attribute measures. Viewing it as a structure of parts, system S was represented as $S_S = (\mathbf{E}_S, \mathbf{R}_S)$, where $\mathbf{E}_S$ was the set of components of the system, and the constructive definition of the structural interrelations $\mathbf{R}_S$ permitted the derivation of S_B from S_S and the black box definition of its atomic components.

We draw on these ideas when defining the elements and structure of P/p graphs.

Product, process and gate

Chapter 4 introduced the idea of viewing products and processes as systems, and defined them both informally. Chapter 5 discussed P/p graphs and their variants, and gave their definitions. We saw that the construction of most P/p graphs called for a type of auxiliary element: the gate. Unlike gates – abstract entities to aid modelling –, products and processes always have real life referents, both being represented by an interpretation of the system equation of expression 11.1.

We have also seen that the distinction between product and process is not inherent in the nature of the referent: it is a matter for the modeller's viewpoint. In our universe time is ubiquitous. If the passage of time is significant from the viewpoint of the problem in hand then the real life entity is modelled as a process. If one needs take no account of time duration in the solution of the problem then the entity is modelled as a product. Measurement assists in making the distinction. If time duration is one of the key attributes of the referent, and if the value of this attribute is non-zero then it is to be modelled as a process. If the time duration attribute can be excluded from the model, or if its value can be taken as zero then we have a product. Naturally, both products and processes may be modelled as black boxes and as structures. Notice the distinction between the duration attribute and the time stamp. The place of the former is in the entity set, $\mathbf{E}_B$, but the latter is in the relation set, $\mathbf{R}_B$ (or $\mathbf{R}_S$).

- The product is the representation of the real-life entity at a time instant, thus, should the duration attribute of a product be measured on a ratio scale, it would have the mandatory value zero. Once a decision is made to model the referent as a product, the zero duration measure is redundant: it may be taken for granted and absorbed into the definition, rather than being stated explicitly in the model.
- By contrast, the time stamp has the function of imposing temporal coherence over the attribute set of the black box model, and over the component set of the structure. The value of the time stamp shows the real time instant – the calendar time – at which the model is a valid representation of the referent. The time stamp must always be stated explicitly. If it is omitted, the model is invalid.

11.2 Products

Recall that the definition of product ties the concept of 'product' to a time instant. This is the essential distinguishing feature of all products, setting them aside from processes. It allows 'product' to be defined autonomously, regardless of the past history of the referent and independently of the process that brought it about. One must bear in mind however that the idea of product being instantaneous is at variance with the everyday use of the word 'product'.

Example 11.1

In everyday language a pair of shoes just produced by the manufacturers will be called the 'product' of the company. On leaving the factory, the shoes may be assumed to have essentially the same attributes as those same shoes at the retailers, and would be considered to be the same product. However, in our terminology the pair is now a different product. Not only has it a different time stamp: at least some of the attributes will have been changed, namely the location, and this change contributes to themodification of the 'value' attribute, since the shoes are now readily available for customers.

Example 11.2

Today's newspaper is not the same product tomorrow. Its date stamp and one of its attributes is changed: it may retail at 50p today, but by tomorrow it will be waste.

Example 11.3

During software development, designs are constantly changing as new facilities are added, previous ones are updated, and time scales and resources are revised. Each stage of development of the design is a distinct product: a different 'version' approximating towards the design of the future system. The time stamp on each version must show when that design was a view of current thinking, allowing the designer to trace the development of the project, and identifying the most up-to-date version of the design.

Example 11.4

Minutes recording decisions taken at Board Meetings are time stamped, registering the starting time and date of the meeting. If a decision taken at a meeting is changed at another meeting of later date, or in case of inconsistency or contradiction between minute items of the same meeting, it is usual to assume that the most recent minute is valid, and previous ones are overwritten.

Note that the time stamp may be given to any accuracy: a nanosecond, a day or a year, depending on the purpose of the model and the nature of the attribute set chosen to represent the referent. In case of Example 11.2 and 11.4, it is usually sufficient to record time to the nearest day.

Product as black box

Referring to expression 11.1, and to the definition of 'product' in chapter 4, we may now proceed to define formally product as a black box:

> **product P** is modelled as a black box by the pair:
>
> $P_B = (\mathbf{E}_{BP}, \mathbf{R}_{BP})$
>
> where $\mathbf{E}_{BP}$ is the finite set of attribute measures characterizing the product P as a black box (including a zero valued duration attribute, often omitted for conciseness),
>
> $\mathbf{R}_{BP}$ is the finite set of interrelations on $\mathbf{E}_{BP}$ which includes:
>
> r_P the 'coattribute' interrelation, assuring *referential cohesion* , stating that all measures in the set $\mathbf{E}_{BP}$ belong to the *same referent,*
>
> t_P the 'time stamp' interrelation over attribute measures in the set $\mathbf{E}_{BP}$, assuring *temporal cohesion,* and identifying the real time instant when the attribute measures are valid,
>
> and BP is a suffix designating black box representation of product P (often omitted for conciseness).

For the sake of conciseness, attribute variables are often defined so that they should be independent of each other; if this is the case then $\mathbf{R}_{BP}$ will have only the two mandatory elements given in the definition. However, where reliability is important, redundancy is deliberately introduced into the attribute definitions; in such cases the interrelation set includes an element which stipulates how one of the attribute values may be computed from some of the others, thus allowing the user of the definition to check correctness. In some cases redundancy may also be introduced accidentally, the modeller being unaware of the interrelation among attributes. Such accidental redundancy may then results in error or inconsistency.

Example 11.1 continued

The location attribute and the value attributeof the shoes in this example are not independent. The value of the shoes might be defined indirectly by using an interrelation over the distance of the location and a constant parameter giving the value of the shoes at the factory.

Product as structure

In many cases it is convenient to define products constructively, giving the structure and the black box model of each element, from which the black box model of the whole can be computed. Referring again to expression 11.1, we can write:

product P is modelled as a structure by the pair:

$P_S = (\mathbf{E}_{SP}, \mathbf{R}_{SP})$

where	$\mathbf{E}_{SP}$	is the finite set of structural elements comprizing the product P,
	$\mathbf{R}_{SP}$	is the finite set of interrelations on $\mathbf{E}_{SP}$ which includes:
	r_P	the 'costructural' interrelation, assuring *structural cohesion*, stating that all elements in the set $\mathbf{E}_{SP}$ belong to the *same referent,*
	t_P	the 'time stamp' interrelation over elements: the common time stamp of the black box products of $\mathbf{E}_{SP}$, assuring *temporal cohesion,*
	r_S	is a finite set of structural interrelations over elements of $\mathbf{E}_{SP}$, assuring that all elements are connetced,
and SP		is a suffix designating structural representation of product P (often omitted for conciseness).

Let us refer again to notion of constructivity defined in chapter 4 and discussed in chapter 10. Accordingly, P_S of product P is constructively defined if it is possible to derive from it the black box model P_B. The time stamp of P_B will carry the common time stamp tp of the product set $\mathbf{E}_{SP}$.

Example 11.5

Figure 10.7 of Example 10.3 presents the resistor assembly Z as a structured product, with atomic components $\mathbf{E}_{SP} = \{Z_{11}, Z_{12}, Z_2, Z_{31}, Z_{32}, Z_{33}\}$. *The structure of Z,* r_S, *defined by the circuit diagram, shows how the components are interconnected. From this, using elementary circuit theory, we could deduce the resistance of the whole assembly Z as a function of the resistance values of its structural components. Altering the value of any component, or the interconnection among the components, would change the resistance of the assembly in subtle ways.*

- *The resistor assembly on the shelf is not the same product as the assembly in operation. Should a resistor heat up in service, the value of its resistance would increase. Using the domain theory of thermodynamics, the operational value of each resistance at a given current loading of the assembly would be calculable from the temperature coefficient attribute of the resistor and its share in the load of the assembly.*
- *Should the resistor assembly be under voltage stress, the voltage would be distributed among the components according to their resistance and position in the structure, changing the value of each resistor to a degree determined by its voltage coefficient.*

The example indicates that the component attributes and the structural interrelations among the components play equally important parts in determining the black box model of the system as a whole. The structure encapsulates knowledge of domain theory which allows the derivation of the black box model from the structure and the component models.

Product cluster

In representing two or more products jointly, it may be convenient to regard them as a cluster. The prerequisites for two or more products to be clustered is that they have a common time stamp.

The attribute measure set of the cluster contains all the attributes of the individual products. Since the combination of products into a cluster is a modelling formality rather than an action of physical reality, clustering takes no time, there is no interaction between the components of the cluster, and the attributes of the individual products remain unchanged. This does not mean that other attributes may not emerge, but these are attributes of the cluster as a whole, as an example will illustrate.

Example 11.6

Planks of wood or mass-produced items are clustered for reference before packaging for transportation. Each plank or each item retains its individual dimensions, weight and other attributes. The cluster as a whole will have a cardinality *attribute: an absolute measure of the number of pieces of wood in the cluster, a new attribute.*

The interrelation set of the cluster contains the individual coattribute interrelations of the components of the cluster and a new cluster-forming interrelation over the products in the cluster which is called the co-product interrelation.

Example 11.6 continued

Note the difference between compiling the batch and clustering. The former is a process, taking time, using manpower and other resources; the latter is a virtual process declaring the identity of the batch and its elements.

Let two products P_1 and P_2 have a common time signature. Then, by definition, P_1 and P_2 may be collected into a cluster and regarded as a single product P which carries the common time stamp. Should some process p (by definition a single-input, single-output representation) require as input both P_1 and P_2, the two products can be modelled as a cluster P: products P_1 and P_2 being linked by a co-product interrelation.

'Product cluster' was informally defined in chapter 5. Formally:

product cluster
a system, defined as $P = (\mathbf{E}_{SP}, \mathbf{R}_{SP})$,
where $\mathbf{E}_{SP} = \{P_1, P_2, \ldots, P_n)$ is a product set,
a product P_i within the cluster is given as
$P_i = (\mathbf{E}_{BPi}, \mathbf{R}_{BPi})$,
and the interrelation set of the cluster is
$\mathbf{R}_{SP} = \{t_P, r_c, r_{c1}, r_{c2}, \ldots, r_{cn}\}$,
where t_P is the time stamp of P, the common time stamp of all products in the cluster,
r_c is the co-product interrelation of the cluster,
and $r_{c1}, r_{c2}, \ldots, r_{cn}$ are the coattribute interrelations of the individual products in the cluster.

Our working definition

Note again that clustering assumes that there is no interaction among the products of the cluster. Thus, if products $P_1, P_2, \ldots, P_n$ are collected into a cluster, each product of the cluster is separately identifiable, and the attributes of the products remain invariant.

Similarly, since a cluster retains the separate coattribute interrelations r_{ci} of its component products and each product's individual attribute measures, the elements of a cluster can be can be *distributed* into its constituents, which are then independent products with identical time stamps.

11.3 Processes

As just seen, a product is instantaneous, its time duration is zero. Any other black box is a process, representing entities that act on products over time to generate new products. The concept of product is essential to the definition of process.

Referring to expression 11.1, we now examine how processes may be modelled both as black boxes or as structures over black boxes.

Process as a black box

Just as in the case of products, processes must be temporally and referentially coherent. In addition, processes are distinguished by special features:

- they *transform* the attributes and time stamp of their input product to generate the output product,
- the attribute transformation is described by *functions*,
- the transformation of the time stamp is by addition of a finite and nonzero *time interval*,
- the transformations absorb finite, nonzero *resources*,
- at any instant the process is, or is not, in a fit *state* to receive an input product, since it may be already engaged in performing a task,
- the process has a well-defined *domain* to which its valid inputs belong.

In addition to these mandatory attributes, processes may be characterized by several other features. For example,

- if man-made, the process has an *owner:* an individual responsible for the execution of the process,
- there is an *agent* (personnel, mechanism or whatever) executing the process.

These characteristics are captured in the informal definition given in chapter 4, and in the formal definition of the process as a black box system offered here:

process p is modelled as a black box by the pair: $p_B = (\mathbf{E}_{Bp}, \mathbf{R}_{Bp})$

where $\mathbf{E}_{Bp}$ is the finite set of attributes that characterize process p as a black box, including

∂t the duration of the process,

$\mathbf{D} = \{D_1, D_2, \dots, D_n\}$, the 'conformance attribute', setting the bounds of the value of each of the n attributes of the input, thus defining the domain of input products on which p can act,

$\pi = \{\pi_1, \pi_2, \dots, \pi_m\}$, the 'transformation attribute': the set of functions defined over the attribute measure set of the input product, each function generating one of the m attribute measures of the output product,

F the Boolean status parameter, indicating the availability or otherwise of p at the instant of arrival of the input,

Ω the nominal measure of the process owner of the process (if man-made),

C the cost of executing the process, a monetary measure in £ Sterling, say, of the resources absorbed by the process,

and $\mathbf{R}_{Bp}$ is the finite set of relations over $\mathbf{E}_{Bp}$, including

r_c the 'coattribute interrelation' over all elements of $\mathbf{E}_{Bp}$, asserting that the attributes belong to the *same* process,

r_t (or t) is the 'time stamp' interrelation over all elements of $\mathbf{E}_{Bp}$, stipulating the time instant when the attribute measures are valid, and

Bp is a suffix designating black-box representation of process p (frequently curtailed).

Let us examine now the process characteristics in more detail.

DURATION ∂T

The duration of a process is the time interval between t_{in}, the time of the input product entering the process, and t_{out}, the time the output product emerges; thus, $\partial t = t_{out} - t_{in}$.

The duration of a process may:

- be explicitly set in advance, as in the instruction "boil the potatoes for 10 minutes", or "on completion of a surgical operation, keep the patient under close observation for two hours",
- have its duration bounded, such as "execute a program instruction every 0.1 millisecond".

All these processes are synchronous: they are deemed to be accomplished within a preset time period of fixed value, by when they are expected to have yielded the required output (properly boiled potatoes, adequately recovered patient, completed computation). For such processes the value of ∂t in the black box model is a constant.

Alternately a process may continue until the attribute measures of the output product reach a predetermined value, as in:

- "boil the potatoes until soft",
- "keep the patient under observation until his breathing, pulse, blood pressure, etc. attain values within normal limits",
- "notify completion of the computational task".

Only when the attribute values of the output meet the set criteria is the process terminated, and only then can the output be passed on for further processing. Such processes are asynchronous. For asynchronous processes ∂t must remain a variable in the black box model: a placeholder for the value to be filled in when the duration measure becomes available.

In requirement specifications it is common to set bounds on the duration attribute of the process.

Examples 11.7

- *Completion dates in contracts, with penalty clauses, levying charges day-by-day if the contract is not fulfilled by the set date: an ordered item is not delivered, highway construction is not completed, etc.*
- *Deadlines for repayment of loans, and extra interests charged, if the deadline is breached.*
- *Upper bound for displaying perishable foods: the 'Sell by' date.*
- *Deadlines set for students to hand in coursework assignments, and marks deducted if the deadline is not met.*

DOMAIN

The domain **D** of a process defines the set of all products acceptable to the process. For an input to be admissible to a process it must satisfy the condition $P_{in} \in \mathbf{D}$. The domain can be given by enumeration, restricted by defining the attributes of products to be included or excluded; it may be given as a product class; it may be defined on some other basis. Here are some examples.

Examples 11.8

A domain may be given:

- *as an enumerated set, such as list of named students accepted to an academic course,*
- *as a class, such as criteria for acceptance of students to an academic course, based on*
  - *minimum age and academic record,*
  - *as a restriction due to local conditions, the acceptance of 20 applicants on a first-come, first served basis .*

FUNCTION

A process acting on an input product generates an output which differs from the input. This can be expressed as:

$$P_{out} = p\,(P_{in}) \qquad \text{(expression 11.2)}$$

where p is the process and P_{in}, P_{out} are the input/output products of p.

Engineers regard processes as transfer functions, which transform inputs to outputs. As we noted before, the transfer function has two effects:

- it modifies the time stamp of the product such that

  $$t_{out} = t_{in} + \partial t \qquad \text{(expression 11.3)}$$

- it transforms the attribute measures of the product

  $$\mathbf{E}_{out} = \pi(\mathbf{E}_{in}) \qquad \text{(expression 11.4)}$$

where $\mathbf{E}_{in}$, $\mathbf{E}_{out}$ are the attribute measure sets of the black box model of products P_{in} and P_{out}, and π is a set of attribute transformations.

If $\mathbf{E}_{out} = \{e_{o\tilde{}ut1}, e_{out2}, \ldots, e_{outn}\}$ and

$$\pi = \{\pi 1, \pi 2, \ldots, \pi n\}, \text{ then}$$

$$e_{out1} = \pi 1(\mathbf{E}_{in}),\ e_{out2} = \pi 2(\mathbf{E}_{in}),\ \ldots,\ e_{outn} = \pi n(\mathbf{E}_{in}) \qquad \text{(expression 11.5)}$$

Note that, in general, the individual attribute values of the output product depend on the total set of input attribute values. To understand this fully, consider the following example.

Example 11.9

A food manufacturer is trying out a new stew recipe in his experimental kitchen. The experimental process is shown in figure 11.1, ∂t signifying the duration of the process (including preparation time and cooking time), E_{in} standing for input attributes (including characteristics of ingredients and fuel cost), E_{out}

representing output attributes (characterization of the taste and appearance of the finished dish).

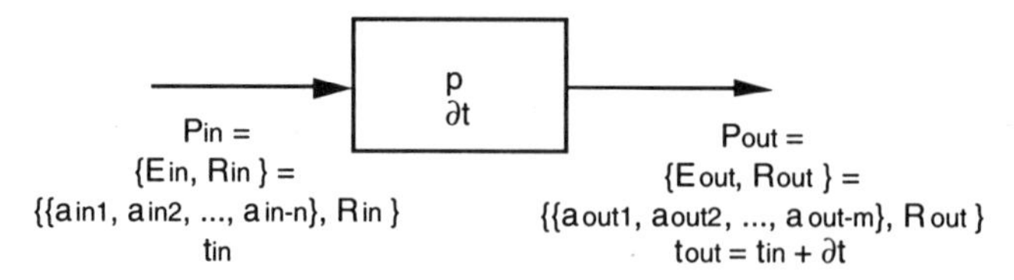

Figure 11.1: Process p executing a transformation of the input product into the output product (b-type key)

Before deciding to adopt the recipe of the tasty stew as one of the new product lines of the company, the dish and the production process must be comprehensively characterized. The process of characterization will take account of the attributes obtained from the experimental process of figure 11.1, together with calculating the nutritional value of the food, its full production cost (including cost of disposal of heat loss, fumes and other waste products), the size of a portion, the selling price, etc. Let's call this process p', with input product $P_{in}' = \{E_{in}', R_{in}'\}$, output product $P_{out}' = \{E_{out}', R_{out}'\}$, and duration $\partial t'$. The characterization will involve many of the departments of the company, requiring expertise in food chemistry, thermodynamics, nutrition, cost estimation, consumer psychology, market assessment, etc. Each specialist may contribute to decidingwhat input/output parameters are neeed for characterizing the process from his/her own point of view. Each person will need only a subset of the input data, but in principle each may have access to all of it.

Figure 11.2 shows the process p' of characterizing the industrial version of the cooking process p and its products.

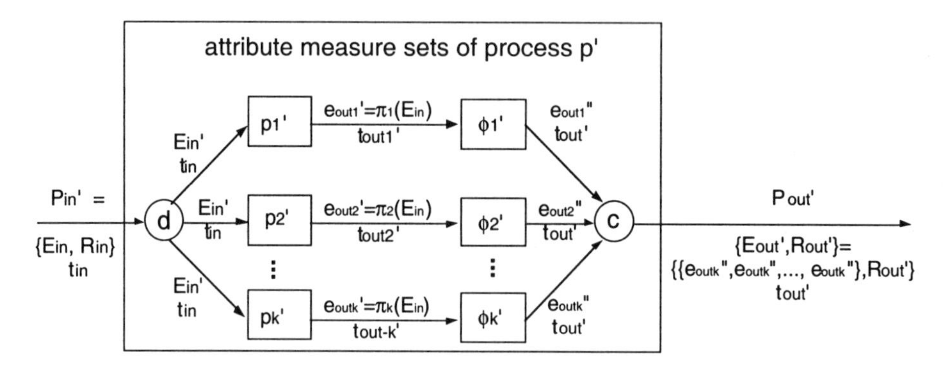

Figure 11.2: Representation of the process p' of characterizing the process p (b-type, reduced representation – see text)

Each subprocess p_i' in the figure is the responsibility of an expert, and each process yields an attribute measure e_i of the output of the industrial process. There are k number of subprocesses: as many as the attributes required for the full characterization of the new product line. The subprocesses are started *simultaneously, but they are independent of each other, each one using the mathematical formulation required by the specific discipline, and will take different amounts of time. To assemble the results into the single product Pout', the output of subprocesses must be stored until all the results become available.*

To emphasize the action performed by process p', figure 11.2 is a 'reduced' representation, omitting the interrelation sets of the products in p' and showing only the subprocess attribute measure sets.

- *The distribution gate d 'broadcasts' the complete attribute measure set E_{in} simultaneously to all subprocesses of p'.*

- *Each subprocess p_i generates an attribute measure set comprizing a single attribute measure $e_{out\text{-}i}$' as a function π_i (E_{in}). The output of each sub process is then input to a null process of suitable duration, generating the tcoincident inputs to the collection gate c.*

The crucial feature of the process definition, assuring its effectiveness in practice, is the independence of the function of subprocesses generating each attribute of the output product. The formulation and solution of complex problems calls for the contribution of experts drawn from several disciplines, each with its own methods and tools, each using a variety of different mathematical idioms of its own. Collaboration is of the essence, but within the collaborative framework each expert must retain autonomy. Figure 11.3 seeks to illustrate this.

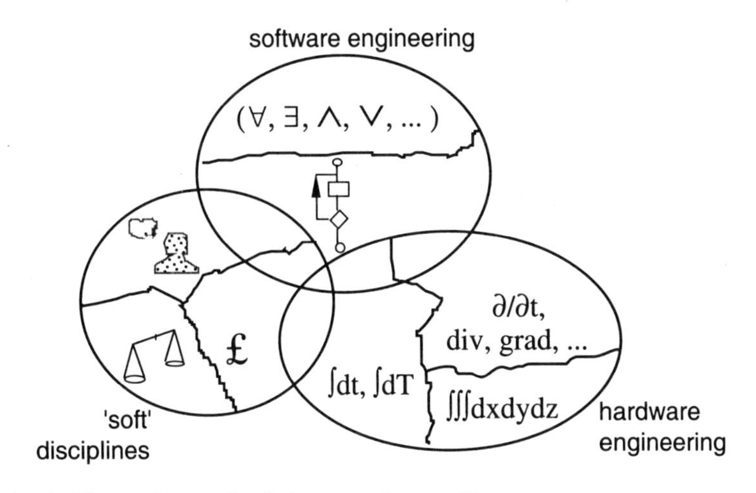

Figure 11.3: The problem of solving complex problems

The figure shows pictorially some 'soft' disciplines such as finance, psychology and law, together with 'hardware engineering' represented by some mathematical symbolisms, and 'software engineering' by logical and flowchart symbols. These three groups of disciplines may all be involved in the solution of a single problem.

Within each group there will be subgroups that have their own domain of specialist expertise, their precisely defined language and method of reasoning. Provided that problems and requirements are characterized by properly defined measures and yield measurably characterized solutions, because of functional independence P/p modelling can accommodate such a diversity of hard and soft disciplines, coordinating the contribution of all experts involved in creating the solution.

STATUS

Product/process modelling is realistic in its approach. Frequently a process is 'busy' processing the previous input. All real-life activities have nonzero duration, and the processes representing them must carry a parameter to show their status as free to accept input or the converse, busy. This two-valued parameter is known as the status parameter, and its value will depend on the real time at which the state of the process is sampled. An atomic process is set to busy between t_{in} and t_{out}, for the complete duration of the process of which it is an attribute. The status parameter is the handle for managing access to the process, as the examples below show. Access management is discussed in more detail in chapter 12.

Examples 11.10

- *The transportation process carried out by a taxicab is free or not free, as indicated by the status 'flag' on the taxicab.*
- *For a new patient the process of healing in a hospital will depend on the availability of a bed.*
- *A CPU (the central processor unit of a computer) processing a 'thread' is not free for any other function.*

OTHER PROCESS ATTRIBUTES

Non-mandatory process attributes offer means of integrating technical and managerial information within the same process representation. In business management, manufacturing and related fields it is necessary to make explicit who is the process owner: the individual who may not actually carry out all, or even any of the functions of the process, but will be responsible for the successful execution of the process: the person at whose desk 'the buck stops'. The owner parameter, designated by the symbol 'Ω', makes it explicit that in professional practice there is no place for excuses, there is no 'shared responsibility', and attitudes such as 'I am the boss, but I have not been told what goes on' are unacceptable.

In similar situations it is also useful to make explicit that all processes absorb resources. In an organization well known to the authors, an inordinate amount of time was spent people participating in large meetings. The situation changed dramatically when a house standard was adopted that all processes must carry a cost parameter. Examining the case for the inclusion of each member in each committee, cutting down on cross-committee representations and ex-officio participations reduced the membership of all committees, shortened meetings without in any way diminishing the quality of decisions reached, and incidentally released personnel for more productive duties.

Yet another useful process attribute is the physical agent that carries out the process. The agent may be a person, a team, a machine, or some composite mechanism.

In some situations other attributes might also be helpful, such as the location attribute of the process, and standards governing it. These are not included in the process definition.

CONDITIONS FOR A PROCESS TO TAKE PLACE

For a process to occur, the input product must be within the permissible domain of the process, ($P_{in} \in \mathbf{D}$), and at the time the product presents itself to the process (t_{in}), the status of the process must be free (F=1).

Process as structure

As an alternative to black box definition, processes may also be defined structurally, using the system notation of expression 11.3.

Formally:

process p is modelled as a structure by the pair :

$$p_S = (\mathbf{E}_{Sp}, \mathbf{R}_{Sp})$$

where	$\mathbf{E}_{Sp}$	is the finite set of structural elements: the black box processes of which p_S is composed,
	$\mathbf{R}_{Sp}$	is the finite set of interrelations which includes
	r_p	the 'costructural' interrelation, assuring *structural cohesion*, stating that all elements in the set $\mathbf{E}_{Sp}$ belong to the *same referent,*
	t_p	the 'time stamp' interrelation over elements: the common time stamp of the black box products of $\mathbf{E}_{Sp}$, assuring *temporal cohesion,*
	$\mathbf{r}_S$,	a finite set of structural interrelation on $\mathbf{E}_{Sp}$, assuring that all elements are connected,
and	Sp	is a suffix designating structural representation of process p (often omitted for conciseness).

The p_s of process p is *constructively defined* if it is possible to derive from it the black box model p_B of process p. The time stamp of p_B will carry the common time stamp t_p of the process set $\mathbf{E}_{Sp}$.

Let us explore the kinds of struct˜ures one may construct out of the three kinds of elements – products, processes and gates – of a P/p network.

The simplest possible structure is a single process, the set $\mathbf{E}_{Sp}$ having exactly one element (figure 11.4). This is a 'degenerate' structure, having only a single component.

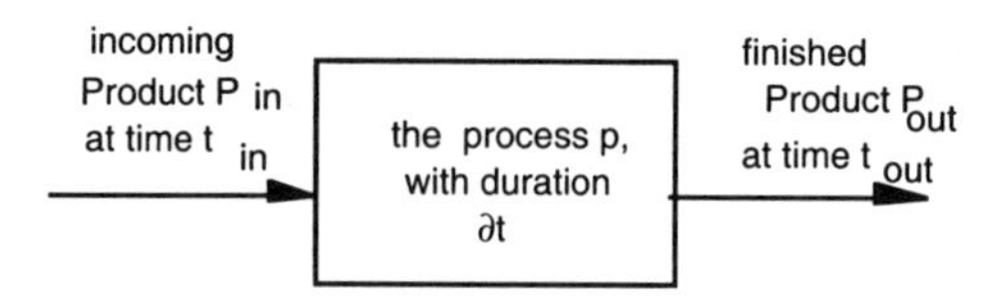

Figure 11.4: Single-element serial structure (b-type)

SEQUENCE OR SERIAL STRUCTURE

The next simplest structure is a process composed of two subprocesses in sequence, the output product of the first process p_1 serving as the input product of the second process p_2. Figure 11.5 demonstrates.

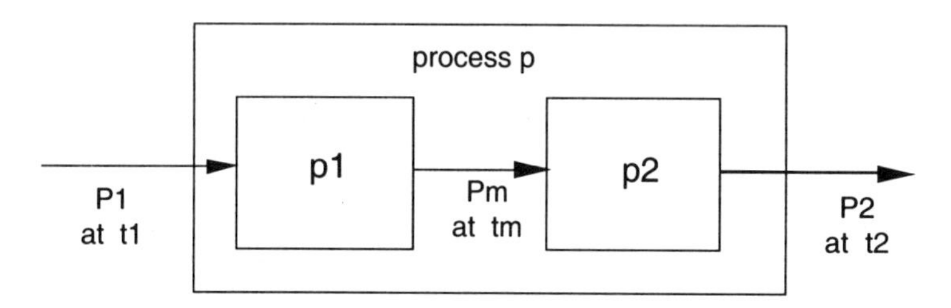

Figure 11.5: Two-element serial structure (b-type)

The serial structure can be generalized to include a finite number of elements connected in a chain.

Assume now that some man-made process p is a two-element serial structure, as in figure 11.5, where all the parameters of the constituent subprocesses p_1, p_2 are hard black box processes, and the structure is constructively defined. This means that we should be able to derive the parameters of the complete process p from the parameters of its constituents. The question is: how?

Let us take one parameter at a time, starting with the simplest.

Duration

If we know that the duration of the subprocesses p_1 and p_2 is ∂t_1 and ∂t_2, what is the duration ∂t of the complete process p?

The answer is obvious: the duration of the complete process p is the sum of the constituent subprocesses: $\partial t = \partial t_1 + \partial t_2$.

Function

If we know that the transfer function of the subprocesses p_1 and p_2 are π_1 and π_2, what is the function π of the complete process p?

Process p_1 operates on the attribute measure set $\mathbf{E}_1$ of the input P_1, trans-forming it to the attribute measure set $\mathbf{E}_m$ of the intermediate product P_m. We can write this as $\mathbf{E}_m = \pi_1(\mathbf{E}_1)$. Next, process p_2 operates on $\mathbf{E}_m$, trans-forming it to the attribute measure set $\mathbf{E}_2$ of the output product P_2. We can write this as $\mathbf{E}_2 = \pi_2(\mathbf{E}_m)$. By substitution, we get $\mathbf{E}_2 = \pi_2(\pi_1(\mathbf{E}_1))$. Thus, the function of process p is the composition of π_2 over π_1. We may write this conventionally as

$$\pi = \pi_2 \circ \pi_1.$$

Domain

If we know that the domains of the subprocesses p_1 and p_2 are D_1 and D_2, what is the domain D of the complete process p?

To fall within the domain of the complete process, any input product P_1 must be acceptable for both subprocesses. The requirements of p_1 can be taken into account directly as D_1; however, the requirements of p_2 must be *transformed back* to the input of p by π_1^{-1}: the inverse function of p_1. The acceptable domain of p is computed as the intersection of D_1 and $\pi_1^{-1}(D_2)$. Thus, we can write that $D = D_1 \cap \pi_1^{-1}(D_2)$.

Status

Assume that the process p is a 'simple' combination of its subprocesses: it is free (F=1) only when both its constituent subprocesses are free (F_1=F_2=1). We can say that F= $F_1 \wedge F_2$. When the process combination is not simple – as in the case of 'pipelined' processes – then other rules apply. This is discussed in chapter 12.

Other parameters

Generalizations are not easy: these must be considered case-by-case. For example:

- It might seem reasonable but it would be wrong to assume that the cost of two processes in sequence is the sum of the individual costs, because some of the resources may be common to the two, and the second process will encounter only the marginal cost, not the complete cost. The complete cost C is derivable from the individual cost parameters C_1, C_2, provided that the formula of cost calculation is stipulated in the interrelation set $\mathbf{R}_S$.
- It would similarly be wrong to assume that the owner of the complete process is the owner of one or the other of the subprocesses. Given two argumentative subprocess owners, good management might require the appointment of a third, independent owner for the process as a whole.

> The attributes of this new owner would arise from the particulars of the situation, including the personalities of the two people already involved, but the derivation of this new owner parameter C would not be calculable: it is beyond the realm of the 'hard' disciplines.

Larger serial structures can be viewed as repeated binary compositions of two-element structures, and hence the above considerations also apply for calculating their parameters.

PARALLEL STRUCTURES – GENERAL CONSIDERATIONS

Figure 11.6 shows the simplest parallel structure, where the process p is composed of two processes p_1 and p_2, linked by a distribution and a collection gate. Here inputs P_1 and P_2 are product clusters whose constituents are P_{11}, P_{12} and P_{21}, P_{22}, respectively. If process p is 'hard', if the attributes of its constituent subprocesses are known and if it is constructively defined, then it should be possible to derive the attributes of p.

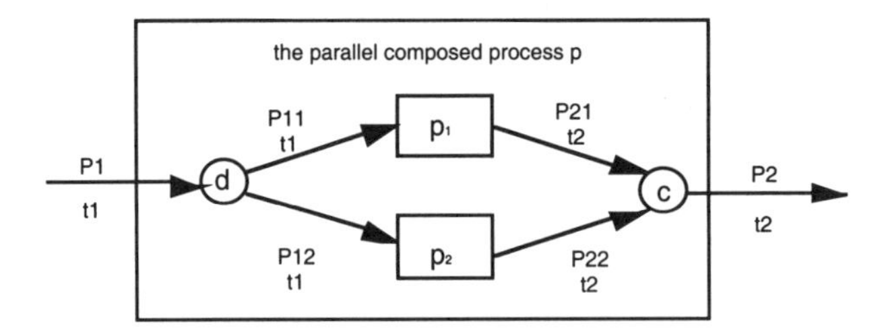

Figure 11.6: Two-element parallel structure (b-type, usual key)

Duration

> P_1 is a cluster; hence, by definition, P_{11} and P_{12} are simultaneous. Similarly, since P_2 is a cluster, P_{21} and P_{22} are simultaneous. This means that ∂t_1 of p_1 and ∂t_2 of p_2 are identical, and equal to the duration ∂t of the complete process: $\partial t_1 \equiv \partial t_2 \equiv \partial t$.

In practice the duration of two real-life processes are never exactly identical. If process p represents the process of manufacturing two parts P_{21} and P_{22} which are to be assembled by some subsequent process then one or the other part will be ready first, and must be stored somewhere until the other part becomes ready. Assume that P_{22} is the tardy one; then the process p_1 will have an internal serial structure, composed of the 'active' process p_{11} followed by the storage process ø whose role is to balance the delay of the two subprocesses of p (figure 11.7).

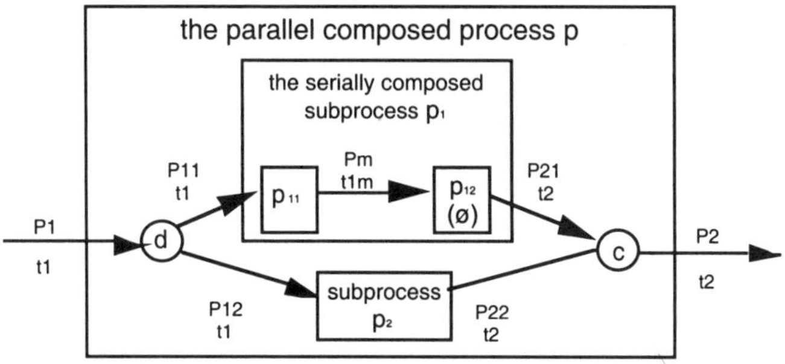

Figure 11.7: Two-element parallel structure of a real-life process (b-type, usual key)

In the following, we assume that any internal structure of subprocesses p_1 and p_2 is hidden, and both subprocesses can be considered 'atomic', as in figure 11.6.

Domain

If D_1 is the domain of p_1 and D_2 is the domain of p_2 then the domain D of the composite process p is derived from D_1, D_2 by the gate rule.

Status

For process p to function, both subprocesses must be free at t_1, the time of arrival of the input. If F_1 is the status of p_1 and F_2 is the status of p_2 then it is evident that the status D of p is the 'and' function of these: $F=F_1 \wedge F_2$.

Function

We know that the function of subprocess p_1 is π_1 and the function of subprocess p_2 is π_2. How do we find the function of process p?

P operates on the cluster P_1. The definition of cluster stipulates that within it the elements retain their identity. Let the two components of the input cluster P_1 be $P_{11}=(\mathbf{E}_{B11},\mathbf{R}_{B11})$ and $P_{12}=(\mathbf{E}_{B12},\mathbf{R}_{B12})$. Likewise, the elements of the output cluster P_2 will be written as $P_{21}=(\mathbf{E}_{B21},\mathbf{R}_{B21})$ and $P_{22}=(\mathbf{E}_{B22},\mathbf{R}_{B22})$. The task of subprocess p_1 is to generate $\mathbf{E}_{B21}=\pi_1(\mathbf{E}_{B11})$; similarly, subprocess p_2 generates $\mathbf{E}_{B22}=\pi_2(\mathbf{E}_{B12})$. Since within P_2 the products P_{21}, P_{22} are distinct, we can simply state that π is a set: $\pi=\{\pi_1,\pi_2\}$.

If the parallel structure is composed of three or more subprocesses, the same considerations apply: larger structures are constructed as pair-wise binary combinations of two-element parallels.

PARALLEL STRUCTURES – SOME VARIANTS

Return again to the two-element parallel structure of figure 11.6, and consider some variants of the operation of the process p, from the viewpoint of the gate functions involved.

- In our previous discussion we assumed that the distribution gate d forwards a product element of the cluster P_1 to *each* of the subprocesses p_1, p_2 gates d, c performing 'inclusive or' functions.
- A specific case of the above is when the cluster P_1 comprises a single information product which is broadcast to both subprocesses p_1, p_2. In this case $P_1 \equiv P_{11} \equiv P_{12}$, and here too, gates d, c perform 'inclusive or' functions. Duration, domain and status parameters are computed just as before, and in this case we can also state that the function $\pi \equiv \pi_1 \equiv \pi_2$.
- Consider now the case when the incoming product, call it P_{11}, may be of any kind (information, material, hybrid), but it is to be sent *either* to subprocess p_1 or to subprocess p_2, but never to both. In this case we can regard the cluster P_1 being composed of two parts: P_{11} and P_{12}, where P_{12} is the 'null product': a product whose attribute measure set is empty. The gate d sends P_{11} to subprocess p_1 or to subprocess p_2, whichever is free at the time; if both are free, the choice is arbitrary. The duration and domain parameters of process p are derived as before, but here the status parameter is $F = F_1 \vee F_2$, and the function is $\pi \equiv \pi_1 \equiv \pi_2$.
- Further variants will include larger structures, such as a process composed of n subprocesses of which m is to operate at any time. Instants of this are processes operating a 2-out-of-5 binary code, or 'multi-casting' processes where a message is sent for processing to selected subsets of n recipients on a network. The process parameters of each such specific case are to be deduced by repeated applications of the considerations discussed above.

SUBSTITUTION

Substitution is the replacement of a structure by its black box representation. Once a black box is characterized, one may suppress the internal structure. As we have seen in Part 1, substitution is an effective means of complexity management, allowing the organization of an unwieldy structure with a large collection of atomic elements into a multilevel hierarchy with a relatively compact manageable structure at each node.

OTHER PROCESS STRUCTURES

If processes are allowed to evolve without sufficient forethought and without the aid of an explicit representation, then their structure can 'grow' unchecked, become quite ramified, and ultimately prove unmanageable. As an example, the P/p graph of a moderately complicated structure was shown in figure 5.21(a) which cannot be simplified by substitution. While complicated structures are easy enough to create, we warn against the use of structures whose constructive definition is not feasible.

Some managers might say that, according to contemporary management thinking, hierarchical structures are passé. Nevertheless, a guideline of effective process management must be retained: however the structure is decomposed into elements, and however the elements are organized to form a system as a whole, the interrelations among the structural components must be simple enough to allow deriving the black box characteristics.

11.4 Gates

Most process structures involve branching and confluence: distribution of products from a single source to two or more destinations, and collection of products from two or more sources. In most other diagram notations this information is only implicit. It is the obligation in P/p modelling to make the rule of collection or distribution explicit, and the gate holds this information.

Gates were introduced in Part 1 of the book and a definition was given in chapter 5, with examples of gate rules listed in table 5.1. This section examines and expands the notion of gates.

Gate attributes

Gates share with processes the characteristic of having products as inputs and outputs, but they do not operate on their input to create their output, and have zero duration. They differ from both product and process by not standing for any entity in the real world, and, since they have no real life referent, they can do nothing; they are simply there to make explicit the algorithm – the rule – by which products are combined or distributed within the P/p structure. If the algorithm given in the gate is inconsistent with reality then one or both are faulty.

Type

In P/p graphs there are only two possible types of gate.

- The collection gate has two or more inputs and a single output.
- The distribution gate has a single input and two or more outputs.

Valency

Valency is the measure of the number of arcs incident on a node of a graph. Figure 11.8 shows two gates, both of valency n+1.

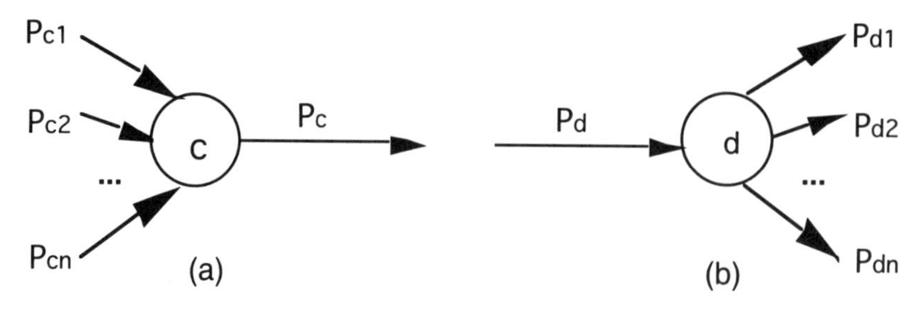

Figure 11.8: Collection and distribution gate of valency n+1 (b-type key)

Timing

The state of a gate is either open or closed, and gates change state instantaneously. The normal state for a gate is closed and when it opens it is only for a time instant (figure 11.9). This timing condition implies that, if a gate is open at time instant t_{in} then t_{in} is the common time stamp of the input and output products of the gates.

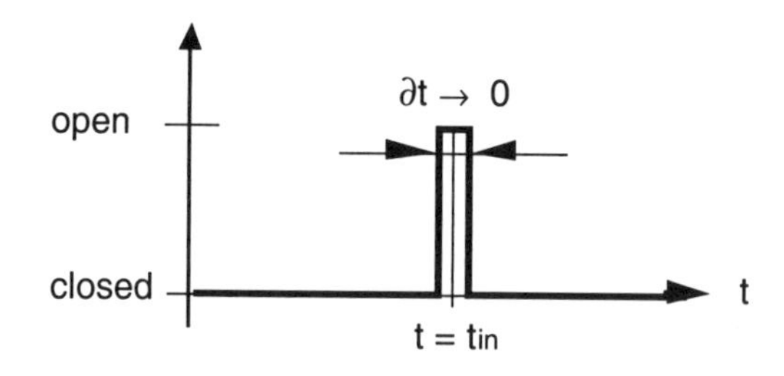

Figure 11.9: Gate timing

Function

COLLECTION GATES

The function of the n-input collection gate is to make a product cluster from the incoming product set in accord with some prescribed rule. We explore the possibilities.

The 'and' rule

The simplest case is when the rule prescribes that *all* input products must arrive simultaneously at any instant, call it t_{in}. Should any proper subset of inputs arrive at any time (in other words, should any of the n inputs be missing), the gate will remain closed. The output of the collection gate at time t_{in} is the set of its n input products formed into a product cluster.

Example 11.11
The rule is a preliminary to the construction of a table when all four legs and the table top are present, together with the construction aids of glue, screws, or whatever.

The 'exclusive or' rule

The next simplest case is when the rule prescribes that *one and only one* input product must arrive at any instant, call it t_{in}. Should any input arrive at any time with all others absent, the gate will open; should two or more input be present at any given instant, the gate will remain closed.

Bear in mind the function of the n-input collection gate: to create an n-element product cluster out of its n incoming products. In case of the 'exclusive or' collection gate the product cluster will consist of one of the input products, P_k, say, and n-1 *dummy* inputs: products whose attribute measure set $\mathbf{E}_B$ is *empty*.

Example 11.12:
The rule applies when actuating a telephone connection by the arrival of a single dial instruction from the many that could have been received.

The 'inclusive or' rule

This is the case of the most liberal gate regime. The gate will open when *any subset* of inputs arrive: any single input, the full collection of n inputs, or anything in-between. Should m number of products arrive at t_{in}, this will be complemented by n - m number of dummy inputs to form the n-element product cluster.

Example 11.13
This rule works when a taxi cab admits up to 5 passengers.

The 'm-out-of-n' rule

The gate has n inputs, but it opens only if a specified number of inputs arrives at a time instant. Let's call this number q, where m < n. It does not matter *which* these inputs are, only the *number* of inputs matter. In this case the n-element cluster will be made up of the q incoming products and n–q number of dummy input products.

Example 11.14
A Binary Coded Decimal digit (BCD) has five input line. If any 2 lines carry the value binary '1', the gate will momentarily open. If the number of '1's is smaller or greater than 2, the gate remains closed. Figure 11.10 demonstrates.

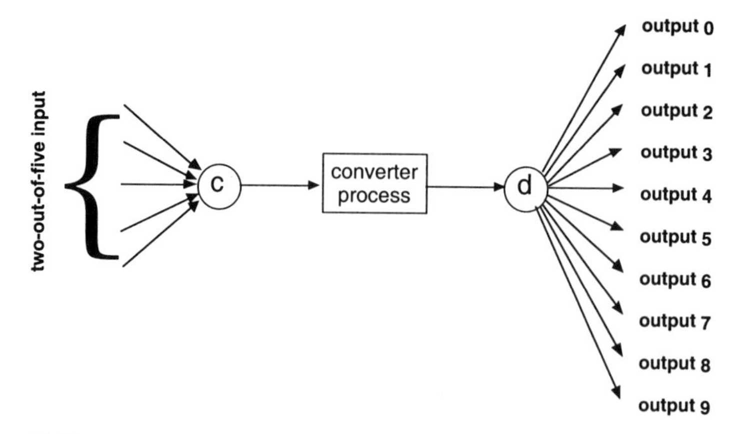

Figure 11.10: Gates flaking a BCD to decimal converter: c is a two-out-of-five collection gate, and d is a one-out-of-ten distribution gate

Other collection gate rules

The gate rule might make specific demands different from those listed above. We quote only one example: the case when there is a *distinguished input* which must always be present, together with a *specified number* of other inputs, it does not matter which.

Example 11.15

The rules governing horse racing stipulate that all registered horses are present and start. Assume that this number is m, where m ≥ 2. For the race to start, at least 3 inputs must be present:

- *the start signal,*
- *at least two horses [1].*

A note on collection gates

When the input products to the collection gate are material or hybrid goods, we need to examine the nature and magnitudes of the attributes of the input products and their relationship with the equivalent attribute of the single output product. Such relationships may provide useful quality checks both on the referents and of the validity of the model. For example, in the case of the mass attribute of material or hybrid products, if the value of the mass attribute of each product Pc_i in gate (a) of figure 11.5 is a_i then for i from 1 to m, $\Sigma a_i = a_P$, the mass attribute of the gate output Pc. This is true of all 'extensive' attributes, such as mass, cost, electrical current and others.

DISTRIBUTION GATES

The function of the n-output distribution gate is to disassemble its incoming product cluster into a set of output products in accord with some prescribed rule. The output products of the gate appear with the same time stamp as that of its input product cluster. Once again, we explore the possibilities.

The 'exclusive or' rule

The simplest case is when the incoming n-element product cluster comprises a single product, call it Pc_k, together with a bunch of n–1 empty products (products whose attribute measure set is empty). The destination of Pc_k is the kth output of gate (b) of figure 11.5. All other outputs of the distribution gate receive dummies.

Example 11.16
The delivery van conveying orders to customers, each receiving a single item.

The 'and' rule

One case is when the rule prescribes that the n-elements of the input product cluster are distributed among *all* the n outputs of the gate. There are various possibilities. One of these is when the incoming product is divided evenly among the outputs.

Example 11.17
A father dividing an apple among his four children, each getting a quarter.

The incoming information product may be *broadcast:* conveyed in its entirety to all output destinations.

Example 11.18
A radio or television broadcast; an audience listening to a lecture.

The 'm-out-of-n' rule

The incoming product may be divided among selected outputs. A case of this is when the information product is *multicast*, sent to a specified subset of recipients.

Example 11.19
All employees of a company are on the circulation list and all would receive some items, such as safety regulations, but other items of information will only be forwarded to individuals of a specific grade.

Example 11.20
Prizes distributed to a selection of students where the selection algorithm will be 'if grade higher than <set value>'.

A note on distribution gates

The considerations given to the values of extensive attributes for collection gates hold equally for distribution gates and may serve as a valuable quality check.

Documenting gates

On a P/p graph all products, processes and gates carry a unique label, but in the interest of clarity of the graphs, information about gates is not included in the graph itself but is kept in associated tables. Table 11.1 shows the template of a gate table.

gate label	
type	collection / distribution
valency	2 / more (specify)
function / algorithm	and / exclusive or / inclusive or / q-out-of-n (specify) / other

Table 11.1: Template of gate table

Defining 'gate'

The thesis of this book is that every real life entity can be represented as a system, using the formalism of expression 11.1. Gates are not real life entities: they are merely modelling aids. Can they nevertheless be characterized as systems?

- Gates have no components and no internal design; thus, they have no structure, and hence no structural representation.
- Gates have attributes, and hence they may be represented as black boxes. We know that they are process-like, having input and output; thus, we can try to use the black box definition of 'process' as a template for their definition.

gate w is modelled as a black box by the pair: $p_B = (\mathbf{E}_{Bw}, \mathbf{R}_{Bw})$

where	$\mathbf{E}_{Bw}$	is the finite set of attributes that characterize gate g as a black box, including
	∂t	the duration of the process whose value is 0,
	γ	the two-valued type attribute (c for collection or d for distribution),
	ν	is the valency: a finite positive integer with minimum value 3,
	π	is the gate rule
and	$\mathbf{R}_{Bw}$	is the interrelation set, including
	t	the common time stamp of input and output,
	r_g	the two-place 'coproduct interrelation' over the product and the product cluster that form the input and output,
with	Bw	as a suffix designating black box.

11.5 Summary

This chapter considers hard systems, and defines products and processes formally, both as black boxes and as structures. It shows the use of constructive models in deriving the attributes of black box models from the structure of their referent. It then talks about gates: modelling aids for explicit representation of process structures.

11.6 Exercises

Exercise 11.1

For the following processes, suggest suitable domains for input products:

- polishing silver,
- loading a laser printer,
- feeding cattle,
- cutting grass,
- earning a living,
- dialing a phone number,
- setting up a Health Service,
- implementing a housing policy.

What attributes of the input and output products could be used to show the effect of the process?

Exercise 11.2

If an input to a computer program generates an error message, is that input within the domain of the process carried out by the program?

Exercise 11.3

A large multinational organization sets its base premises in New York and distributes price lists to five Regional Headquarters in Rio, London, Berlin, Tokyo and Johannesburg. Each of the regional offices has the authority to modify the prices according to local conditions.

Draw a P/p graph of the processes involved. Identify attributes and suggest values for all products and processes in your graph. Characterize all gates you have used.

Exercise 11.4

At the time of writing, used car prices are some 30% higher in the UK than in Continental Europe.

Draw a P/p graph of the possibilities available to a British purchaser: overpaying locally, Internet purchase, crossing the Channel and any others you may envisage. Aggregate cost across the options. Identify and characterize all products, processes and gates.

Exercise 11.5

A company has a central office which is on its warehouse premises. Customers order through the various branch offices and only the branches deal with customers. The orders are sent nightly to the central office for processing and subsequent dispatch with a time lag of no more than 48 hours. If a particular line is out of stock then central office notifies the customer of the anticipated delay.

Construct a P/p graph of the complete process. You may find it enlightening to build the input product from its constituents and identify attributes by constructivity.

Exercise 11.6

A postal area employs 17 postmen, each delivering mail to a selected sub-area.

Devise a basis for partitioning the incoming mail into 17 sackfuls, one for each postman. Draw up the P/p network of the sorting process and the gate algorithms involved.

Devise a method for monitoring and adjusting the partitioning algorithm such that each postman should carry approximately equal workloads.

11.7 Reference

1 Checked with the Jockey Club, 16.2.2000.

Part 3

Chapter 12 Process management

This chapter offers an example of the use of P/p modelling in handling technical problems. Several examples were considered for possible inclusion here:

- Life history models that allow the manager to follow the changes in a developing industrial project, giving check points and measures to monitor progress.
- Modelling for quality management, starting with the operational model of the processes of the organization, the development of a quality strategy, and the design of the Quality Management System over the operational model, to implement the strategy.
- Modelling of protocols for communication systems of aircraft.
- Modelling the signalling system of part of an underground railway.

Of these and others, we selected process management. The issues considered here are everyday situations, such as the possibility of a process being busy when required, a process receiving the wrong kind of input, or requiring to allocate different priorities to different classes of input products.

This chapter is not a text on management: it does not seek to provide a comprehensive review of the subject, nor does it recommend ways of dealing with all problems of process management. Instead, the aim is to show how P/p modelling makes situations explicit, aiding the process owner to plan for adversities and eventualities, consider alternative strategies, and maintain control of problematic situations. Only hard processes are considered.

12.1 A first look at process management

The process parameters D (the domain definition) and F (the status parameter) guard both the product and the process, assuring that the process is ready to accept the product, and no unsuitable product enters the process: otherwise the product, the process, or both, might be damaged or destroyed.

Examples 12.1: Cases of inappropriate input

- *the meat grinder processing a bag of nails?*
- *emergency patient taken to a hospital without Emergency Department,*
- *lorry required to carry overload,*
- *student seeking admission to a university course without having the requisite entry grades.*

Examples 12.2: Cases of process unavailability

- *attempting to withdraw money from the bank when all tellers are busy and there is a long queue,*
- *dialling an engaged number,*
- *attempting to purchase a ticket for a show when the house is sold out,*

- *attempting to book a non-smoking room at a hotel when all such rooms are occupied (although plenty of smelly rooms might still be available).*

When a product P_{in} arrives at the input of a process p, two *processing criteria* must be satisfied for it to receive service:

- The product P_{in} must be a conformant input product of process p, falling within p's domain as defined by D. This means that the attribute measure set $\mathbf{E}_{in}$ of $P_{in} \in D$. For convenience, we write this simply as $P_{in} \in D$.
- The process p itself must be accessible at the time of arrival of P_{in} (conventionally, F=1).

There are several ways of testing that the processing criteria are met. For example, we might demand that the following assumptions should be satisfied:

- All processes must broadcast their status parameter, and these parameters should be available from an 'infrastructure facility' called the 'Process Manager'.
- All processes include a protective decision process which tests for the processing criteria, and diverts P_{in} if the criteria are not satisfied.

Figure 12.1(a) shows a fragment of a network, including the process p and its protective test g. Here g is a cactus: a single input, two-output component designated by a triangular symbol, such as seen in chapter 5. The function of g is to ascertain that P_{in} is within the domain of process p ($P_{in} \in D$) and that at t_{in} process p is free (F = 1). If so, P_{in}' proceeds to p; otherwise it is diverted.

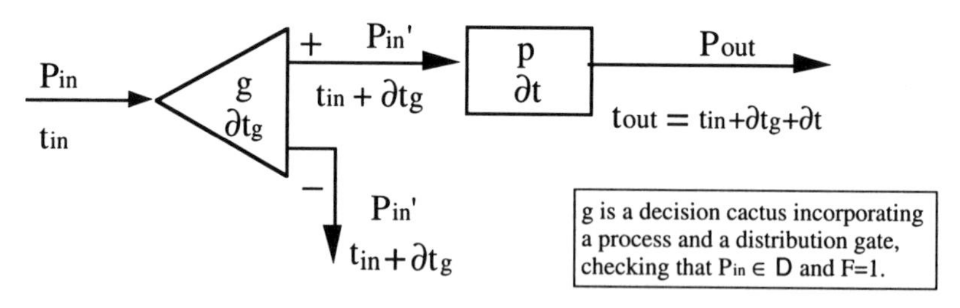

Figure 12.1(a): The process p with its protective decision cactus g (b-type key)

The internal structure of the cactus is given in figure 12.1(b), comprising a test process p_{test}, followed by a two-output distribution gate d. Since figure 12.1(b) defines g as a P/p network, figure 12.1(a) itself may be regarded as a P/p network.

Depending on the outcome of p_{test}, a binary parameter (+ or –) is attached to the attribute measure set of product P_{in}, without changing any of the product's attribute measures. To indicate this, the outputs of g are labelled +P_{in}' or –P_{in}'.

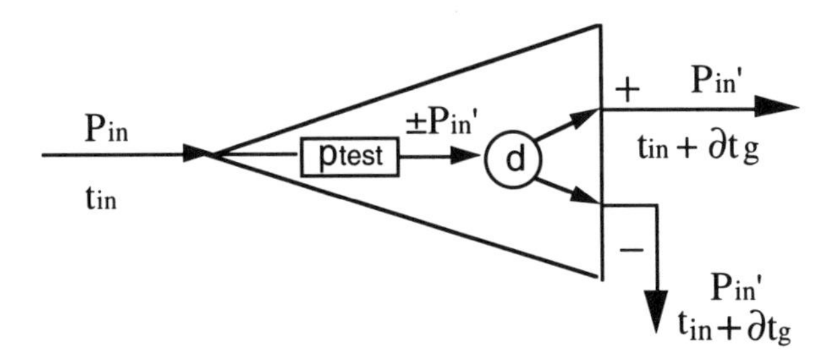

Figure 12.1(b): Internal structure of cactus g (b-type key)

The test process p_{test} takes time, hence the decision delay ∂t_g of cactus g is nonzero, but let us assume that ∂t_g is negligible compared with the duration ∂t of the subsequent process p, so that t_{out} is well approximated by $t_{in}+\partial t$, and $P_{in}' \equiv P_{in}$ (figure 12.1(c)).

Throughout most of our discussions in this chapter, we shall neglect decision delays in comparison with the delay of other processes. Neglecting ∂t_g in the case above allows us to change our view of g as a *cactus* incorporating a process to that of a *gate* governed by a predicate, and define it as in figure 12.1(c). This means that both the input and output of g is P_{in}, timed at t_{in}, the output carrying a + or – label to indicate the outcome of the test. However, one must bear in mind that, unlike gates, decision processes are 'real' processes, and their delay must be included in the P/p graph explicitly wherever it is significant in comparison with the delay of the preceding or subsequent process. As a reminder, it is advisable to retain the triangular decision symbol, instead of using the circular gate symbol.

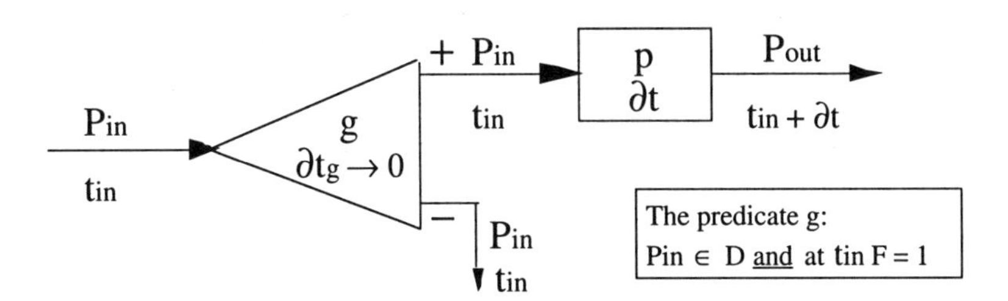

Figure 12.1(c): The process p with its protective decision g, assuming that delay $\partial t_g << \partial t$ (b-type key)

Consider now the negative branch of figure 12.1(c). Product P_{in} failed the test, and its fate depends on the *reason* for its rejection.

- If $P_{in} \notin D$ (P_{in} is nonconformant, one or more of its attributes falling outside the domain of process p defined by D) then the product should be diverted because it is unsuited to the process p.
- If the product and the process are suited to each other ($P_{in} \in D$, all attribute measures of P_{in} are conformant) but the process is inaccessible at the arrival time t_{in} (F = 0) then the product may be delayed in a null (storage) process until p becomes available.

Assume that at the time of arrival of product P_{in}, process p is part way through its work on some previous product P_{in0}, and cannot be interrupted. At time $t_0+\partial t$ process p concludes its operation on P_{in0}, and P_{out0} emerges. Process p flags its availability, and a version P_{in}' of the product P_{in}, now aged – having languished in a null process – enters process p.

Figure 12.2 isolates and expands the elements which control the input to process p, separating the access requirement (F=1) from the domain membership requirement ($P_{in} \in$ D). We discuss these presently under sections entitled 'Conformance Management' and 'Access Management'.

Note that the predicate in figure 12.1(c) indicates a logical 'and' relation between the conformance test of domain membership and the access test of process status. Since logical relations are commutative, the outcome is independent of the order in which the two tests are carried out. Figure 12.2 shows the case where conformance testing is conducted first, g_1 representing conformance management, and this is followed by g_2 representing access management.

In many practical situations it is advisable to give time precedence to conformance testing: one would normally seek to eliminate unsuitable products at the earliest opportunity, preventing them from taking up space, or getting mixed up with, or contaminating, other products. However, in principle the order of the tests of conformance management and access management is arbitrary, and the two mechanisms of 'process management' can be interchanged.

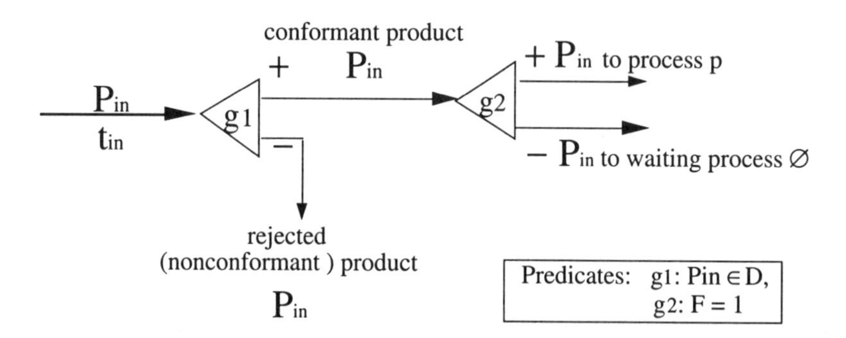

Figure 12.2: The process management mechanism of p (b-type, usual key)

In addition to managing conformance and access, process management often has the additional function of managing *priority*. This means varying the order of performing processing tasks because of the particular urgency of a process function (such as stopping bleeding when dealing with an emergency), or because of the special significance of a product (such as the lift serving the Managing Director's floor ahead of other callers in the queue). In the following sections we deal with each of the process management functions (conformance, access, priority and interrupt management) in turn.

12.2 Conformance management [1]

Conformance of the atomic process

Assume for the moment that process p is free to receive a conformant product (figure 12.3). In this case the conformance test g is necessary and sufficient to protect the process p from unsuitable incoming products. Ideally, such a conformance test should be carried out for all processes as an instrument of quality assurance.

The input product P_{in} of process p is the output product $P_{out\text{-}previous}$ of some other process $p_{previous}$. Responsibility for conducting the conformance test may be given to the owner of p, to the owner of $p_{previous}$, or even to a third party. The following discussion is equally valid, no matter *who* is charged with protecting p and P_{in} against nonconformance.

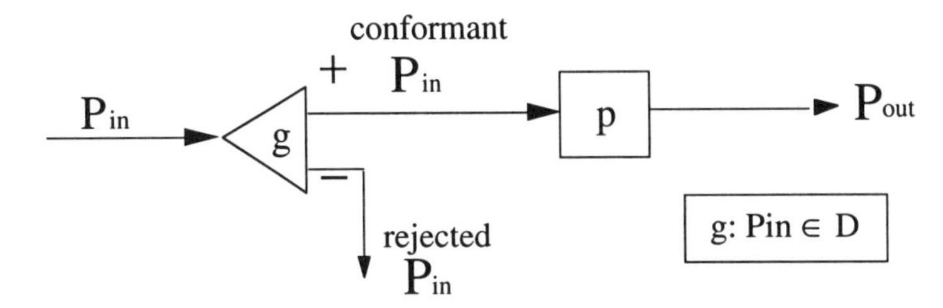

Figure 12.3: Conformance management of the atomic process p (b-type, key and timing omitted).

Conformance of the serial process

If p is composed of n subprocesses in series (figure 12.4(a)), process p should only be entered by product P_{in} if it is guaranteed that all intermediate products, P_1, P_2, ... P_{n-1}, will be conformant. If no such guarantee is available then it would be desirable, but expensive, to provide tests and escape routes for nonconformant intermediate products (figure 12.4(b)).

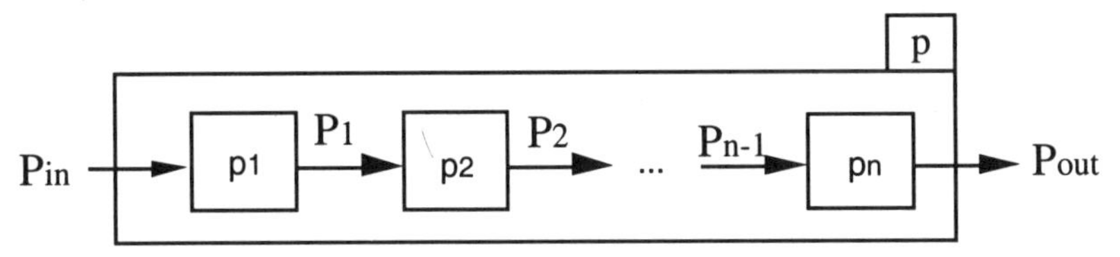

Figure 12.4(a): The n-element series process (timing omitted)

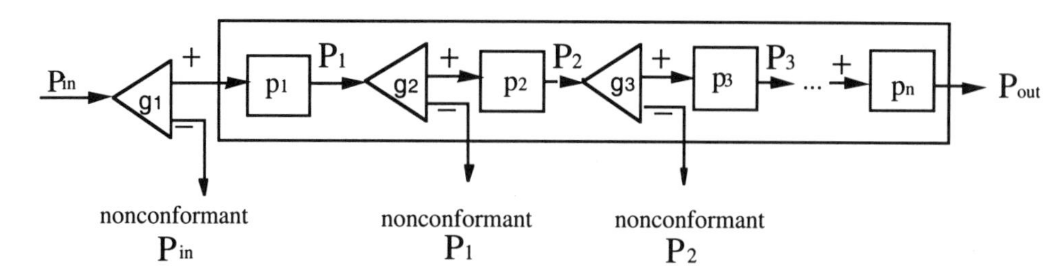

Figure 12.4(b): Conformance management of the n-element series process (key and timing omitted)

Let us consider figure 12.4(b) in more detail. The '+' outcome of gate g_1 assures that all attributes of P_{in} are conformant. This means that P_1 will also be conformant, provided that process p_1 performs correctly. Likewise, if P_1 passes the conformance test of g_2 then P_2 will be correct, unless p_2 is at fault. This applies all along the sequence, hence the conformance tests of the intermediate products of the serial process are in effect quality tests not only of the intermediate products but also of the constituent subprocesses.

In the comprehensive quality regime of figure 12.4(b) the processes leading to the successful product P_{out} will have passed a series of conformance tests, each with positive binary outcome. Combining the results of the subprocess tests g_1 to g_{n-1}, we may write the condition for test g of the complete process p as:

$$
\begin{aligned}
g: P_{in} \in D \text{ if } \quad & g_1: P_{in} \in D_1 \textit{ and} \\
& g_2 : P_1 \in D_2 \textit{ and} \\
& \ldots \qquad\qquad \textit{and} \\
& g_n : P_{n-1} \in D_n.
\end{aligned}
$$

Using the logical notation '$\wedge$' for *and*, and given that we define g_i as $P_{n-1} \in D_i$, we may write:

$$g: P_{in} \in D \text{ if } \wedge_i\, g_i \text{ for } 1 \le i \le n \qquad \text{(expression 12.1)}$$

In practice the fully comprehensive quality regime of figure 12.4(b) would seldom be economical; instead, it is usual to adopt a more modest quality procedure, testing the input product P_{in} prior to entry into the serial process, and thereafter testing only a few strategically selected products along the route. Assuming for example that p is composed of p_1, p_2, p_3, p_4 as a four-element sequence and p_3 is a critical process whose input must be specifically protected then the process will have two guards g: $P_{in} \in D$ at the input and g_3: $P_2 \in D_3$ at the critical intermediate point.

The parallel process

Figure 12.5 shows conformance management for process p whose distribution gate d performs an 'and' function, such that subprocesses p_1, p_2 operate simultaneously. The attribute measures of both components of P_{in} must satisfy the conformance criterion of the corresponding subprocess:

$$g_1: P_{in1} \in D_1 \text{ of } p_1 \text{ and } g_2 : P_{in2} \in D_2 \text{ of } p_2.$$

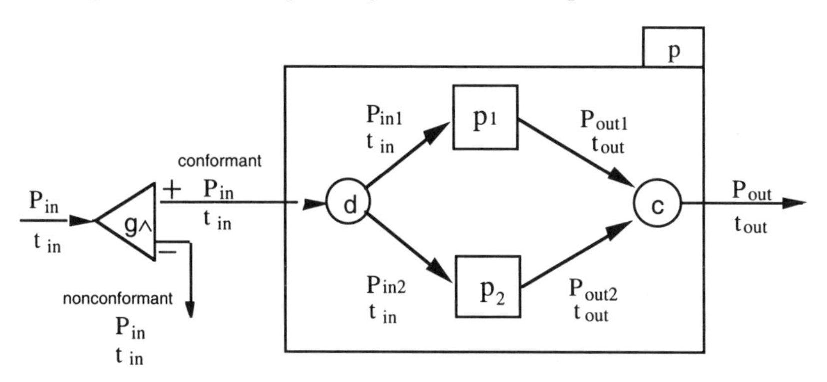

Figure 12.5: Conformance management of the two-element parallel process (usual key)

The protective decision test $g_\wedge$ must be carried out before P_{in} enters process p, and must guarantee both; thus,

$$g_\wedge: P_{in} \in D \text{ of } p \text{ if } g_1 \wedge g_2.$$

Generalizing for an n-input parallel process, and using logical notation, defining g_i as $P_{n-1} \in D_i$, we obtain :

$$g_\wedge: P_{in} \in D \text{ if } \wedge_i\, g_i \text{ for } 1 \leq i \leq n \qquad \text{(expression 12.2)}$$

Note that the form of expression 12.2 is similar to that of expression 12.1, but the meaning is different. In the serial process P_i was an intermediate product; here all products $P_{in\text{-}i}$ are part of the input vector of process p.

Non-simultaneous processes

Where the distribution gate d performs an 'exclusive or' function feeding two processes p_1 and p_2, either p_1 or p_2 can be active, but never both. Here the conformance test of p_1 and p_2 may precede gate d, or it may be carried out independently, as in the network fragment of figure 12.6. The same applies for three or more non-simultaneous processes.

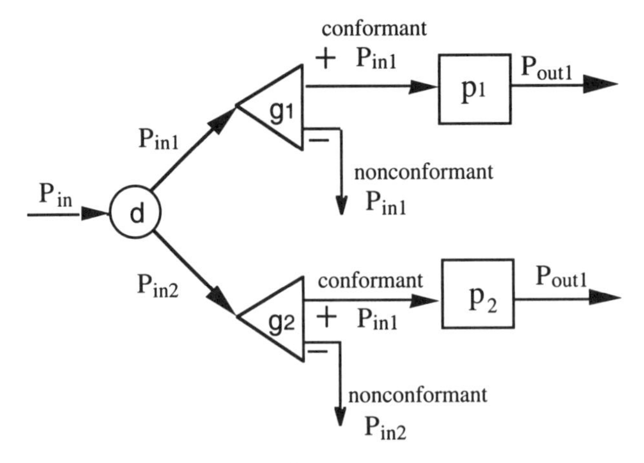

Figure 12.6: Conformance management of network fragment with two non-simultaneous subprocesses (b-type key, timing omitted)

Conformance management of P/p networks

Consider now a network p as a series/parallel nested structure resolved to n atomic process components. If a comprehensive quality regime is called for, and if the conformance criteria for all processes and subprocesses of p are defined in the usual form $g_i : P_i$ _ D_i, then the conformance criterion for the network is:

$$g: P_{in} \in D \text{ if } \wedge_i d_i \text{ for } 1 \leq i \leq n \qquad \text{(expression 12.3)}$$

The form of expression 12.3 is the same as that of expressions 12.1 and 12.2, but once again the meaning is different. Here P_i designates an input product to *any* subprocess of p: it might be part of the 'global' input P_{in} to process p, or a 'local' input to a process anywhere within the P/p network.

12.3 Access management

When all input products of a P/p network are conformant and no input product can claim priority over any other, then access to subprocesses is determined on the basis of the status attribute, F.

Access to an atomic process

Refer to figure 12.2, where g_1 is the conformance test with negligible duration and g_2 controls access. If the input product P_{in} to the atomic process p has passed the conformance test g_1 at a time when p is not accessible then P_{in} can be eventually admitted to process p after a delay. The duration of the access delay is unknown.

Let us assume that, no matter how long the delay, patience will not be exhausted, and the relevant attributes of P_{in} will not change. Then there will be no rejection exit from g_2, hence g_1 ceases to be a decision process and becomes a delay process of duration $\partial t \geq 0$. In this case the function of the access manager is a simple null process, the time of termination being determined by the event of p becoming free (F=1). Figure 12.7 shows the atomic process p, complete with its conformance manager g_1 and access manager ∅.

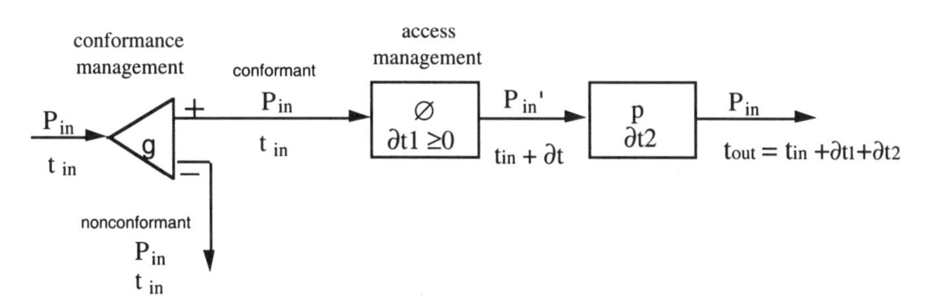

Figure 12.7: Process p with its conformance and access manager (usual key)

Let us look at the implementation of access management in more detail.

Figure 12.8 shows a process p in operation on a previous product P_{in0} at the arrival of a new input P_{in1}. The protection mechanisms are shown in figure 12.9, where conformance management and access management are carried out by decision processes g_1 and g_2, respectively.

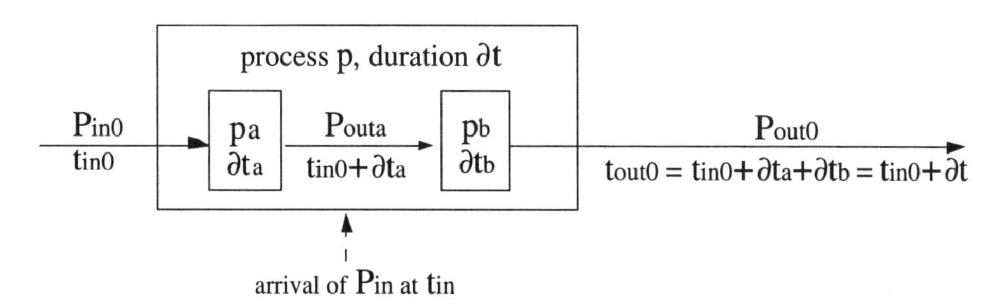

Figure 12.8: The process p acting on product P_{in0} when a new product P_{in} arrives (usual key)

Assume that the processes are overseen by a process manager who keeps an eye on the status of p, and after a delay ∂t_b (implemented by the null process ∅) signals that the process has now finished its work on the previous input P_{in0}, its status has changed from busy back to free, and can now attend to the new input P_{in}. The arrangement of figure 12.9 can be extended to manage a queue of n incoming products, servicing the queue on a first-in-first-out basis.

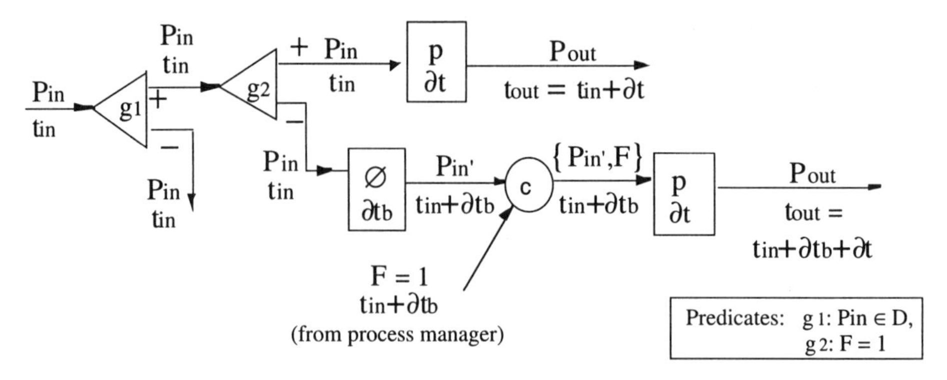

Figure 12.9: The process p with discriminating protective decision processes (b-type key)

Access to serially composed processes

THE 'SIMPLE' SERIAL PROCESS

Figure 12.10 shows a process p_s composed of subprocesses p_1 to p_n in series. The process is such that p_s is inaccessible to further inputs until all its subprocesses are free. We call such a serial process 'simple', and the suffix 's' denotes this. If F_1, F_2, …, F_n are the status parameters of the subprocesses p_1, p_2, …, p_n, then the status parameter F_s of the simple serial process p_s is the 'and' composition of the status parameters of its n constituent processes. Since the status parameter is modelled by a boolean variable, we may derive the value of F_s as a logical function of the status parameters of its constituents:

$$F_s = \wedge_i(F_i), \qquad \text{(expression 12.4)}$$

where F_i is the status of the ith subprocess of p_s.

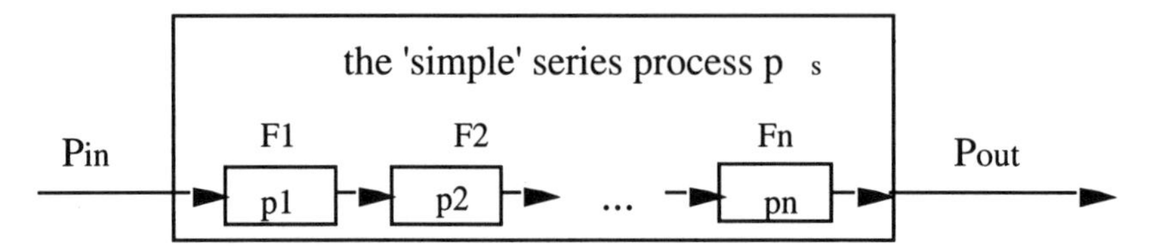

Figure 12.10: The simple series process p_s which is free if $F_s=\wedge_i(F_i) = 1$

In the case of the simple serial process, since the constituent stages are inaccessible, the series as a whole may be treated as a single process. This is in contrast to the 'pipeline' process of the next section where access management to the constituents is a major factor.

THE 'PIPELINE' PROCESS

A 'pipeline' p_p is a serial process which is structurally identical to the simple series process p_s, differing only in the manner in which access to the subprocesses is managed. Under suitably controlled conditions a pipeline admits new input products even when some of the subprocesses are still busy on previous tasks.

The reason for using a series process as a pipeline is economy. All processes absorb resources, and may themselves be regarded as resources in need of husbandry. If some atomic process p has fixed duration ∂t and is used n times over a time period Δt then we may define the 'utilization efficiency' e_a of the atomic process as $n \times \partial t / \Delta t$.

Generalizing this for the case when each operation of the atomic process p might take different amounts of time, the utilization efficiency becomes:

$$e_a = \frac{\Sigma_i \, \partial t_i}{\Delta t}$$

where ∂t_i is the duration of the ith time when p was in use during the period Δt.

Pipelines are economical arrangements where each atomic process in a serial composition is enabled to admit a new product just as soon as it completes its operation on the previous one. When the first input P_{in1} enters the pipeline at t_{in}, subprocess p_1 becomes active for a period of ∂t_1. Then, while the rest of the subprocesses progress their task on this input, p_1 is free to accept a new input P_{in2}. In the limiting case all n subproceses of the pipeline might be busy simultaneously, acting on a succession of products P_{in1} to $P_{in\text{-}n}$, thus increasing the utilization efficiency of each subprocess, and of the process p_p as a whole. If p_p is used in this way, it could be declared free (its F parameter set to 1) as soon as p_1 is free, regardless of the status of any of its other subprocesses:

$$F_p = F_1, \qquad \text{(expression 12.5a)}$$

where F_p is the status of p_p
and F_1 is the status of the first subprocess of p_p.

Such an arrangement spells danger. If one or more of the processes along the line take undue time, the pipeline may become overcrowded, products coming out of a previous subprocess while the next process is still busy, having nowhere to go.

To guard against this, expression 12.5(a) must be supplemented: access to p_p must be restricted to assure that the duration of each subsequent process is never longer than the previous process:

$$\text{For each subprocess } p_i \text{ in } p_p, \quad \partial t_i \leq \partial t_{i-1} \qquad \text{(expression 12.5b)}$$

Figure 12.11 shows an n-element pipeline and the condition of its access management.

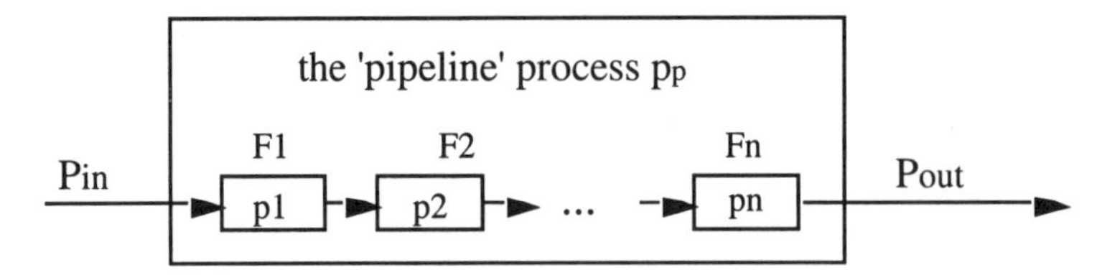

Figure 12.11: The pipeline process p_p is free if F_1=1, given that $\partial t_i \leq \partial t_{i-1}$ (timing and key omitted)

Note that a serial process made up of a finite but large number of elements, each with nonzero but small duration, can be used to model a true pipeline, such as the flow of a liquid through a pipe.

Access to parallel processes

Figure 12.12 shows the process p_r, parallel composed of n subprocesses which operate simultaneously, gate d distributing an input to each of the subprocesses p_1 to p_n. Since in a simultaneous parallel process all subprocesses start at the same time, there is a logical relationship on the status parameters: the status parameter F_r of the whole process p_r is the 'and' composition of the status parameters of its subprocesses:

$$F_r = 1 \text{ if } \wedge_i F_{ri} = 1 \quad \text{for } 1 \leq i \leq n \qquad \text{(expression 12.6)}$$

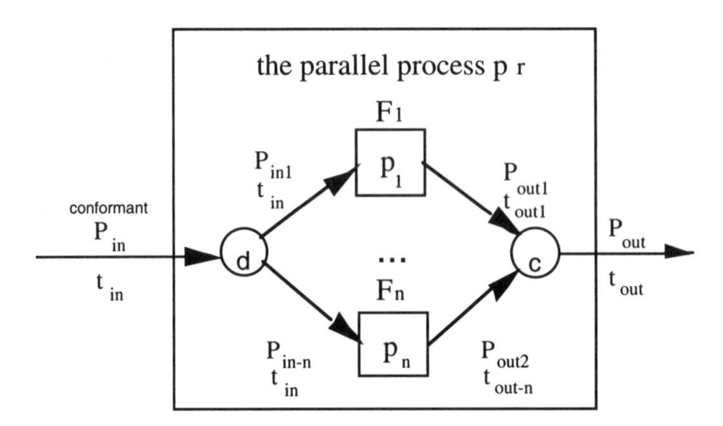

Figure 12.12: The parallel process p_r which is free if $\wedge_i F_{ri}$ for $1 \leq i \leq n$

The case would be different if the input to the subprocesses of the parallel structure of figure 12.12 would be governed by an 'exclusive or' gate. Here we have an 'alternative' parallel process where one and only one subprocess could receive an input at any time instant, and some subprocess p_i might be busy on a previous task while another subprocess p_j would be free to receive the next input to p_r.

The simplest alternative parallel process is one where the subprocesses are similar, so that any free subprocess can attend to any new input. We don't deal with this in detail, but demonstrate it on two examples

Example 12.3: The simplest case of alternative parallel structure
An instance of a parallel process governed by an 'exclusive or' distribution gate 'd' is the checkout system of the supermarket where some cashiers may be busy servicing customers, while others may be ready to attend to another customer. Each customer is attended to by one and only one cashier. The gate 'c' governing the output is also 'exclusive or', implemented by the exit door of the store through which only one customer can pass at a time.

Example 12.4: An alternative parallel structure
Consider a bank where some of the tellers deal with domestic customers, others serve at an international counter, yet others deal entirely with queries on accounts or customers wishing to open or close their account. (It is a frequent source of frustration that all tellers of the class you require are busy, while others are quietly shuffling papers.)

Access to P/p networks

In the general case a process represented by a P/p network is a multilevel structure, such as a series/parallel nested composition over atomic subprocesses. Since the status parameter of a process at any level of the hierarchy is a logical function of the status parameters of its subprocesses, one can derive the status parameter F for the complete process p as a logical function of the status of the atomic processes of the structure, using the notions outlined above.

Project management by 'phases'

In chapter 2 we gave several definitions of 'project'. In a business context projects are usually undertaken under contract, defining the specifications of the product which the project yields, and setting limits to the time and resources available for completion.

In terms of P/p modelling, a project is a carefully managed process: planned, organized, and implemented under managerial control, testing progress at predetermined times, as well as at times when specified targets are reached. A known method of management is to plan a major project as a sequence of three or four well defined 'phases', rather like the process in figure 12.4(a), each phase constituting a semi-independent project in its own right. To ensure the integrity of each phase, it is usual to appoint a different manager to take charge of each phase.

Progress from phase to phase is strictly controlled by testing the *conformance* of the product passing from one phase to the next (as in figure 12.4(b)), and it may be part of the phase manager's responsibility to ensure that the input product to his/her process phase meets its specifications.

Access is also controlled, but the control is different from the cases we encountered before. It is not a matter for the process of a phase being otherwise engaged when its input product arrives: the phase team and phase resources (space, instruments, materials, information, infrastructure, etc.) are assembled for the appointed time, specifically designed for processing a single product. The starting time of each phase is set out in the project plan, and it is the responsibility of senior management to ensure that appropriate personnel, space and material resources are available to start each phase at the appointed time. An essential predetermined test is to check that the phase is fit to start.

The project may be subject to time and resource overrun, or it may fail altogether, because of:

- failure of any of the *phase managers* to deliver a conformant output (a product with time stamp consistent with the target date, its attribute measures meeting the specifications),
- failure of *senior management* to assemble one of the phase teams and phase resources by the appointed time.

P/p models are powerful aids to project management. They ensure that the project plan is explicit, comprehensive and feasible, available to all concerned, and contains adequate guards and contingencies. They set out clear tasks for each phase, clarifying the role and responsibility of all concerned. They facilitate control of the operation of the project, define the measures of acceptance tests and document operational and quality procedures. They are explicit and documented in accord with clearly defined syntax, serving the needs of internal quality management and facilitating external audits.

12.4 Priority management

Where multiple inputs await entry to a single process, an order of priority must be established and its enforcement managed. Such a situation might arise because, for example, several products arrive simultaneously, or because some items have accumulated already and are awaiting their turn, but a new high-priority item appears. Priority management must take at least two factors into consideration: *urgency* and *fairness*.

Products can vary in importance, demanding more or less urgent attention. Priority may be determined by several factors, among them the characteristics of the incoming product, or of the processes to which the product will be subject.

- Product-driven priority may occur for reasons such as a product having already been the subject of delay, or a product just arriving but being of higher priority than any of those already in the queue.
- Process-driven priority might arise when some process p_1 produces different sorts of outputs for several processes, among them a process p_2 that must run continuously or is particularly costly, requiring a steady flow of inputs for achieving high utilization efficiency. In this case process p_1 often has to give priority to those input products whose destination is process p_2.

Consider the case when the 'importance attribute' of products can be regarded as a constant, and recorded as an integer a_h in the attribute parameter set of each product.

The domain of the parameter is {1, 2, ..., n}, the symbol 1 denoting (for example) a product with lowest priority and n the highest.

Example 12.5

One operating system assigns priorities to the execution of applications, for instance, assigning priority 9 to background processes, 13 to foreground processes and 31 to processes carried out by the operating system itself.

Example 12.6

Where more than one group of office workers make use of the same printer, one group may be assigned a higher priority than others, enabling urgent documents to be printed before those less urgent or more time consuming.

Example 12.7

The lift control system of a hospital is designed to give top priority to calls to or from the floor of the Intensive Care Unit, next highest priority to other medical departments, next highest to administrative departments, and bottom priority to calls to and from the refectory.

If several products are waiting at the entrance to a process, *fairness* demands that note should be taken of the order of arrival, such that no product should be held up indefinitely. Products unable to gain immediate access to the target process p acquire a 'fairness attribute' a_∂: a variable which the priority manager itself is able to modify. Since the product entering the priority manager is 'instantaneous', i.e. carries the date stamp of its instant of arrival, a_∂ must preserve the time at which the waiting process commenced.

The priority manager mechanism may be designed to implement a variety of strategies. It may do so by computing the 'priority attribute' a_p of a product P, defined as a function of its importance and fairness attributes:

$$a_p = f(a_h, a_\partial) \qquad \text{(expression 12.7)}$$

In expression 12.7:

- a_h is a scalar constant, determined by the problem.
  An emergency at a doctor's surgery (a_h=2) will take precedence over routine procedures (a_h=1). Emergency telephone calls (a_h=2) will have priority over routine calls (a_h=1). More refined priority management regimes will be more discriminating, with the importance parameter a_h having a wider domain.
- a_∂ is an objective interval measure of time, evaluated by the priority manager, designating the time interval between the present and the arrival of the original product and is variable.
- f is the priority function, defined by the designer of the process, and is thereafter kept invariant throughout p's operation, until the process is redesigned or is reassigned by the system administrator to optimize a multifunctional system. In effect, f is a utility function, imposing the designer's preferences on the objective measures a_h, a_∂.
- a_p is a scalar utility measure, determining choice among products which present themselves simultaneously at the input to the process.

The priority management regime above imposes 'partial order': a_p clearly discriminates between some products and others, but two or more products may have the same priority attribute value. Since only one product can enter a process at a given time, the priority manager must resolve such conflicts, imposing 'total order' over products which would otherwise have identical values of a_p. Possible ways of achieving this is to make more refined choices by considering additional priority criteria, or to leave the choice to chance, using a randomiser.

Example 12.8: Networking
The ethernet standard defines means of avoiding collisions on a network (CSMA/CD) , stating that should two frames be transmitted onto a network simultaneously with subsequent collision, each waits a random period before attempting to retransmit.

Figure 12.13 shows the 'priority manager cactus': an n-input, n-output cactus resolved into a P/p graph. The priority manager has nonzero delay, and incorporates a priority evaluator which selects one from a group of products, all arriving at the same time t_{in}, all competing for the attention of some process p. The distribution gate d routes the successful product to the target process p. The priority manager preserves the attributes of all incoming products: its function is only to select one of them by comparing their priority measures. Normally the input with highest priority measure would win, but if more than one has the same value then selection is in accord with some explicit strategy, such as selecting a product at random. Input products failing to be selected are either discarded or delayed and submitted to another priority evaluation later, when p becomes free. Assume for the moment that the input product P_{in-2} wins the race; then P_{out} will be the delayed P_{in-2}.

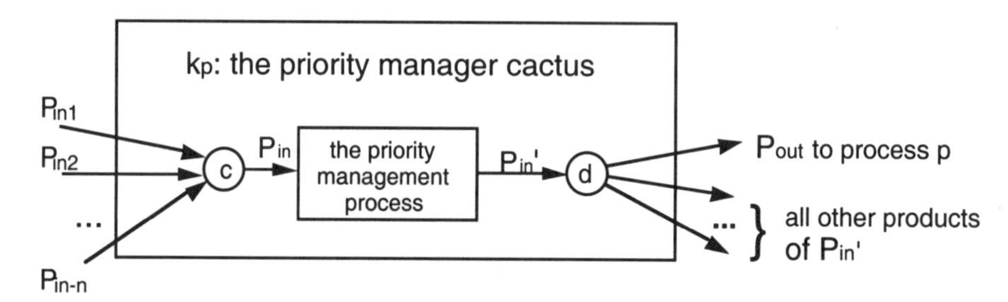

Figure 12.13: Priority manager imposing 'total order' (b-type, timing omitted)

Once conformance is assured and total order is imposed on priority, the access manager takes control, and may or may not delay acceptance further. At this stage the accepted product's priority attribute ceases to be relevant and may be discarded, unless needed for subsequent processing, such as for interrupt management.

Designing the priority function

The simple form of the priority function f is to form as the unweighted sum of the fairness and importance parameters, having expressed a_∂ as a scalar: a multiple of a suitable time interval.

$$a_p = a_h + a_\partial \qquad \text{(expression 12.8a)}$$

This means that unsuccessful candidate products have their importance parameter incremented by the value of a_∂ which increases each time the product is detained, improving the chance at the next presentation to the priority manager.

A variant of expression of 12.8(a) may assign different weights to the two parameters in the form

$$a_p = A \times a_h + B \times a_\partial, \text{ where A and B are constants} \qquad \text{(expression 12.8b)}$$

An important version of the priority function may be used in real-time systems to guarantee that an artifact is given a high value of importance attribute so as to assure that it obtains service within a preset time bound. Here the priority function might be conditional, to give:

$$a_p = a_h + a_\partial \;\text{ if }\; a_\partial < a_{\partial\text{-max}}, \text{ and}$$

$$a_p = a_{p\ max} \text{ otherwise,}$$

giving a_p top priority among all products.

Priority strategies

In real life one encounters a wealth of priority strategies, some explicit and declared, some veiled or hidden. Here we discuss only a few simple strategies, leaving it to the reader to represent the implementation of these and others in a P/p graph, using the ideas and methods learned.

SELECTION BY IMPORTANCE

A simple version of priority management is one where the losers of the priority management process are discarded and disposed of in some way. Here, on entry the importance attribute a_h is the only basis of selection, $a_p = a_h$, since the discarded products do not wait for further attention, and there is no fairness attribute. The priority manager performs a compare-and-select process, comparing the value of the importance attribute of all incoming products and choosing the highest, once again using the randomizer in case of a tie.

SELECTION BY FAIRNESS

Consider now the case where all products carry the same priority value, and priority depends on the order of arrival. In this case a_∂ is the only basis of comparison and selection, $a_p = a_\partial$. The way in which a_p is used is a matter for deliberate strategy, and we show below only two of many possibilities: (1) management by queue, and (2) management by stack. The design and operation of both the queue and the stack might be described in a P/p model, but this implementation detail is not discussed here.

Management by queue

Where more than one product is available and all products are equally important, selecting the product which has been waiting longest is the strategy represented by the queue, and service by process p is allocated in accord with a 'first-in-first-out' protocol. The priority manager chooses the product with the highest value $a_\partial = a_{\partial\text{-max}}$, and also controls access to the queue. In case of a draw, one may either use a randomizer, or introduce an auxiliary parameter that can make a more meaningful distinction. There are many examples of this queuing discipline, such as waiting for a bus, waiting for service at the post office, etc.

Management by stack

Another well known strategy is that of a 'last-in-first-out' protocol. Here the priority manager will choose the product with the lowest waiting time, once again randomizing (or employing a secondary parameter) to resolve a tie. Yet again, the priority manager compares and selects, but this time it chooses $a_\partial = a_{\partial\text{-min}}$.

The stack is a means of data management in computing. It also occurs in personnel management where the organization is 'downsizing', making people redundant, first dismissing those who entered employment last.

12.5 Interrupt management

Interrupts may occur because of a variety of causes, from the mundane to the dramatic. An interrupt may be initiated by appearance of a high priority product in need of attention by a process already engaged on a task, by a signal from a sensor communicating priority requirements to a process in progress, by the occurrence of some preset real time instant when the process must be interrupted, or by some sudden disaster — lightning strike, earthquake — which terminates the process without prior warning. The interrupt might give rise to delaying or abandoning work on an artifact; it may cause a total shut-down or complete destruction of the process. From the viewpoint of their management we discriminate three cases, and offer a definition for each:

- *scheduled* interrupts,
- *unscheduled* interrupts,
- *catastrophic* interrupts.

Scheduled (or operational) interrupts

Some interrupts are the normal part of daily life.

scheduled interrupt
a product occurring at a planned time instant to halt a process for a set time period because this is managerially expedient
Our working definition

They occur at planned times, when the operational process has to be halted for a set period, for example because of safety. The task of management is to assure that all part-products of the interrupted process are in a stable state, ready for storage until the processing is restarted, and interruption is safe: it does not endanger the human operators, the machinery the materials and other resources involved in the process. P/p modelling assists in the effective management and documentation of scheduled interrupts, and demonstrating effective management to all concerned.

Here are a few examples of operational interrupts.

Examples 12.9 Manufacture
Single-shift manufacturing processes are specifically devised for stopping at the end of the day, when the processing of several artefacts are still in progress, part-way towards completion. At the end of the day work is interrupted in accord with well defined procedures for ensuring that material, equipment and other resources are left in a safe state for work to continue next morning.

Continuous (three-shift) processes may also be halted operationally by planned interrupts to facilitate preventive maintenance or complete shut-down for major overhaul.

Example 12.10 Other scheduled interrupts
Normal operations in hotels, schools, offices and other public buildings are operationally interrupted for fire drills. Personnel are trained to adopt set procedures to guide the public out of the building along planned routes, and ensure that equipment in the building is left in a safe state.

P/p modelling helps in describing the timing, procedures and mechanisms of scheduled interrupts, and the admissible state to which products and processes must be brought by the time the operational processes are halted.

Unscheduled interrupts

We define:

> **unscheduled interrupt**
> an unplanned but foreseeable product that halts a process for an indeterminate time period
>
> Our working definition

The well-managed process is devised to cope effectively with interrupts of this type.

ATOMIC PROCESSES

By definition, an atomic process cannot be interrupted. If process p is modelled as atomic, and a product arrives at the input while p is engaged in a previous task, the product would be ignored, the access parameter F of p indicating that p is busy. If it is foreseeable that interruption of p might be necessary or desirable, and if the management seeks to retain control of the process by keeping a valid representation of its progress, then there is no option but to model the process *not* as an atomic process but as a structure of atomic processes.

Breaking down the atomic process to two serial subprocesses

Consider some process p which can operate on a range of products of varied priority, and is liable to interruption by the arrival of one or more high-priority product. Here are two examples.

Example 12.11: Computing

In computing, unscheduled interrupts are part of normal operation, and machines are designed to cope with them. A process in progress may be interrupted by a rival process, generally an operating peripheral device, seeking attention. This will initiate storage of incoming signals and current values of variables, pass control from the process in progress to the interrupter, and, after the interruption has been dealt with, allow the machine to return to normal working. Should this not have happened then a system crash may occur. Such use of interrupts is a consequence of the serial nature of single processor systems, and allows processes to compete for limited processor time.

Many examples of operational interrupts in computing are hidden from the user; others are apparent, such as halting computation by periodic 'save' mechanisms and 'background printing'.

Example 12.12: Casualty

Casualties of a major road accident arrive in a busy hospital where all staff is already engaged in carrying out necessary tasks. The hospital has set procedures for rapidly bringing its normal processes to a safe state. This includes assuring that the condition of all existing patients is stable. Only then can staff turn their attention to the incoming new patients whose condition requires priority treatment.

Once the condition of the new patients is stabilized, they will take their place among others, and priority will be determined in the normal manner, as outlined in figure 12.14. This means that in due course interrupted treatments and other processes will be resumed in accord with the criteria of priority and fairness.

Figure 12.14 is the familiar structure of a two-element serial process, preceded by the priority manager cactus k_p. Process p is partitioned into two atomic subprocesses p_1 followed by p_2. The input product P_{11} enters the priority manager together with others, and wins the competition for the attention of p. Since k_p has nonzero duration, P_{11} had been delayed. P_{11}' – the product entering p – has the same attribute measures as P_{11}, but has a later time signature.

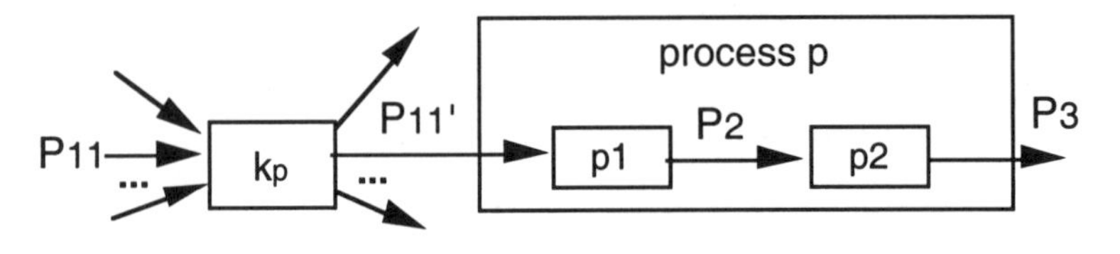

Figure 12.14: Two-element serial process preceded by priority manager (b-type, timing omitted)

Assume now that a product P* arrives while p_1 is in progress. Since p_1 is atomic, it cannot be interrupted; thus, P* must be stored until p_1 completes. At the end of p_1 the delayed newcomer P*' must compete with the intermediate product P_2. If P_2 wins, process p_2 starts and p concludes. However, if P*' wins then product P_2 must give way, and the new input, designated P*'' since it is now *twice* delayed, enters p_1. This is as far as figure 12.15 represents the process.

What happens to unsuccessful products after an interrupt? The primitive approach would be to discard them. A more effective method is to devise the two subprocesses of p such that it is safe to leave the intermediate product P_2 of the first subprocess p_1 pending, to be stored until the interruption is dealt with and work on it can be resumed.

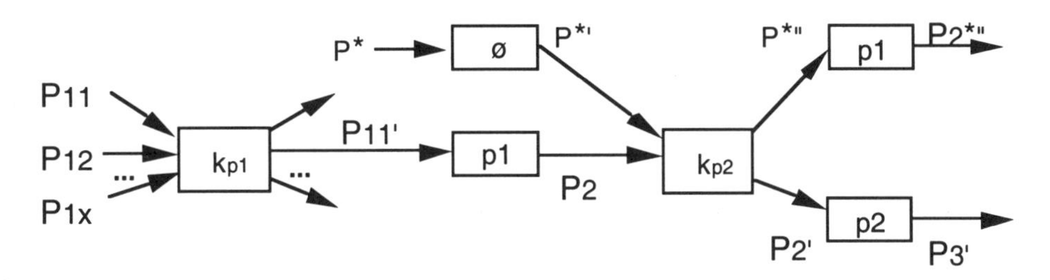

Figure 12.15: Priority and interrupt management: the early part of a two-element serial process (b-type, timing omitted)

Figure 12.16 shows a two-element sequential process comprising subprocesses p_1 and p2, from the viewpoint of the initial input, call it P_1, which had won the priority race, and is now delayed to be P_1'. The interrupt manager k_{int} is interposed between p_1 and p_2. When subprocess p_1 completes, its output P_2 carries a priority measure a_h. At this point the priority of P_2 is assessed in k_h.

- If any new input product arrives whose priority measure is higher than that of P_2, then P_2 is passed to a store process ø until process p completes dealing with higher priorities.

- If there is no new input, or if the priority measure of the new input is not higher than that of P_2, then P_2 is passed to subprocess p_2, and the process completes.

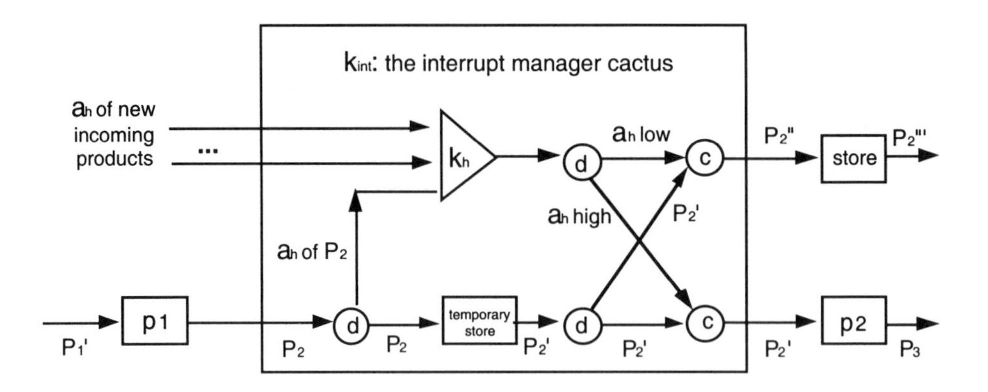

Figure 12.16: Two-element serial process with interrupt manager (b-type, timing omitted)

GENERALIZING THE INTERRUPT MANAGEMENT OF ATOMIC PROCESSES

In most practical cases effective interrupt management calls for composing processes not of two but of several atomic subprocesses. The serial structure should be such that it should be safe to interrupt the process whenever it reaches any boundary between adjacent processes, and store the intermediate product for the period required to attend to the priority task. At each boundary point one would examine the whole set of waiting products and act first on the highest priority product which might be in store. Note that this arrangement does not tie the interrupts to specific *times*: priority management is driven by asynchronous *events* throughout process p.

Figure 12.17 shows how interrupt management is generalized to a process with three or more subprocesses. Note that the interrupt manager k_h incorporates its own short-term storage process, maintaining the intermediate product for the duration of sorting out priority.

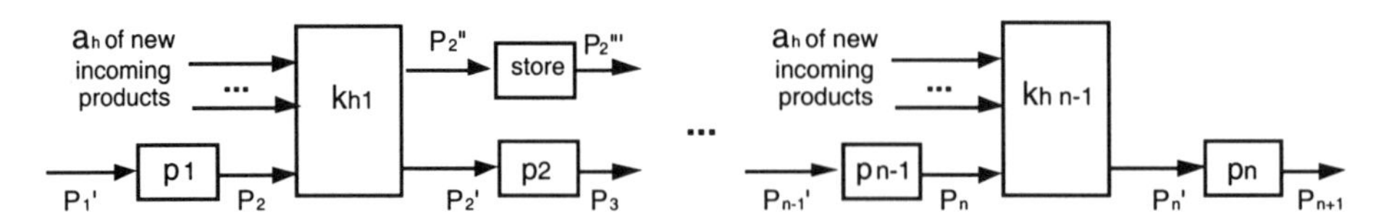

Figure 12.17: n-element serial process with interrupt manager (b-type, timing omitted)

DEALING WITH INTERRUPTS IN STRUCTURED PROCESSES

When a process is modelled as a structure of atomic processes then the interfaces between the structural elements offer ready-made opportunities for interposing interrupt managers. However, interrupt management costs money and absorbs time; thus, interrupt use must be selective. Moreover, the structured process may include subprocesses which are too lengthy to be allowed to stand as atomic, and interrupt management requires breakdown of these into sequences. Thus, interrupt management of structured processes must be handled judiciously.

SOME GENERAL COMMENTS ON MANAGING UNSCHEDULED INTERRUPTS

In the discussion above we have considered interrupt management from the viewpoint of the individual artifact which has to take its chance in competition with others, and might languish in the vicinity of the required process for a considerable time if more urgent products arrive.

The designer of the process must also consider the situation from the viewpoint of the process and its context. All processes absorb resources. Choosing an interrupt management strategy must take account of the cost of providing storage for waiting products. The number of waiting products should be kept short, as should be the average waiting period.

The management of unscheduled interrupts should not be a matter of fire fighting, or coping with difficulties when they arise. It should be treated as a design problem to be dealt with at the time of planning processes. P/p modelling helps to articulate the eventualities that have to be taken care of, and assists in finding safe, reliable, cost-effective solutions.

Catastrophic interrupts

Catastrophic interrupts are unplanned, unscheduled. They might be foreseen, but are deemed to be beyond the manager's power of planning and control. They may be caused internally, the process itself breaking down, or else be the result of forces external to the process. They might be caused by some infrequently occurring external force which had been excluded from the process model deliberately, or by the disruption of some resource which is essential to the process, and whose presence had been taken for granted by the modeller.

Earthquakes, bomb blasts, lightning strikes are possible causes of external catastrophic interrupts. Such interrupts may cause physical damage to products, to process, or to human beings associated with the process. In computational processes essential information may be lost by media failure. Where catastrophic events have taken place (the Marchioness river disaster, oil refinery blow-outs, landslides, explosion in mines), it is often because documented safety procedures are not implemented. Conversely, many catastrophes have been averted by prompt human action which implements, and even goes beyond, planned safety procedure. The subject is fascinating, instructive, and not always depressing [2].

Catastrophic interrupts need to be precipitated by 'acts of god'; they need not be dramatic, and they don't need to have tragic consequences. We define:

catastrophic interrupt
a product that halts a process for an indeterminate time period, although it had been planned as atomic
Our working definition

When a catastrophic interrupt occurs, the *model* fails. Interrupts of this kind cause the real life process to take leave of its model, so that the manager in charge of the process loses control: is no longer able to describe, let alone predict, the happenings in the process and the state of its products. This means that when the cause of the interrupt disappears, it may not be easy, or even possible, to restore the process to operation, or rescue the resources involved.

The aftermath of a catastrophic interrupt includes questioning the validity of the model. Such interrupts usually lead to the refinement of models, taking account of those previously excluded factors which caused the disruption. This in turn leads to improvement of the processes themselves, the inclusion of guards and recovery mechanisms, or the enhancement of the infrastructure on which the processes rely.

FAILURE MANAGEMENT

Failure management aims to avert or mitigate catastrophic interrupts, seeking to convert them to unscheduled interrupts. We distinguish here between (1) refinement of the *model,* and (2) improvement of the *process* and/or the *environment* of the process, incorporating *guards* and *recovery mechanisms.*

Refining the model

As we have seen, a catastrophic interrupt is the failure of the model which had been unable to represent the cause of the interruption. Following the catastrophic interrupt, it is the task of interrupt management to review the model to discover why it had failed, and how it should be amended to account for the cause of the interrupt, should it recur.

Guards

Interrupt management must consider what safety checks can be incorporated and what precautions can be taken to prevent abnormal interrupts. Guards may be *preventive,* either seeking to avert the cause, or monitoring the environment so as to predict the impending interrupt. In the latter case the guard operates similarly to priority interrupts, the interrupt prediction signal taking topmost priority, giving the process advance warning to abandon normal operation and institute built-in shut-down procedures.

Recovery mechanisms

Recovery mechanisms are invoked when an interrupt has occurred and led to a process shut-down, but the cause of the interruption had disappeared, or had been dealt with. The recovery mechanism is *remedial*, restoring normal operation rapidly and safely.

Some examples of interrupts

The examples below give account of a number of situations, some routine and some quite serious, where interrupts occur. To guard against an interrupt giving rise to catastrophic failure, one needs an explicit representation of the situation and of the mechanisms of managing it. P/p modelling assists by making the effect of the interrupt explicit, thus aiding the management of interrupts.

Example 12.13: Electricity supply

A potential source of catastrophic interrupt is the failure of the public electricity supply in processes reliant on the supply. Different strategies of failure management may be adopted, assuring that the process is maintained, or at least that control is not lost:

- *If the process tolerates scheduled interrupts, it can be designed to have its own short-term passive internal supply (by use of capacitors), allowing the process time to reach a safe condition before shutting down. An example occurs in computing where the power supply of the equipmentis maintained for a limited period, long enough for assuring that the system, all the applications and all unused files are saved in non-volatile memory, and files in use are brought into a recoverable state.*
- *If the process must not shut down under temporary power failure, as is the case for the operating theatre of a hospital, a local power source (domestic generator or high-capacity battery) is provided as standby. The local source is designed to keep the process going for several hours or even a few days, until the public supply is restored.*
- *If the process must not shut down even if the power fails semi-permanently (for example as a consequence of a major act of war), elaborate standby power supply arrangements are instituted for maintaining continuity of critical processes and securingfor them alternative power to almost indefinitely.*

Example 12.14: Printing

Printing a document is a routine task, often treated as an indivisible atomic process. However, the 'paper out' alert informs the user of an interrupt, illustrating that the process is divisible into many small units, such as the printing of a single page.

Yet further granularity is introduced when we consider a paper jam. Here the interrupt shows the printing of a single page being made up of even smaller units separated by signals from sensors along the paper channel.

Example 12.15: Background printing

Consider the interrupt mechanism of printing from the viewpoint of a printer driven from a computer, operated in a 'background printing' mode. Here the computer attends to a number of competing tasks of which printing is only one, and the printing process itself is granular.

Example 12.16: Computing

At the processing level, where several active programs are sharing the same processor, means must be in place to allow fair sharing of processor time. There are two methods of implementing this: preemptive and cooperative multitasking. In the first, the operating system decides when to interrupt a running process and in the second the process itself voluntarily steps aside. The points at which this can occur are at the end of 'threads', tasks composed of sequences of instructions, or if finer granularity is needed then the execution of a single instruction may be regarded as an atomic process.

Example 12.17: Gas leaks

Gas leaks are the potential cause of catastrophic interrupts of the life of the community and the subject of risk analysis. However, consider now the issue from the viewpoint of the finances of the gas supply company. To repair the damage costs money, not to mention the potential cost of compensation in case of disaster, and the consequential loss of business when – following the inevitable adverse publicity – customers transfer to other energy suppliers. Moreover, shut-down means loss of revenue.

The task of interrupt management is to minimize the actual and potential loss, which means simultaneously minimizing:

- *the* frequency of occurrance *of leaks,*
- *the* severity *of leaks,*
- *the* region *over which the supply must be shut down once a leak has been detected,*
- *the* time *taken for diagnosing the cause and effecting a remedy,*
- *the* time *taken for restoring the supply to all customers.*

Example 12.18: *Pipelines*

When considering the problem of interrupt management of a pipelined serial process, one must note that the pipelined subprocesses are interdependent. All subprocesses in the pipeline will need to be blocked as they terminate their execution following a priority interrupt. Means must be provided to buffer intermediate outputs in readiness for future resumption of operation. Safety critical procedures must also be set in motion.

12.6 Summary

This chapter shows the power and adaptability of P/p modelling in articulating problems of process management, and assisting managers in handling such problems.

The success of projects depends on the managers understanding of the products and processes involved, and the interrelationships among the subprocesses. This chapter discusses various aspects of process management. Starting with guards and constraints on individual processes, it first identifies two major issues: conformance management and access management. The former governs the suitability of the product entering the process, the latter the state of the process itself, and its ability to accept the product. These two strands are followed from the single, atomic process through to compositions of processes, demonstrating the use of P/p modelling in dealing with individual processes and complex process structures.

The chapter goes on to discuss two further issues: priority management and the management of interrupts. The handling of products of differing priority is through introducing a priority function: a utility measure subjectively defined by the manager of the process as a function of objective measures. The chapter outlines several possible priority strategies.

When considering interrupts, three cases are distinguished: (i) benign, useful operational interrupts, such as periodic shut-downs for preventive maintenance, (ii) unplanned but foreseeable interrupts, such as necessary for safety management, and (iii) catastrophic interrupts. This last need not necessarily spell disaster, but it always means that the manager loses control, the interruption driving the process beyond the bounds of validity of its model. The chapter extends to the discussion those kinds of catastrophic interrupts which can give rise to disasters, and refers to some issues of disaster management.

12.7 Footnotes

1 For definition of 'conformity' see chapter 14.

2 Tragedies averted are not usually publicly documented as such but, among others, the Civil Aviation Authority's reports of near misses bear ample testimony to such incidents. Indirect evidence is also furnished by the supply of manual overrides to many automated systems.

Chapter 13 Organizational maturity and quality management

In today's competitive environment the sustained profitability and very survival of organizations depend on their maturity. "Determining an organization's capability and maturity" was one of the stated aims of a recent Colloquium [1], and we quote here from our contribution to this topic. The Colloquium was prompted by the realization that, in general, the maturity of organizations is relatively low.

Even in organizations where process modelling is deliberately pursued and company-wide measures are imposed as management aids to assessment and guides to improvement, not infrequently the process models are deficient and the measures ill defined. Such organizations may satisfy the *form* but not the *spirit* of maturity assessment and quality management: they will carry the bureaucratic burdens of such audits without obtaining their benefits.

The latter part of this chapter examines the maturity of organizations in the light of the requirements of the new version of the international quality certification standard.

13.1 Background

In everyday parlance 'maturity' is defined as 'the state of full development' [2]. The notion has been introduced into the business context by the Software Engineering Institute (SEI) of Carnegie Mellon University for assessing the capability of organizations whose business is software development [3]. SEI's 'Capability Maturity Model' (CMM) and its 'maturity measures' have also been extended to systems [4]. CMM is stated to be a "descriptive model of the stages through which organizations progress as they define, evolve and improve their processes". SEI offers no definition of 'maturity', but proposes to measure it on an integer scale of 1 to 5, naming the levels as 'initial', 'repeatable', 'defined', 'managed' and 'optimizing'.

The notions of gradation and level-by-level advance are helpful, and CMM's detailed assessment criteria are stated. The maturity measure of the organization is derived from the assessment of detail by means of a formula. Although the scale is defined only at integer values, this formula frequently yields fractional measures such as 2.75 or 3.5. Since the formula is not published, organizations are not in a position to check the correctness of the external evaluation, and are unable to make full use of the process internally in self-evaluation and maturity improvement.

SEI's maturity assessment initiative came at the right time: customers needed some objective basis of appraising and selecting suppliers, and suppliers themselves were keen to evaluate the state of their organizations and mark their advancements. SEI's trademarked 'Capability Maturity Model' started a trend, and was followed by others. It may well have been the background for the definition of the 'Performance

Maturity Levels' offered as '**Guidelines** for self-assessment' in ISO/FDIS 9004:2000. The standard does not give a definition for the concept of 'maturity', but recommends the measure of its 'levels' on a 5-point integer scale (table 13.1).

It would be an interesting exercise to compare or evaluate the definitions and uses of CMM and ISO, but this is not our purpose here.

The subject matter of this chapter is a suitable basis of maturity measurement, but its purpose is not only, and not even primarily, normative. It differs from CMM and ISO, both of which require a mature organization to pursue a systematic and methodological approach, but neither of which recommend a methodology. Instead, this chapter demonstrates how the systems approach and P/p modelling described in this book would aid the progress of organizations, stimulate their progress towards excellence, and, incidentally, offer them the basis of demonstrating and measuring maturity.

Maturity level	Performance level	Guidance
1	No formal approach	No systematic approach evident, no results, poor results, or unpredictable results
2	Reactive approach	Problem– or corrective-based systematic approach; minimum data on improvement results available
3	Stable formal system approach	Systematic process-based approach; early stage of systematic improvements; data available on conformance to objectives and existence of improvement trends
4	Continual improvement emphasized	Improvement process in use; good results and sustained improvement trends
5	Best-in-class performance	Strongly integrated improvement process; best-in-class benchmarked results demonstrated

Table 13.1: Performance maturity levels defined in ISO/FDIS 9004:2000

To avoid confusion with the 'levels' of CMM and ISO, we refer to our maturity grades as 'stages'. Definitions of stages are not imposed externally: they arise naturally from methodology itself. There is no attempt to line these up with the maturity levels of CMM or ISO, although we shall have occasion to remark on their consistency: an organization at a higher stage of development will confidently expect to attain a higher maturity measure of CMM or ISO.

13.2 P/p graphs for representing progress of maturation

A mature organization models its operation, plans its goals of improvement as measures for timed objectives, and demonstrates the achievement of its goals by measures of its model. Any measurement scheme will award a high maturity measure to such an organization.

It would be unrealistic to expect a company to leap from a state of relative immaturity to operation in accord with a clearly articulated and measurably defined process model. The maturation process is complex. To make progress, higher management must devote corporate effort to ensuring that the organization realizes its situation and makes progress towards improving it. For this, management must appreciate the need to model the operation of the organization. Since the maturity of the organization as a whole depends on the maturity of all its parts, progression towards maturity must involve the whole staff and much of the constituency, the models must be comprehensible for those concerned, and the measures must be both independent of the evaluator and checkable by the evaluated.

We chart the maturation of an organization in a P/p network: a sequence of subprocesses, each producing as output a stage of development of the organization. After the earliest stages of relative immaturity, each stage of development yields the representation of the operation of the organization the form of a *network.* Each type of network is defined in the Glossary, each being an advancement compared with the previous, the 'maturity' of the network defining the stage of maturity of the organization, each stage corresponding to enhanced staff skills, defining the operation of the company more and more rigorously. Similarly to the level-by-level progression of CMM and ISO, the target of the progression is a formal model of the operation of the organization, furnished with properly defined variables and measures, such that the model can not only facilitate demonstrable *improvement* but also support planned *optimization.*

The progression towards a fully fledged P/p model may vary from organization to organization, depending on its initial stage and development strategy. Figure 13.1 shows cases where the complete maturation process may start from two different states of the company's development: the 'Undocumented' stage (P_A), or the 'Mess' (P_B). These alternative starting stages, together with each stage of the maturation process, is described below. The figure uses the enriched P/p notation introduced in tables 4.1 and 4.2 of chapter 4.

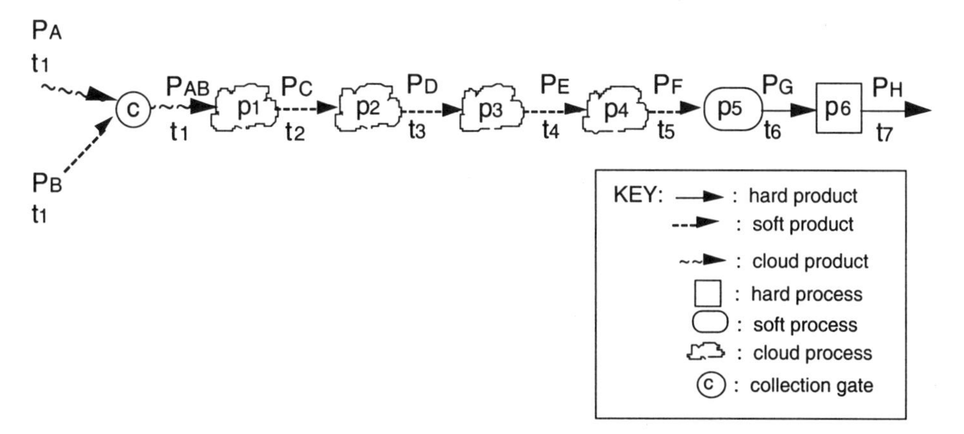

Figure 13.1: Maturation process of an organization shown in a P/p graph

Starting stages P_A, P_B

P_A: the 'Undocumented stage':

There is no written process representation; nevertheless, good practices may be followed, and handed down by custom. Such might be the case in a skilled craft workshop.

P_B: the 'Mess':

Some kind of process documentation exists about the current activities of the organization, usually in the form of text and informal diagrams, but there is no defined documentation standard, hence no basis for systematic checking of the completeness, consistency or correctness of the representation of the operation of the organization.

Preliminary stages P_C to P_E [5]

P_C: the 'Diagram stage':

The operation of the organization is represented in line drawings. Consistent use of diagrams has been established, and the diagram admits some degree of quality assurance; for example, there is a key to each diagram explaining the symbols used, and there is an explicit statement of the purpose of the representation against which one can check the relevancy of the features of the process representation.

P_D: the 'Network stage':

The process diagram is now represented in a consistent manner by a directed graph where clear distinction is drawn between 'passive' objects and 'activities' (e.g. the graph might be a-type or b-type). All parts of the graph are uniquely and consistently labelled, and the meaning of the labels is well defined.

P_E: the 'Cactus network stage':

The network is now defined as b-type, arcs representing passive entities and nodes designating activities. Each node has at least one input and one output, but the valency is unconstrained. The complete network and any of its internal nodes may be a cactus.

Advanced stages P_F to P_H

P_F: the 'P/p network stage':

All arcs are 'product-like': their key attributes are listed and given at least by verbal description. All nodes are single-input, single-output entities whose function is at least verbally defined. Aggregation and disaggregation of product-like entities is by use of collection and distribution gates whose rules are at least verbally given.

P_G: the 'P/p framework stage':

All arcs are formally defined as products or product types, the latter representing verbally defined key attributes by variable definitions. All nodes are formally defined as processes or process types in terms of their function, together with representation of their key attributes by measures or variable definitions. All gate rules are formally defined.

P_H: the 'P/p model stage':

All arcs correspond to formally defined products; all nodes to formally defined processes or gates, with all attributes defined by measures.

A comment

The maturation process just described represents steady progress, each stage being a definite advance on the previous, although this is not apparent from figure 13.1. Only at stage P_G does the organization reach sufficient maturity for its operation to be modelled in measurable terms, and benefit from this thereafter.

13.3 Using the P/p graph for measuring maturity

The P/p graph of figure 13.1 may represent the maturation process of the whole organization, or of any of its parts. The list below summarizes the main features of the measurement process.

- The definition of each stage of maturity beyond Stage C rests on the concepts of the *systems methodology* defined in the Glossary. Whether an organization has attained a stage or not is not a matter of opinion, nor is it a subject of value judgement: it is a matter of fact.
- There is no need to map observations of the stages of maturity into *measures*: the stages shown on figure 13.1 serve *directly* as ordinal measures of maturity.
- As the figure shows, the measure has a seven-valued *ordinal scale*:

  (A or B), C, D, E, F, G, H.
- The grades of the scale correspond directly to the representation of the organization: the further along the grade in the alphabet, the more mature the organization. To make it evident that maturity is measured on an ordinal scale rather than on a ratio scale, the scale uses an *alphabetic* rather than a numerical *symbol system*. There is no letter in the alphabet between C and D, and this should make it explicit that there is no equivalent here to CMM's fractional grading.
- Once an organization attains stage H in maturity development, there is no scope in figure 13.1 for formal advancement to a higher stage of maturity. However, this does not mean stagnation, as will be discussed in a later section of this chapter.

Model-based measurement of maturity

Throughout this book we emphasize that assignment of numbers to a thing does not necessarily amount to measurement. To use a famous quote: "However reliable the test or reproducible the measurement, without a theoretical framework into which that quantity enters, it is useless [6]". Maturity assessment as presented here uses the theoretical and conceptual foundations of P/p modelling and model-based measurement, with measures derived directly from the documentation of the operation of the organization, the most mature stage being the case where representation is formal, the attributes well defined, and given as measures.

The two-part assessment process – a maturity audit

As we know, representation of the operation of an organization is essential for its effective management, and is the prerequisite of maturity measurement. However, the *maturity of the representation* is not the same as the *maturity of the organization.* Managers of a mature organization have a representation of the operation in their charge. Assessment must be *open:* carried out against declared criteria, and in accord with stated procedure. As in expert auditing, and as is the standard procedure of quality management, maturity assessment proceeds in two parts:

PART 1 examines the documentation against the declared assessment scheme, and

PART 2 examines the operation against the representation, checking consistency, detecting any case where the documentation is fiction, divorced from reality.

To put it in other words, when preparing for maturity assessment, members of the organization must first *say what they do*, and next they must prove that they *do what they say.*

13.4 Preparing an organization for maturity assessment

A *mature* organization is ready for assessment at any time. All that is required is to inform the staff, bring the measures of the model up to date for the specific day, present the model and its measures in the required medium for PART 1, and be ready to welcome the assessors on the appointed date for PART 2.

For an organization of relative *immaturity*, preparation for PART 1 of assessment may mean modelling the operation of the organization for the first time. Management must also acquaint the staff with the representation submitted to the assessors; otherwise how could the operatives convince the assessors in PART 2 that they know what they are doing, and do what is stated in the documentation? Thus, model-based measurement of maturity:

- induces *management* to examine the operation of the organization and represent it in some format, thus gaining deeper understanding of the processes in their charge, and
- involves *staff* in maturity assessment of the organization, the involvement itself being a source of motivation for all concerned, improving staff morale, and developing the kind of corporate spirit characteristic of successful organizations.

Guidelines for modelling the operation of the organization

Even in a relatively immature state, the organization would have some form of black box representation of its operation, if only for the purposes of annual financial audit and biennial reporting to external stakeholders, such as the shareholders of a public company. Beyond this, a mature organization will operate in accord with a well developed structural model, resolved into properly defined black box atomic elements. One expects that such a model would represent each kind of activity of the operation of the organization, and also give details of activities of major importance. However, common sense dictates that it would be unreasonable, uneconomical and quite unproductive for such a model to break down each minor task, each support function into minutia of structural detail. The question is: to what structural depth should the model of a mature organization penetrate?

In search of an answer, let us refer to the bipartite trees of chapter 10, with the complete organization at the root of the tree, and the atomic parts at the leaves.

- The first task is to represent the operation of the complete organization as a black box process.
- Next, the black box is to be refined into a process structure represented as a P/p graph (at the appropriate stage of maturity). The graph should show the breakdown the operation of the organization into major operational functions, the P/p graph defining the interrelation among these structural elements, product and process tables giving the black box model of each part. The support functions must also be shown in the representation, if only to identify their role in the organization, the persons responsible for them, with their resource requirements accounting for some parameters in the black box model of the complete organization.
- At this point managerial judgement comes into play. Each black box node of the bipartite tree must be examined to decide whether or not to define them in further operational detail. If not, then the node becomes a leaf of the tree; if yes, the node is broken down into a process structure given as a P/p graph with black box elements at its leaves.
- The process continues until the structure is completely defined, all leaf nodes being given as black boxes whose detail is deemed adequate.

The decision concerning depth of modelling detail need not be final. If a minor part of the operation assumes greater importance or proves troublesome, the level of structural detail must be increased. As an example, it would not usually be necessary to have a P/p model of the operation of the works canteen of a manufacturing company, but if salmonella poisoning breaks out one day, the P/p model becomes a necessity, and should be maintained for an agreed period of time, such as a year, after the outbreak. Conversely, if a previously critical part of the operation becomes so well established that it is now routine, the level of detail should be reduced in the interest of saving administrative cost and curtailing unnecessary bureaucracy. it must be defined support function

It is the task of the maturity assessor – or any auditor – to question the rationale behind the representation. The management should have a reasoned answer, and preferably a justification in terms of the performance record and other attributes of the part of the operation, as to why the model details one part of the operation rather than another.

13.5 Conducting maturity assessment

Maturity assessment can be carried out *internally* as the means of self-assessment. It can also be performed by a *second party*: a prospective customer appraising the capability of the organization to act as supplier. Assessment can also be carried out normatively by a disinterested *third party*, establishing the status of the organization in accord with an agreed standard.

Let us emphasize again that maturity assessment based on P/p modelling is entirely open, the result is achieved objectively, and the scale is independent of the evaluator. Thus, the appraised organization or organizational unit may check the correctness of the grading, appeal against the result if an appeal is justified, and the matter can be settled factually. The grading, derived as an explicitly defined maturity function over the characteristics of the P/p graph, can be linked to levels of CMM or ISO. Should the organization require third party assessment by one of these organizations, the P/p-based maturity assessment can be used as a preparation. Thus, P/p modelling is a method which does not only support the organization in reaching a high level of maturity, but also provides a mechanism for proving that specific maturity levels have been achieved.

While the maturing process of figure 13.1 and its scale of measurement are generic, the procedures described here are examples. They need not be dogmatically imposed, but should be devised to suit individual organizations.

Assessing the maturity of a small organization

Assume first that the organization is small enough for its maturity to be assessed by examining its characteristics as a single entity. The two-part procedure outlined in section 13.3 may work as follows:

PART 1: OBTAIN THE 'PROVISIONAL MATURITY MEASURE' (PMM)

Examine the *documentation* of the operation of the organization.

- If the operation is 'Undocumented' or if the documentation is a 'Mess' then PMM = AB.
- If the documentation is text supported by diagrams then PMM = C.
- ...
- If the documentation is a P/p framework then PMM = G.
- If the documentation is a P/p model then PMM = H.

PART 2: OBTAIN THE 'ACTUAL MATURITY MEASURE' (AMM)

Examine the operation of the organization, checking each constituent subprocess against the documentation.

- If the operation is fully consistent with the representation then the Provisional Maturity Measure PMM is confirmed as the Actual Maturity Measure (AMM) of the organization: PMM = AMM.

- If the operation does not conform fully to the documentation but the deviations are few and minor then the organization is given a deadline by when to bring its operation in line with the documentation; meanwhile the maturity measure is 'Unconfirmed' (UMM).
- If the deadline is not met, or if the deviations from the documentation are major or numerous then the organization is nonconformant to *its own standards*. This means that the organization is operating without valid documentation, and could only pass the maturity assessment at the grade AMM=A.

  Such an organization should revise its process representation to assure that it is not fictitious but realistic, and recommence maturity assessment in due course.

Assessing the maturity of larger organizations

Let us turn our attention to a larger organization subdivided into a number of parts (Divisions, Departments, Groups, or whatever), and assume that the maturity of each of these can be assessed independently by the two-part procedure applicable to small organizations. Assume also that the part-by-part assessment has been carried out, yielding a set of Actual Maturity Measures, but this is not yet the maturity measure of the organization as a whole. The reader will anticipate that aggregation of the individual measures will be a two-part process:

PART 1: OBTAIN THE 'PROVISIONAL MATURITY MEASURE' (PMM)

Examine the documentation of the operation of the whole organization in terms of the operation of its parts, and assign to this the appropriate value of Provisional Maturity Measure of the corporation as a whole.

PART 2: OBTAIN THE 'ACTUAL MATURITY MEASURE' (AMM)

Examine the actual operation against the documentation. Let us assume here that the Provisional Maturity Measure is confirmed, and we have obtained the Actual Maturity Measure of the corporation.

At this point in the assessment process we have (n+1) number of Actual Maturity Measures: AMM_1 to AMM_n for the n parts of the organization, and AMM_0 for the top level.

The organizational maturity measure can be obtained from these by various formulae. Let us adopt the harsh formula based on the maxim that any organization is as strong as its weakest part. Assume that an organization consists of four divisions and has scored Actual Maturity Measures as:

Part of the organization	Division 1	Division 2	Division 3	Division 4	Organiza-tional level
AMM score	$AMM_1 = D$	$AMM_2 = G$	$AMM_3 = C$	$AMM_4 = H$	$AMM_0 = D$

The corporate maturity measure AMM_{corp} of such an organization is C.

In organizations structured as multilevel hierarchies, maturity assessment is carried out level-by-level, aggregating the measure for each higher level from the measures of the level below in accord with the procedure just described. The method is equally applicable to organizations that adopt non-hierarchical management structures, such as a matrix. In such a case the column-wise and row-wise operation of the matrix is assessed independently, and then aggregated as discussed above.

13.6 Effects of maturity assessment on the organization

Whatever the method of maturity assessment, it compels organizations to look at themselves and review their procedures. However, in many cases preparation for maturity assessment *detracts* rather than assists the organization: it absorbs resources which could otherwise be used for constructive purposes and enhancement of the capability of the organization.

This is not the case with P/p modelling which is both the instrument of maturity and the aid to the development of the organization and of its deliverables. Applied judiciously in accord with guidelines based on common sense and economic sense, the effort invested in maturity assessment yields skills of P/p modelling which the management and the personnel of the organization can then utilize subsequently in their daily tasks of running the organization and producing its deliverables.

Since the assessment method is known to all, it is conducive of healthy competition among units of the organizational structure, stimulating less developed units to advance to best practice. Interdepartmental competition is constructive rather than damaging: since the over-all appraisal depends on the result of the weakest, more developed parts of the organization are motivated to assist their peers.

13.7 Continuing maturity enhancement

In P/p-based maturity assessment Stage H marks the desirable state of the mature organization operating in accord with a fully developed P/p model. Having achieved such a stage, the organization need not be smug and complacent: it should continue the maturing process, improving the efficiency of its processes and the quality of its products in search of excellence. Improvement must be *demonstrated*, and convincing demonstration needs *measurement*. From grade AB to H, maturity improvement could be measured objectively on the seven-level ordinal scale given in section 13.2, the measures representing characteristics of the *representation*.

To measure subsequent progress of an organization already at Stage H operating under a fully fledged P/p model requires devising some other scale of measurement *within Stage H*. These measures all correspond to the same *type* of representation – a P/p model –, and within this, the grading of the organization relies on the type and value of the *measures* themselves.

Now is the time to see what concepts CMM and ISO associate with advanced grades of maturity.

- Operating at Stage H, armed with measures of a fully developed P/p model, should comfortably put a company at the middle point of *Level 3* in the CMM or ISO scale.
- Both CMM and ISO emphasize that, for advancing from Level 3 to *Level 4*, organizations must demonstrate *continuing improvement.*
- ISO describes the top Level 5 as 'best-in-class', and CMM designates the fully mature *Level 5* as '*optimizing*'.

We may use the process definition of P/p models to distinguish between three ranks within Stage H, each rank inheriting the characteristics of the previous, with enhancements. We enthusiastically embrace the first and second of these ranks but have reservations about the third; nevertheless, to capture the ideas of the two distinguished bodies of third-party auditors, we define all three. The outcome is a three-valued ordinal scale within Stage H, designated by alphabetic characters.

Table 13.1 shows the definitions of the complete measurement scale, and a fuller explanation of the P/p model' scales is given overleaf.

Starting stages	Undocumented (A)	There is no written process representation.
	Mess (B)	Process documentation exists, e.g. text and informal diagrams.
Preliminary stages	Diagram (C)	Complete process is represented in line drawings. Consistent use of diagrams established.
	Network (D)	Process diagram represented by a directed graph; clear distinction between 'passive' objects and 'activities'. All parts uniquely and consistently labelled, all labels well defined.
	Cactus (E)	B-type network; valency is unconstrained.
Advanced stages	P/p network (F)	All arcs 'product-like'; all nodes single-input, single-output with function at least verbally defined; aggregation and disaggregation of product-like entities by gates, with rule at least verbally given.
	P/p framework (G)	All arcs formally defined as products or product types; all nodes formally defined as processes or process types; all gate functions formally defined.
P/p model stages (H)	Measured (Ha)	All arcs products and all nodes processes or gates; all attributes defined by measures.
	Continuous improvement (Hb)	Model includes two sets of 'rate-of-improvement' attributes, measuring (i) the *planned* change of selected process attributes over a set period, (ii) the *actual* change of the same attributes over the same period.
	Optimization (Hc)	The black box model of the organization includes: – a set of *objective functions* defined over selected key parameters, – the *actual* values achieved.

Table 13.2: Ordinal scale of maturity measurement based on P/p graphs

13.8 Quality management

At present the ISO 9000 series of international quality certification standards is under revision and the new standard is about to be issued. The Final Draft of the standard is already available [7], specifying requirements for quality management systems. It states that the Standard "promotes the adoption of a *process approach* when developing, implementing and improving" quality management systems. It describes the process approach as "the systematic identification and management of the processes employed within an organization and particularly the interactions between such processes", and emphasizes that "objective measurement" is one of the distinguishing features of the process approach. The Standard also offers a figure, reproduced in Figure 13.2 below, as "a conceptual illustration of one model of the process approach", and states that the figure "covers all the requirements of this international standard".

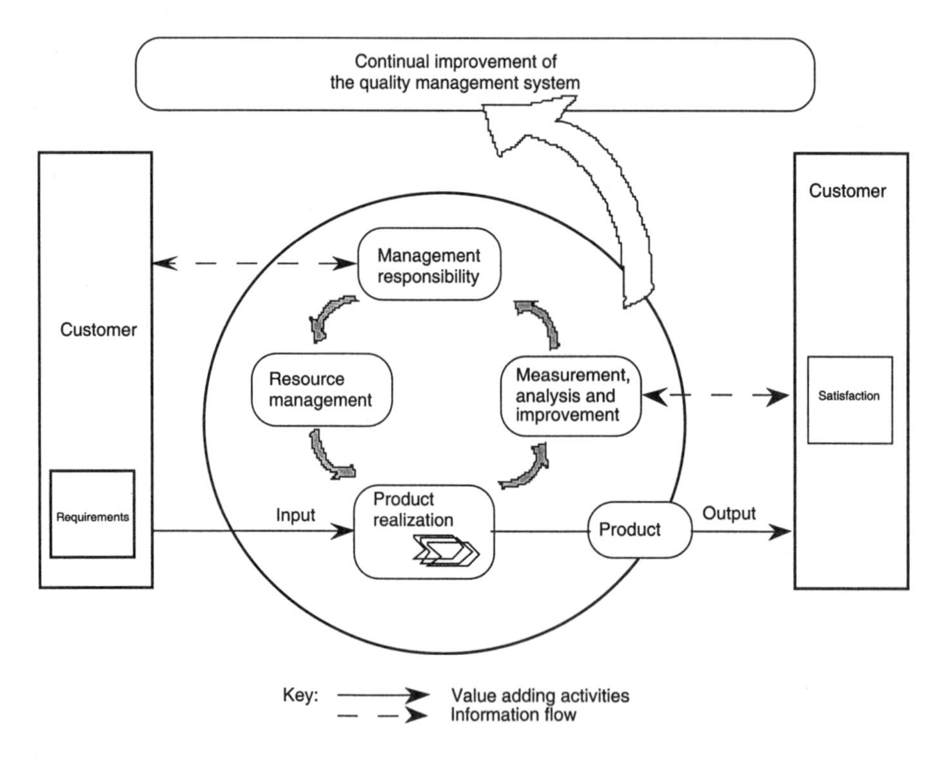

Figure 13.2: "Model of a process-based quality management system" – reproduction of Figure 1 of the standard ISO FDIS/9001:2000 [8]

The figure will now be discussed in the context of an example of developing the quality management of an organization with the aid of the standard.

Using the Standard

The Top Drawer Organization, a prestigious management consultancy, is preparing for certification under ISO 90001. Senior Management is committed to achieving a high maturity level. The Quality Manager is instructed to use advanced methods of process modelling and use the model published in the Standard itself as the starting point for modelling the quality management system (QMS) of the Organization.

The Quality Manager is knowledgeable about systems methodologies, is skilled in Product/process modelling and model-based measurement, and is familiar with the P/p graph of the maturation process given in figure 13.1. He welcomes the opportunity to use his systems skills, and is encouraged by the Standard's commitment to the "process approach".

The Quality Manager's strategy

The Quality Manager decides that the Top Drawer Organization should aim to reach at least the lowest 'Advanced' maturity stage: the 'P/p network stage' of table 13.2. This demands modelling the quality management system of the Organization as a P/p network, using Figure 1 of the Standard as a basis of high-level graphical representation. Thereafter, the text of the Standard would serve as a guide to devising the detailed implementation of the QMS, and documenting it as a structure of P/p networks.

To start his task, the Quality Manager subjects Figure 1 of the Standard to systematic investigation. Experienced in the quality assurance of diagrammatic representations of systems, he needs positive answers for the following questions:

1	Is the referent clearly defined?
2	Is the figure a graph?
3	Is the graph directed or undirected?
4	Is there a key?
5	Are the symbols of the key consistent with the symbols of the figure?
6	Is the key comprehensive?
7	Is the graph labelled?
8	Is the meaning of all labels defined?
9	Is the labelling consistent with the key?
10	Is the labelling internally consistent?
11	Is the directed graph a network?
12	Is the network a-type or b-type?

List 13.1: Questions for investigating the maturity of a figure with the view of using it in company documentation

Using List 13.1 as an aid, the Quality Manager argues as follows:

- If the investigation results in positive answers to all 12 questions and the network turns out to be b-type then Figure 1 of the Standard is consistent with maturity stage E (the cactus network stage), ready for refinement into a P/p model (maturity stage F).
- Should the network prove to be a-type, then the figure is at maturity stage D (the network stage). Now the first task is to convert it to b-type to reach stage E, and then proceed with refinement into a P/p model.
- Should the investigation yield any negative answers then one must first identify the maturity level of a system based on such a figure, and then attempt to enhance the maturity of the figure to reach stage E.

The Quality Manager investigates Figure 1 of the Standard

The following is a record of the results of Quality Manager's investigation:

QUESTION 1: WHAT IS THE REFERENT?

The identity of the referent is ambiguous: figure and caption are not consistent.

- The caption of Figure 1 of the Standard states that the figure is a "model of the process-based quality management system" of the supplier's organization, and the text of the Standard explains that the QMS is described in four 'Clauses' of the Standard, namely:

  Clause 5: 'Management responsibility',
  Clause 6: 'Resource management',
  Clause 7: 'Product realization',
  Clause 8: 'Measurement, analysis and improvement'.

  These correspond to the four boxes inside the centre circle of the figure.
- By contrast, the figure has four additional boxes:

  Customer Requirements,
  Customer Satisfaction,
  Continual improvement of the quality management system,
  Product.

The Quality Manager decides to set aside the issue of the identity of the referent, hoping that it will clarify in the light of further examination of the figure.

QUESTION 2: IS THE FIGURE A GRAPH?

No. The figure is not a *graph* but a *diagram*, since it contains a mixture of directed, undirected and two-way directed edges.

The Quality Manager reluctantly concludes that there is no point in proceeding with the investigation: irrespective of the answers to the rest of the questions, documentation based on such a figure would, at best, be at maturity stage C (the diagram stage) of table 13.2.

The Quality Manager develops the figure

The Quality Manager must proceed with developing Figure 1 of the Standard. He returns to List 13.1, attempting to achieve positive answers with the aid of the text of the Standard, and, where this is not sufficient, by making reasoned – or at least reasonable – *assumptions*. The first such assumption is that the Standard intends the figure to be a graph.

QUESTION 3: DOES THE STANDARD INTEND A DIRECTED OR UNDIRECTED GRAPH?

Clearly, a directed graph is intended. All but one of the edges – the one labelled 'Output' – carries an arrow, and the intended direction of the undirected edge is implicit. The Quality Manager assumes that the flow in the undirected edge is from 'Product (Realization)' to Customer (Satisfaction)'. Doubling up on the two-way arcs, he arrives at a directed graph, and may now proceed to:

QUESTION 4: IS THERE A KEY?

Yes, Figure 1 of the Standard gives a key.

QUESTION 5: ARE THE SYMBOLS OF THE KEY CONSISTENT WITH THE SYMBOLS OF THE FIGURE?

No. One of the symbols of the key is a unidirectional dotted arrow, and there is no such symbol in the figure.

Based on the key, the Quality Manager *assumes* that the intention of the Standard would be realized by *doubling up* on the dotted arrows, one unidirectional arrow pointing *away from*, the other *towards,* one of the two boxes labelled 'Customer'.

QUESTION 6: IS THE KEY COMPREHENSIVE?

No. The diagram contains nine kinds of symbols:

- five sorts of arcs (solid line without arrow, solid line with unidirectional arrow, dotted line with two-way arrow, thick gray arrow, thick white arrow), and
- four sorts of nodes (heavy rectangle, thin rectangle, circle, rectangle with rounded corners).

Of the nine symbols of the diagram, the key specifies only *one* of the arc symbols and *none* of the node symbols.

In the absence of indications to the contrary, the Quality Manager *assumes* that the drawing style has no significance: the meaning of all the arcs of the directed graph is consistent, and, similarly, all the nodes have the same kind of meaning. This allows simplification of the figure.

He must also remove the ambiguity of the 'Product' box being cut into two by the central circle of the original figure. The Quality Manager *assumes* that the 'Product' box is completely outside of the central node. (He might just as easily have assumed that the central node contains 'Product' in its entirety.)

Taking stock of progress so far, the Quality Manager draws up figure 13.3: a modified version of figure 13.2 which incorporates the assumptions the Quality Manager made so far. The figure is a directed graph comprising five rectangular nodes and solid arrows, the node at the centre being a nested structure with a four-node substructure.

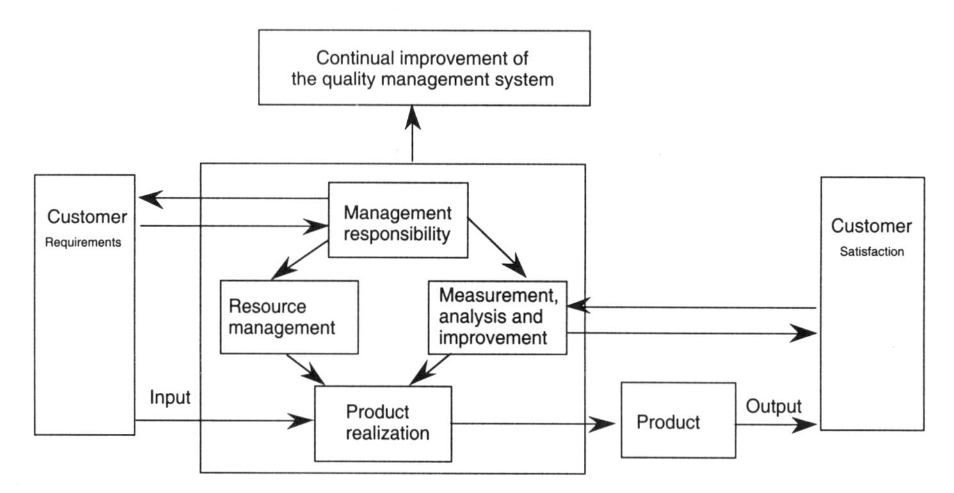

Figure 13.3: An intermediate stage of transforming Figure 1 of ISO/FDIS 9001:2000 into a network (key in text above)

QUESTION 7: IS THE GRAPH LABELLED?

No. Although the graph of figure 13.3 carries all the labels of Figure 1 of the Standard, there are missing labels:

- the central node (the one with the structure nested within) is unlabelled,
- only two of the arcs are labelled.

QUESTION 8: IS THE MEANING OF ALL LABELS DEFINED?

No. Node labels are either defined in the Vocabulary of the Standard or are explained in the text, but the two arc labels ('Input' and 'Output') are undefined.

QUESTION 9: IS THE LABELLING CONSISTENT WITH THE KEY OF FIGURE 1?

No. The two unidirectional solid arrows of Figure 1 of the Standard are labelled 'Input' and 'Output'. Common sense dictates that these terms should denote passive entities (see our own Glossary definition). However, in the key the solid arrow is given as 'Value added activities'.

The Quality Manager *assumes* that the key is to be changed such that all arcs should represent passive entities.

Question 10: Is the labelling internally consistent?

No.

- Within the unlabelled central node, the nodes labelled 'Resource management', 'Product realization' and 'Measurement, analysis and improvement' are activities corresponding to Clauses 6, 7, 8 of the Standard. The fourth node ('Management responsibility') corresponds to Clause 5, which stipulates what 'top management' *shall* do to satisfy the requirements. Thus, the text makes it quite clear that this node is also intended as an *activity*.

  To make the intention of the Standard explicit, the Quality Manager decides to *assume* re-labelling the box 'Management activity'. (He makes a note that, for preserving consistency between figure and text, this implies modifying the title of the corresponding Clause 5 of the Standard.)
- Of the four labelled nodes, one (the 'Continual improvement of the quality management system' node) appears as *activity* and three ('Customer Requirements', 'Product' and 'Customer Satisfaction) as *passive entities*.
- 'Product' is a term defined in the Standard as "the result of a process" – clearly a passive entity. The 'Product' in the figure is the result of the 'Product realization' activity within the quality management system. Nothing is lost, and the diagram is clarified, if one omits the 'Product' box. We *assume* this, and simply re-label the outgoing arc of 'Product realization' as 'Output product'.

As a result, all nodes, except 'Customer Requirements' and 'Customer Satisfaction', are activities.

Question 11: Is the directed graph a network?

No. The graph of figure 13.3 has a no incoming and no outgoing arcs.

- The 'Customer Requirement' and 'Customer Satisfaction' boxes are clearly beyond the intended boundary of the model: the caption of the figure and the text of the Standard reveal no intention of wishing to model Customer actions, only to display the *interaction* between the organization and its customer. The Quality Manager decides that nothing is lost by *assuming* that he may omit the two Customer boxes, leaving it to the incoming and outgoing arcs to specify the interactions. (He is glad to note that this not only simplifies the figure but also brings it closer to its caption – see discussion under Question 1.)
- The 'Continual improvement of the quality management system' node has an input but no output. Nothing can be gleaned from the syntax of

the diagram, but the text of the Standard comes to the aid of the figure: Clause 8.5 is entitled 'Improvement', and Clause 8.5.1 is dedicated to 'Continual improvement'.

In view of this, the Quality Manager concludes that 'Continual improvement of the quality management system' should not be drawn as a node *outside* of the bounds of the QMS, but should be part of the 'Measurement, analysis and improvement' node.

The new assumptions yield a potential network of four nodes, corresponding to the four of the Clauses of the Standard (figure 13.4), with all nodes, but only two of the arcs, labelled.

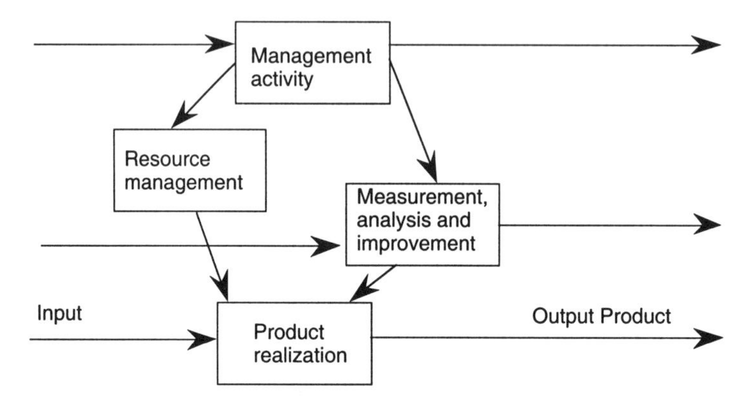

Figure 13.4: A potential network arising from modelling the process-based quality management system of ISO/FDIS 9001:2000

QUESTION 12: IS THE POTENTIAL NETWORK a-TYPE OR b-TYPE?

The potential network is b-type.

The Quality Manager's cactus network

The Quality Manager can now represent the operation and continual improvement of the 'process-based quality management system' in the single cactus of figure 13.5, resolved into the first-level structure in figure 13.6, with all nodes and all arcs labelled.

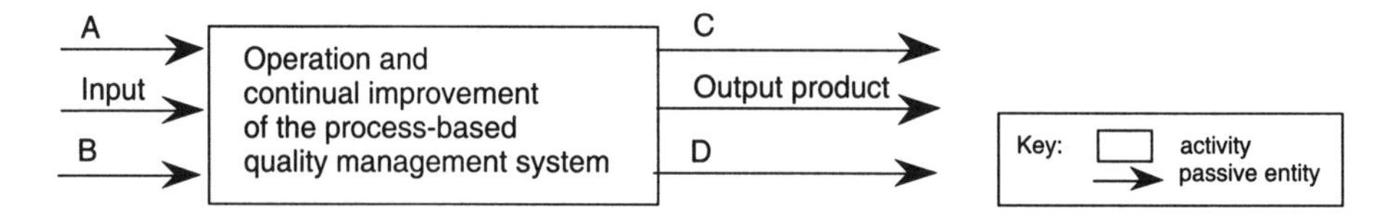

Figure 13.5: Cactus representing the process-based quality management system

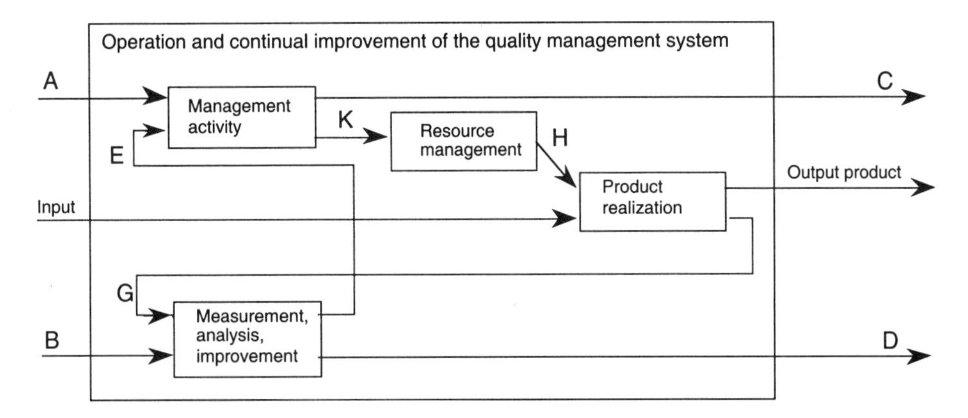

Figure 13.6: Internal structure of the cactus of figure 13.5 (key as before)

Figures 13.5 and 13.6 are now to be subjected to the scrutiny of the questions of List 13.1. If this yields positive answers then the Quality Manager has succeeded in his strategy of establishing figures which are consistent with maturity stage E (the cactus network stage). The results of this investigation are shown in List 13.2.

1	Is the referent clearly defined?	Yes
2	Is the figure a graph?	Yes
3	Is the graph directed or undirected?	Directed
4	Is there a key?	Yes
5	Are the symbols of the key consistent with the symbols of the figure?	Yes
6	Is the key comprehensive?	Yes
7	Is the graph labelled?	Yes
8	Is the meaning of all labels defined?	No!
9	Is the labelling consistent with the key?	Yes
10	Is the labelling internally consistent?	Yes
11	Is the directed graph a network?	Yes
12	Is the network is a-type or b-type?	b-type

List 13.2: Questions and answers: investigating the quality of figures 13.5 and 13.6, with the view of using them in modelling the quality management system of the Top Drawer Organization

Clearly, the job is not quite done yet: the figures are labelled, but some of the labels are undefined. For interpretation of the activities, the representation can rely on the text of the Standard. However, the passive entities of the figure carry nominal labels only. These admit to different interpretations, and the interpretation might alter the *relative timing* of the passive entities, the *internal organization* of the quality management system, and even the *black box representation* of cactus network itself. How to proceed?

INTERPRETING THE LABELS OF THE SINGLE CACTUS OF FIGURE 13.5

Working top-down, the Quality Manager decided to turn his attention first to the representation of the QMS in the single cactus of figure 13.5.

The meaning of the single node is determined by the text of the Standard, but the meaning of the arbitrarily chosen alphabetic arc labels was open to the Qualoty Manager's own interpretation.

- He considered opting for arcs A and C to represent (possibly multiple) interaction between the Customer and the Organization, eliciting the requirements carried in the arc labelled 'Input'.
- The 'Output Product' is delivered to the Customer, and this might evoke Customer's comments of satisfaction or dissatisfaction. The Quality Manager chose to assign this meaning to arc B. Arc D would then need to represent the Organization's responses to complaints.
- The Quality Manager considered the importance of the relative timing of the passive entities in the arcs, and *noted* that relative timing might vary from one use of the Standard to another. For example, if the whole procedure is started by an enquiry of the Customer then A might be the first event of the whole transaction, followed by the Organization's response in C; then would come 'Input', followed by 'Output product', then the Customer's rejoinder B, and finally D, the reaction of the Top Drawer Organization. On the other hand, if the transaction is initiated by the Organization offering a product or marketing a service, then quite a different sequence of events would result.
- The Quality Manager observed further that the figure might be used only to represent financial and legal aspects of the operation, in which case arc interpretations would be quite different; for example, the exchange of A and C might yield a contract between Customer and Organization. Now the specification of 'Output product' would be part of the contract rather than a separate entity, and the 'Input' arc would be redundant. Arc B might carry payment under the contract, and arc D might represent penalties payable by the Organization in case of non-fulfillment.

The Quality Manager was pleased to observe the versatility of the figure: this was consistent with the intention of the Standard and the claim of the systems methodology to be general. He concluded that it would be too restrictive to assign fixed meaning to the arcs, since the interpretation depended on the use to which it is put. Instead, he decided to include in the Quality Manual figure 13.5, together with a table for defining, for each specific use, *at least* the relative timing of the passive entities and the meaning of arcs A, B, C, D. This would involve determining which input plays a role in the generation of each output, allowing checking that the inputs are available in good time. With this proviso, he felt that figure 13.5 was fit to be used in the documentation of an organization at grade E maturity.

Considering further development of the figure when progressing towards grade F maturity, the Quality Manager had no difficulty in transforming figure 13.5 to a black box P/p network by adding a properly defined gate on both the input and output side.

INTERPRETING THE LABELS OF THE CACTUS NETWORK OF FIGURE 13.6

This four-node network is the structural elaboration of the single cactus of figure 13.5. The definition of the actions in the nodes is given in Clauses 5, 6, 7, 8 of the Standard. The structure gives rise to four new arcs (E, G, H, K), and these require interpretation. Here again, the Quality Manager observed that the meaning of the arcs and the relative timing of their contents might vary and must be defined depending on the particular application. He decided to deal with the definition of arcs in the same way as in case of the single cactus of figure 13.5.

The Quality Manager noted further that the network of figure 13.6 contained a cycle involving all four elements. The cycle was inherent in the Standard, prescribed in its Figure 1. There was no difficulty in identifying the figure and its accompanying table as representing the quality management system of an organization of grade E maturity. He decided to include in the Quality Manual figure 13.6, together with a table for defining *at least* the relative timing of the passive entities and the meaning of the arcs. As in case of the single cactus of figure 13.5, tabulating arc definitions and timings would allow determining which inputs play a role in generating each output, and this would aid checking that the inputs are available when required.

Next, the Quality Manager considered further development of the figure in course of progression from grade E to grade F maturity. He identified the need:

- to add and define several gates,
- to transform the cyclic cactus network of figure 13.6 into an acyclic P/p network.

How to proceed?

At this stage the Quality Manager identified two options:

- to *enhance the maturity* of his networks, moving from the representation of the QMS as a pair of cactus networks to their representation as P/p networks, or
- to *refine* the cactus network to the next level of detail, filling the nodes of figure 13.6 with structural content, using the text of the Standard as guidelines.

Each of these options has advantages and disadvantages, and we leave the Quality Manager of Top Drawer to his deliberation deliberate which way to proceed. The use of properly defined networks will aid the Quality Manager, Senior Management, staff and customers of the Organization in understanding the demands and recommendations of the Standard, and will compensate by explicit assumptions for any of the Standard's ambiguities and shortcomings. Later on, having developed a quality management system which satisfies stage F (P/p network) maturity requirements, the ambitious and competent Quality Manager of Top Drawer will confidently investigate advancement to maturity grade G, and beyond, staying comfortably within the requirements of the Standard, but using more closely defined and more explicit documentation than the Standard itself.

13.9 Summary

Maturity assessment has become an important feature in business life. Assessment should not simply be normative: it should also serve as an instrument of development.

This chapter presents a stage-by-stage maturing process. When the organization advances from the starting and preliminary stages of maturity, its progress is measured by the distinction between three kinds of P/p graphs: P/p networks, P/p frameworks and P/p models. The last marks the highest stage of maturity: the organization operates in accord with a formal model, its key attributes measured, and has an infrastructure in place for collecting, disseminating and utilizing this management information. Once the P/p modelling stage is reached, measurement facilitates setting new targets and monitoring achievement: planning, organization and control of a programme of continual improvement of the performance of the organization.

Throughout the maturing process of the organization, maturity assessment can be carried out internally, or by second or third party. Based on the maturity grades defined in this chapter, the assessment method is open, objective, and conducive of a corporate spirit within the organization. Since the same information is used, and the same skills are needed, for maturity assessment as for managing and operating the productive processes of the organization, maturity assessment is a powerful aid to organizational development.

The same skills also come into play when the organization seeks quality certification. The chapter investigates the new, 'process-oriented' ISO 9000 series of quality standards, showing how the management of the organization might go about interpreting and the requirements of the Standard, and provide objective evidence of meeting them.

13.10 Footnotes and References

1 Myers, M, Kaposi, A, Britton, C: 'Charting a path to the Maturity of the Organization'. IEE colloquium on Successful Introduction of Systems Engineering into an Organization, Feb 23 1999

2 Webster's New World Dictionary, 3rd College Edition

3 CMM: SECMM-94-06-/CMU/SEI-96-HB-004 v1.1, March 1996

4 SEI adopts the definition of MIL-STD 499B: "An integrated composite of people, products and processes that provide the capability to satisfy a stated need or objective." The reader might wish to analyze this definition

5 Chapter 4 distinguishes between three types of P/p graphs: P/p models, P/p networks and P/p frameworks. We make use of this distinction in modelling the maturing process and defining the stages of maturity of organizations.

6 K H Kyburgh: "Theory and measurement". Cambridge University Press, 1984

7 ISO FDIS/9000:2000, ISO FDIS/9001:2000, ISO FDIS/9004:2000.

8 Figure 1 from BS EN ISO 9001:2000 is reproduced with permission of BSI under licence number 2000SK0529. Complete standards can be obtained by post from BSI Customer Services, 389 Chiswick High Road, London W4 4AL.

Chapter 14 Contract management

This chapter focuses on the use of a systems approach in business. We concentrate on 'balanced transactions': an interaction among parties that is to have mutual advantage. Parties enter into balanced transactions voluntarily, each participant performing an action with the agreement of the other.

In balanced transactions each party has something to offer and something to gain. In private life the motivation for entering into a balanced transaction may be emotion, tradition, convenience, or a need for companionship. Even where the framework is formal, such as a couple entering into a marriage contract as a basis for a series of balanced transactions, the parties seldom make their expectations explicit: they simply assume that the nature of the obligations arise from the situation. Failure to provide what the other party tacitly expects can lead to misunderstanding, conflict, and ultimately alienation: legal wrangles, divorce, family feuds, broken friendships, or wars between neighbours. As an example, a professional couple of our close acquaintance, both aged 30, decided to get married without agreeing first whether or not to have a family. They were divorced within the year – a sadly representative case of marriage going wrong because of unstated assumptions.

Enriched with 'soft' products and processes, P/p modelling can be applied to representation of balanced transactions of any kind. In this chapter we illustrate the use of P/p modelling in exploring the nature of *business transactions*: particular kinds of balanced transactions that take place in an industrial, professional or commercial context, involving work and financial reward. We identify the key characteristics of business transactions, shared among a wide range of interactions between people and organizations. We show how the terms of the business transactions may be formalised into *contracts*. We make reference to *quality*: a familiar notion which, in this context, encompasses contractual obligations, mutual satisfaction, and the potential success of the business transaction. We then demonstrate how Product/process modelling can assist in representing both the contract and the actual execution of the transaction, making explicit the obligations of both parties, facilitating analysis of conformance, and aiding the assurance of quality. Examples of some representative kinds of business transactions show the use of Product/process modelling in practice.

14.1 The business transaction

A balanced transaction in industry, business and professional life takes place between two parties, a *supplier* and a *customer*. Figure 14.1 is not a P/p model, not even a P/p network: it is a diagram representing a simple business transaction, illustrating the key features. The parties enter into the transaction because, in due course, the customer expects to be enriched by a *deliverable*, and the supplier by a *consideration*.

Parties to the business transaction may be individuals or groups, businesses or government departments, multinational companies or complete nations. People involved in carrying out the activities of the transaction may be unskilled workers, highly skilled craftsmen, administrators, or specialist professionals. The business transactions into which they enter can be simple or complicated, varying from the local and immediate to the long distance and long term. Business transactions may be *external*, such as between two independent companies, or else *internal*, as happens when the supplier company as a whole acts as a customer to one of its departments, or an individual employee within the firm acts as the ultimate internal supplier to one of the organizational units of the company. The task of the systems professional is to uncover the underlying common ground among a bewildering variety of business transaction scenarios, using a common language of representation that fits them all, facilitates understanding by all concerned, and reduces the ground for dissatisfaction, conflict and risk.

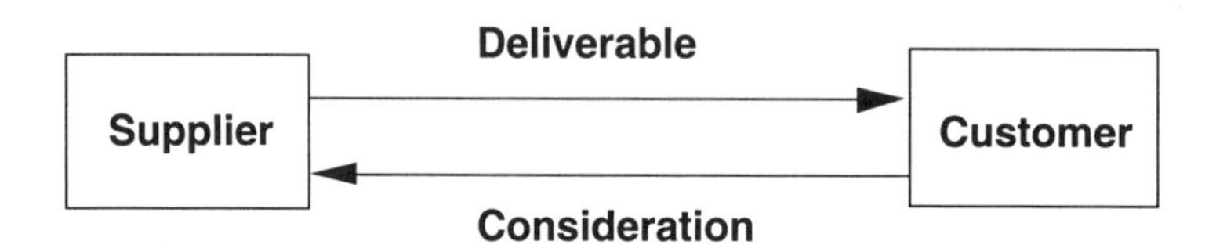

Figure 14.1: Diagram representing a business transaction (no key)

As figure 14.1 shows, there are four elements to a business transaction:

1. The *customer* – an individual or organization – who plays a dual role in the transaction: as *recipient* of the deliverable, and as *provider* of the consideration.
2. The *supplier* – an individual or organization, again with a dual role: as *provider* of the deliverable, and as *recipient* of the consideration.
3. The *deliverable* – the entity passing from the supplier to the customer. The deliverable may be any kind of system:
   - goods: tangible objects, mass-produced or hand-crafted, off-the-shelf or bespoke, or else abstract items: information, professional advice, plans, designs, other kinds of intellectual property;
   - services: menial, commercial, craft or expert, immediate or deferred.
4. The *consideration* – the entity passing from the customer to the supplier – may also be of many sorts:
   - payment of money in a single sum or in stages,
   - recompense in kind, such as money, or the supply of a different kind of deliverable in exchange.

The ISO 9000 quality standard offers definition for two of the four elements of the business transaction:

customer
organization or person that receives a product
ISO/FDIS 9000:2000

and

supplier
organization or person that provides a product
ISO/FDIS 9000:2000

These definitions are unbalanced: they concentrate on the deliverable, but omit the consideration. They are also too broad; for example, by these definitions a beggar is a customer and a charitable donor is a supplier. We propose instead:

customer
organization or person that requires a product and can provide another product as consideration [1]
Our working definition

and

supplier
organization or person that has a product to offer and expects a product in compensation
Our working definition

Using these definitions, we can now continue to define the other two elements of the business transaction:

deliverable
product passing from supplier to customer
Our working definition

and

consideration
product passing from customer to supplier
Our working definition

This leads to the definition of the complete business transaction:

business transaction
process involving a customer and a supplier in the interchange of a deliverable against a consideration
Our working definition

Balance is an essential feature of the business transaction. This is shown in the *symmetry* between the definition of customer and supplier, and between deliverable and consideration. Figure 14.1 would be equally valid with the arrows reversed and the boxes suitably relabelled.

About the deliverable and the consideration

The deliverable may be any kind of product: material, information, service, or whatever. To characterize a deliverable, it is necessary to model its key features, representing them by measures. Among these would be the specification of the deliverable, the identity of the supplier, a unique identifier as a nominal measure of the deliverable, and the time stamp: the real time instant when ownership passes from supplier to customer. In a like manner, the consideration is characterized by measures of its key attributes, among them the identity of the customer as the source, and the time at which ownership passes from customer to supplier. Here are some instances of deliverables and considerations.

Example 14.1: Deliverables

- *a motorcar, a loaf of bread, a family house,*
- *an address list of potential customers,*
- *a film on video cassette,*
- *the text of an international standard,*
- *a collection of designs for a fashion show,*
- *the measurement results of a test,*
- *services for public transportation,*
- *gardening, painting and decorating,*
- *maintenance of industrial plants, computers or domestic appliances,*
- *professional services: health care, education, legal advice,*
- *administrative or other services: financial services of a high-street bank or the finance department of a company, investment advice,*
- *travel agents' services, insurance brokers' services, computer application help lines.*

Example 14.2: Considerations

- *monetary payment, as in the case of cars bought for cash or on hire purchase, or when purchasing property in cash or through a mortgage,*
- *stage payments on development of a weapon system under contract, when the project reaches set milestones,*
- *payment in three stages for computer networks installed over a period of time, the first payment being due on confirmation of order, the second on completion, and the third after a satisfactory period of operation in service,*
- *monetary recompense for services, such as the monthly or weekly salary and annual bonus of employees,*
- *recompense in kind: barter transactions, such as exchange of houses, supply of an advertising firm with computers in return for advertising services, a lawyer waiving her fees when advising a restaurateur client in exchange for a number of meals at his restaurant.*

14.2 The contract

Definition

To carry out a business transaction, the customer and the supplier enter into an agreement, known as a *contract*. The new draft quality standard (ISO/FDIS 9000, 9001, 9004) offers no definition, but the version of the standard still in force at the time of writing states:

> **contract**
> agreed requirements between supplier and customer transmitted by any means
>
> ISO 9001:1994

To obtain a more informative definition, we note that the legal notion of contract implies that a business transaction is typically a two-stage procedure (figure 14.2), each stage involving the customer and the supplier, each stage incorporating four elements, similarly to those identified in figure 14.1.

At Stage 1 an *offer* is made by one party to supply a deliverable against a consideration, and an *order* is forthcoming from another party.

At Stage 2 a *deliverable* is provided by the first party in fulfillment of the order, and a *consideration* is made available by the second party, both the deliverable and the consideration being traceable to the *same contract.*

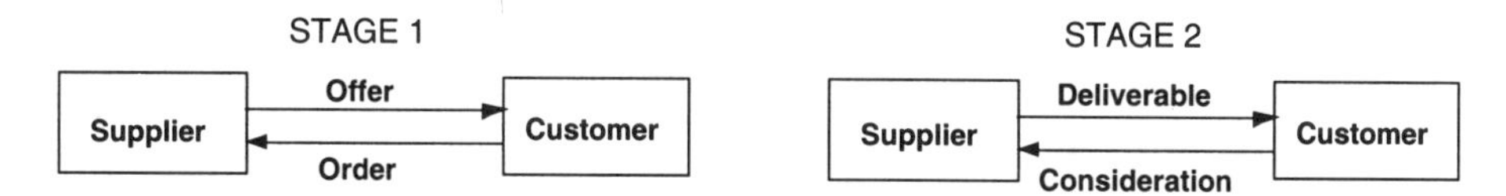

Figure 14.2: Diagram representing the contract and the business transaction (no key)

We may now define:

> **contract**
> an information product representing a formal agreement between supplier and customer regarding a business transaction
>
> Our working definition

Contract as a product

The contract is a product with a time stamp indicating the date at which the parties entered into the agreement. The attribute measure set of the contract as a product would normally include the following:

THE IDENTITY OF THE CUSTOMER

This is given as a nominal measure: a unique symbol designating a particular individual and no other.
The symbol may be a string of alphabetical characters, such as the name of the person or the company, provided that the name is unusual, but if the customer's name is John Smith or Mary Brown then the name itself might not satisfy the uniqueness criterion, and must be supplemented in some way.

THE IDENTITY OF THE SUPPLIER

This too is a nominal measure, and similarly to the customer, the designation must be unique.

THE SPECIFICATION OF THE DELIVERABLE *AS A PRODUCT.*

The specification would normally include the list of key attributes and the value of measures which the deliverable must satisfy.

Examples 14.3

- *the size (A4), grade (100 gram/m^2), colour (white), texture (velour), quantity (1 ream), price (£25) of paper bought over the counter at the stationers,*
- *the name of the composer (Händel), the title of the piece (Messiah), the conductor (Colin Davis), the recording medium (compact disc), and the required date (2 weeks from the date of the item ordered from the record shop or requested from the local lending library).*

Quite frequently the specification of the deliverable sets limits on the measures of the required attributes, defining a range of acceptable values, rather than stipulating for them a given value.

Examples 14.3 continued

The specification of the paper might state that it can be white or any pastel shade, and its cost can be up to *£25.*

The piece of music may be any oratorio by Händel, it may be performed under any one of three leading conductors, and the CD is required at any date up to *2 weeks from the date of order; the price of an air ticket would cover the transportation of the passenger and up to 20 kg weight of personal luggage; the label on the jar specifies that the fruit content of a brand of jam is no less than 50% of the total volume.*

THE SPECIFICATIONS OF THE CONSIDERATION *AS A PRODUCT*

As for the deliverable, the consideration is characterized by a set of attribute measures (or ranges of measures). One of these is a nominal measure of the nature of the consideration (payment, recompense in kind, etc.). If the consideration is a payment, then, alongside the sum and date when it is due, the measures of the specification might stipulate the mode of payment, the bank to which the sum is payable, the currency, etc. Payment may be due on receipt of the order, on receipt of the goods, within 10 days of delivery, or whatever.

THE STARTING DATE *OF THE CONTRACT.*

The starting date may be the same as the date stamp, or – if the contract comes into force at a later date – it is a different parameter. Either way, it is a measure of *real time*, given to appropriate accuracy. In case of a long-term transaction it may be sufficient to give the calendar date as the measure of time. In case of an urgent purchase or some time-critical transaction, time might be measured to the nearest minute, or even to the fraction of a minute.

THE PERIOD OF VALIDITY *OF THE CONTRACT.*

The period of validity may be given as a ratio measure of time: the time duration from the starting date (for example, the contract is valid *for 30 days*), or as a real-time measure of expiry (the agreement set out in the contract is valid until 31st December 2000).

OTHER ATTRIBUTES

Besides these elements characterizing the products of the business transaction, many contracts extend to specification of some of the attributes of the *process* the supplier should follow, such as actions that the supplier must take, resources (personnel, materials, equipment) which the supplier must employ in course of providing the deliverable, 'milestones' to be reached at set times as a condition of continuation with the contract, dates by when part-deliveries must be made, standards which must be observed, tests which must be applied to determine conformance to contractual requirements, guarantee and maintenance certificates which must accompany the deliverable, etc.

Clauses of the contract may also bind the customer, for example to advance stage payments, or provide surety for part or all of the consideration for the duration of the supply process. The customer may also be bound to facilitate the supply of the deliverable, as shown in the next example.

Example 14.4

> *The customer is the owner of petrol station and the supplier is a company manufacturing automatic monitoring equipment for petrol pumps in the forecourt of garages. The customer is obliged in the contract to make provisions, among others, for space, power supply, facilities for installation of the equipment, and personnel and facilities for conducting acceptance tests. The customer is also obliged in the contract to guarantee appropriate operational environment for the equipment.*

Long-term contracts would frequently include penalties on either or both parties, as a recompense for delay or breach. Legal contracts would imply observance of laws concerning responsibility for goods and services supplied.

Formal agreement as contract

As the definition implies, a formal agreement always amounts to a contract, even when it is not in writing. However, not all contracts are enforceable in law. For example, a contract is not legally enforceable if:

- the agreement is *not voluntary*, either party applying coercion to bring it about,
- supply of the deliverable involves some *unlawful act*, such as breaking copyright or patent restrictions, smuggling or stealing an object, harming people or damaging public property,
- the prospective supplier is *not the rightful owner* of the property that is the deliverable of the business transaction,
- the supply of the given type of *goods* is *prohibited or restricted*, as would be the case with certain types of drugs,
- the prospective *purchaser* is *prohibited by law* to be a customer, for example an underage minor purchasing alcoholic beverages,
- the prospective *supplier* is *not fit* to enter into the contract, such as a medical advice offered by a person who is not a medical doctor, taxi service provided by a person without a valid driving licence, etc.

14.3 Quality in the business transaction

Let us recall the definition of 'quality' offered in chapter 6.

Quality of the contract

A 'good' contract is explicit and unambiguous: its terms are clear, guiding the actions of supplier and customer, permitting them to check the *actual* business transaction against the contractual requirements. The systems professional's task is to facilitate the whole business transaction, enabling the parties to make explicit the terms of the contract and the characteristics of the actual transaction, and allowing them to check the latter against the terms of the former. By skilful use of appropriate methods and tools, the systems professional should help in avoiding misunderstanding between the parties, prevent dispute or reduce the chance of their occurrence, and establish the necessary conditions of a mutually satisfactory business transaction. As the title of the book indicates, we suggest that legal experts drawing up or analyzing contracts might benefit from systems expertise.

Conformity

The quality standard defines:

conformity
fulfillment of requirement

ISO/FDIS 9000:2000

If the attribute measures of the deliverable are consistent with the specification set out in the contract, and if the deliverable is available to the customer at or within the stated time, then the deliverable is 'conformant', and the supplier has met his/her formal obligations under the contract.

The reasonable customer would accept a conformant deliverable, and would provide the agreed consideration. If the attribute measures of the consideration are consistent with its specification, and it is available to the supplier within the stated time, then the customer has also met his/her formal obligations under the contract, and the business transaction is complete, but does this mean that the business transaction has been mutually advantageous? As the definition of 'quality' implies, conformity is no guarantee that all interested parties have been satisfied.

The current interpretation of quality places heavy demands on participants in the business transaction. While conformity simply means meeting the stated terms of the contract between customer and supplier, quality additionally demands meeting the requirements of a broad constituency of interested parties, where some of the requirements may not be explicit, but are implied by the contract, as consequences of the circumstances of the contracting parties and the situation which surrounds the business transaction.

The customer's view of quality

Practice shows many cases where the deliverable is conformant, but the customer is dissatisfied. This can occur for many reasons, and a few of these are listed below.

DEFICIENT CONTRACT

The specification may have stipulated attributes of the deliverable that the customer regarded most essential at the time; however, by necessity, any attribute list is but a partial representation of the customer's wishes. The customer may have realized subsequently that some important feature had been left out of consideration, or had been omitted from the list by mistake.

Example 14.5

> *A chain of garages had ordered new petrol pumps that allow the customer to choose between paying at a conventional till or by inserting a credit card directly into a slot in the pump. The pumps came with a built-in printing facility that automatically generated a receipt. Many customers did not wait for their receipt, and the forecourt was soon littered with these unwanted pieces of paper. The Chairman demanded to know why the specification of the pump did not include an option for the customer to choose whether to have a receipt or not.*

FAULTY SPECIFICATION

The contract may have covered all relevant features of the deliverable, but some attribute measures may have been wrongly specified.

Example 14.6

The builder erecting a new house for one of the authors of this book ordered the kitchen furniture on the basis of the dimensions of the unplastered walls, only to find on delivery that not allof the items fitted into the space available.

CHANGING REQUIREMENTS

At the time of drawing up the contract, the specification of the deliverable may have been adequate in every sense, but by the date of the delivery circumstances may have changed, and at the time of supply the deliverable fails to meet the current requirements.

Example 14.7

From the field of educational services, consider the dilemma of providing undergraduate courses in some fast-changing area of science or engineering. Industrial employers are the main customers for the graduates delivered by Universities, and hence Universities consult industry fully, to obtain a specification for the graduates to meet the requirements of prospective employers. Now remember that the 'lead time' for an undergraduate course is 4-5 years: this is the time elapsing between initiating a new course, and the first batch of graduates emerging. In this period technology will have advanced, and industry's requirements will have changed. The customer-oriented University has at least three different ways of providing a course of inadequate quality:

- *If the curriculum accords with industry's requirements at the start of the course development process, by the time the first graduates emerge the technology-sensitive part will be obsolete: 4-5 years out of date.*
- *If the curriculum anticipates the technology change, the University may misjudge the direction or the rate of technological progress. The result is, again, inappropriate technological preparation of graduates.*
- *If the curriculum focuses on the 'fundamentals' of the subject, excluding the contentious technology-sensitive material, the course will be judged too academic, technologically underdeveloped, and out of touch with the University's industrial customer base.*

NONLINEARITY – THE DELIVERABLE CAUSING A CHANGE IN THE REQUIREMENTS

The contract for an important long-term project may take account of the expected change in the customer's needs during the development period, and at the time of its supply the deliverable meets the requirements fully. However, when the finished deliverable enters into service, it has such a powerful effect on the environment that it almost immediately fails to meet the new demand.

Example14.8

The M25 motorway around London was designed to meet the year-by-year rise of traffic flow, but the designers did not anticipate the change of pattern of road use caused by the motorway itself. As a result, almost from the start the motorway was overcrowded.

IN SUMMARY

As the examples illustrate, there can be a great difference between the deliverable being *conformant* – fulfilling the terms of the contract to the letter, and the deliverable being of adequate *quality* – meeting the requirements of the customer.

The shortsighted supplier may adopt a rigid approach to the business transaction. Using contractual demands as sole guidelines, the 'minimalist' supplier would be content with providing a conformant deliverable, regardless of achieving customer satisfaction. Such a supplier may win the immediate battle of the dispute over the given transaction, but stands to lose the long-term war for reputation and the continued custom of the client.

The wise supplier takes a long-term view, regarding the given transaction in a wider context. Aiming for quality, the supplier seeks to achieve the satisfaction of the customer, even if this means exceeding the demands of strict conformance.

The supplier's view of quality

Could the case arise when the customer provides the consideration that conforms to the terms of the contract, and yet the supplier is not content?

Of course, there are many cases when the supplier underestimates the time or the cost of producing the deliverable. For example:

- The deliverable may involve the use of imported materials; in course of the supply process the home currency may be unexpectedly devalued, adding significantly to the supplier's costs.

- The supply process may be labour-intensive, and the new rates under pay bargaining may add an unexpected increase to the supplier's costs.

In such cases the supplier loses on the transaction, or may altogether be bankrupted by it: having made the delivery and received the agreed consideration, the supplier may be forced to close the business. The customer may have made a good bargain on the given transaction, but will have lost a tried-and-tested supplier, and the source of skilled after-sales service. Is this good business? Is it in the customer's interest?

Recall figure 14.1 which shows the symmetry of the business relationship. From the supplier's viewpoint, the entity received is the consideration. For the success of the business transaction it is not sufficient that the deliverable should have adequate quality and the consideration should conform to the terms of the contract. The quality of the consideration must also be adequate, meeting the implicit requirements of the supplier.

The wise customer is mindful of the supplier's viewpoint, and regards the given transaction in a wider context. In the interest of future supply – and in the interest of the customer's own reputation –the satisfaction of the supplier must be assured, even if this means renegotiating the terms of the contract.

The customer / supplier relationship

Rather than competing and contesting conformance, mature and quality-conscious business partners establish a collaborative relationship, aiming to achieve a mutually satisfactory business transaction. On termination of such a transaction, there should be a solid foundation of trust between the parties: on this they can then confidently build future transactions to mutual advantage.

Widening the notion of 'customer'

A business transaction between two contracting parties is never in isolation: every transaction takes place in a broad social and environmental context. Enlightened business practice, codes of professional ethics, and full interpretation of the notion of quality require that each business transaction should reflect social and environmental needs. Although each contract must narrowly identify the customer as the party providing the consideration, the advanced notion of quality demands that the notion of 'customer' should extend to all who are – directly or indirectly – affected by the business transaction. Thus, it is not sufficient that the specification of the deliverable should capture the paying customer's needs; it must also accord with the requirements of the broad customer base, conforming to national and international standards and environmental demands. In this wider interpretation of the concept of customer, the *deliverable* may contain society's approval of the supplier, sought through media attention, thus fostering a positive image that may in turn lead to business advantage. This may be direct, such as extension of the customer base, or indirect, such as tax relief, or the granting of licences for development of environmentally friendly processes.

Example 14.9

Rapid expansion was experienced by a cosmetics and toiletries firm that adopted the policy of avoiding animal experimentation in the development of its product ranges, and publicized the policy widely.

Quality and the systems professional

The systems professional's role is to apply methods and tools for the assurance of quality, and to promote the maturing of the organization (see also chapter 13).

- The supplier must test the quality of the deliverable at the end of the supply process, before its release to the customer. If the deliverable fails this final quality inspection, it must be rejected. Final quality inspection is an essential task, and if it is the sole means of establishing quality, we call it *punitive quality assurance.*
- A more advanced regime is *incremental quality assurance.* Here the organization is not content with detecting inadequate quality: it has procedures for tracing the history of the faulty deliverable through the whole supply process, facilitating diagnosis and elimination of the cause [2].
- Quality inspection of the finished deliverable, and traceability of the supply process are necessary, but still not enough. *Quality improvement* requires that the supplier's organization continuously enhances the specification of its output and increases the efficiency and effectiveness of its processes for the benefit of all concerned.

- The most advanced form of quality assurance is to aim for *constructive quality*. This requires the use of formal models, together with methods and tools of measurement and analysis throughout the supply process, from requirements analysis through design and implementation to final delivery, assuring that quality is not an afterthought, but a guide throughout the creation of the deliverable. Constructive quality methods include reliable prediction of quality, monitoring of all parts of the supply process, and continuing improvement (and optimization?) of the processes themselves through more advanced instrumentation, improved documentation and use of better trained personnel.

14.4 Product/process model of business transactions

The deliverable – the object of the business transaction – may be an off-the-shelf standard item ordered by the customer after inspection; it may be a 'customized' item specially adapted by the supplier to the individual customer's need; it may also be a specially designed, bespoke item, such as a spacecraft, a new weapon system, or a suit of clothes made to measure, developed to the customer's own specification and supplied under contract. The nature of the deliverable will influence the processes making up the business transaction, and P/p models are useful tools for representing this. We give a few examples below, unfolding the diagrams of figure 14.2 into P/p graphs.

Business transactions for ordering a standard item

Figure 14.3 represents a business transaction between supplier X and customer Y.

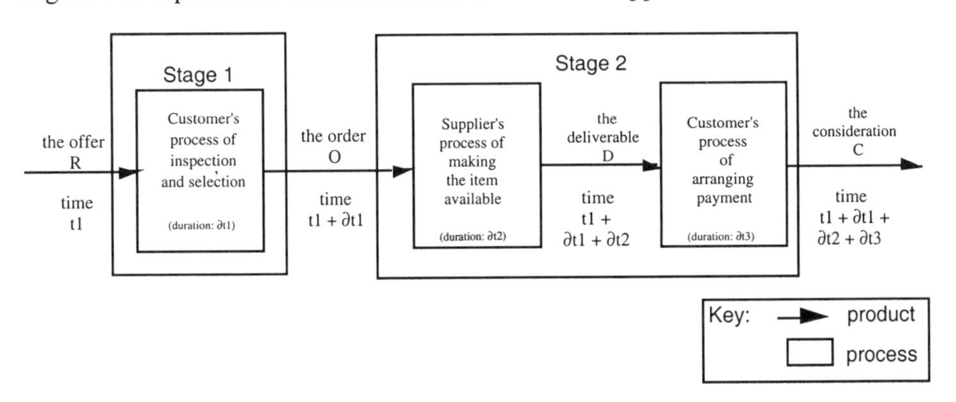

Figure 14.3: P/p graph of a business transaction involving a standard item

In the figure:

- Supplier X represents a shopkeeper who has numerous items on offer, some of which may be purchased on the spot, others being for display only. At some time t_1 customer Y walks into the shop, inspects the items on offer, and selects the one that suits his requirements. Since this is a display item and not for sale, at time t_2 customer Y places an order O with supplier X. This is the end of Stage 1 of figure 14.2.

- The contract stipulates the specifications of deliverable D and the date by when supplier X must make the delivery, together with the price (an attribute of consideration C), and the time period within which customer Y must make payment available. If both parties meet the terms of the contract then this is the end of Stage 2 of the business transaction of figure 14.2.

Figure 14.3 is suitable for representing Stage 2 of many other types of business transactions, among them an over-the-counter purchase of a finished article. In such a case customer Y issues order O verbally by nominating the required item on offer, and agrees to purchase it at the price which supplier X stipulates. The order initiates the supply process whose time span ∂t_2 should be a fraction of a day: the few minutes needed to lift the desired item from the shelf or bring it up from store, and then to wrap it up. The duration ∂t_3 of the customer's process is also a few minutes: the time for transferring the cash, presenting and validating a credit card, or writing out a cheque. The parties of the transaction may only be vaguely aware of the terms of the contract implicit in the issuing, accepting and acting upon the order in such a situation.

Business transactions for customized items

A customer who is not completely satisfied with the ready made article might only need some minor modification of the goods on offer. There might be a preliminary negotiation between customer and supplier regarding the adjustments of features, leading to agreement about the nature of the alterations and the price of the customized item. Responsibility for this preliminary phase may rest with the customer whose enquiry (E) initiates the negotiation. Figure 14.4 shows a business transaction which, besides the processes of figure 14.3, includes a negotiation phase. The measures of the order O will reflect the outcome of the negotiation. The P/p graph is not detailed enough to display the role of the customer and the supplier in the negotiation process: for this, we would require an expansion of the first process of the graph.

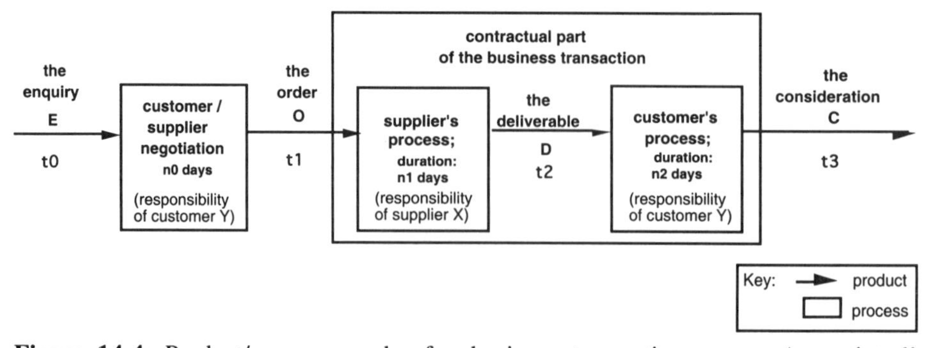

Figure 14.4: Product/process graph of a business transaction over a 'negotiated' customized item

The negotiation is not always successful, and the customer has the right not to proceed to placing the order. Figure 14.5 compresses the contractual part of the business transaction into a single process box, but shows the customer's option when the negotiation fails. The P/p graph suppresses the extra time and effort needed by the supplier to carry out the task of creating the non-standard item to the customer's specifications. As a variation on this type of order, a custom application – such as a database – would be ordered via a consultant who then sets up the database to the client's requirements.

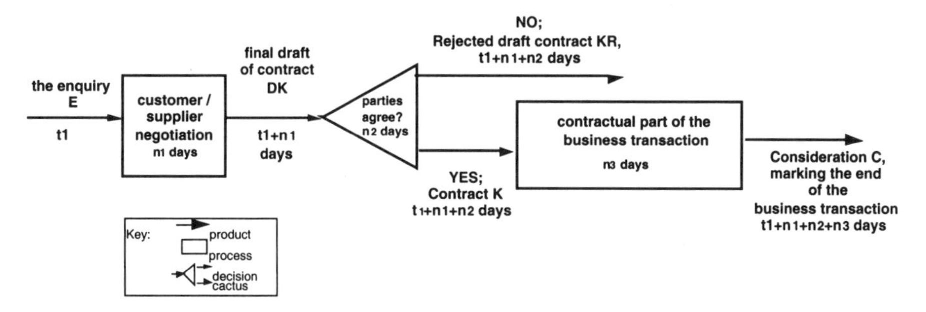

Figure 14.5: Product/process graph of a negotiated business transaction showing escape route

Mass customization

We must make a brief note here of an interesting kind of business transaction, based on a supply process of *mass customization*. This is in sharp contrast with mass production, where the *supplier* has the initiative for product development, and *pushes* the ready-made deliverable to the customer, whose only option is to buy the item or not.

In case of mass customization, much of the design initiative rests with the *customer* who can select measures for several attributes from a wide variety of options, and can *pull down* from the production line the custom-designed artefact of his/her choice.

Mass customization affords staggering variety. An example is a manufacturer of agricultural machinery offering some 87,000 different versions of a type of equipment, simply by allowing the customer to choose from 2 or 3 values for each of 14 attributes of the machine. The reader should check the arithmetic!

Business transactions for bespoke articles

Items made to order require a transaction of greater sophistication. Here the customer might enter into protracted negotiation with the supplier before placing the order, as there are many more specification details to settle than in case of customization. In critical cases of important large projects using new technology, the negotiation process may incorporate a feasibility study: a preliminary supply process, when the customer examines the outcome in detail, and reserves the right not to proceed with ordering the main deliverable. Even so, the feasibility process is essentially similar to the case of figure 14.4, and the order, when released, will embody all the decisions taken in the pre-order negotiation stage.

There are many situations where the supply process for the bespoke item is *long term.* In such cases it is usual for the customer to get involved in the control of the supply process, wishing to be satisfied that adequate progress is being made, and if not, initiate corrective action, or terminate the contract prematurely. In such cases the contract must specify the structure of the supply process in adequate detail, and stipulate aspects of the customer process, should stage payments be involved. The P/p model of such a business transaction would comprise an alternating sequence of customer / supplier processes, with several escape routes for both parties. This is the kind of elaborate business transaction which would benefit most from representation in a P/p model which clarifies the process, and makes responsibilities, conditions and timings explicit, and hence preempts mis-understandings, arguments and legal wrangles.

The extended business transaction

In some long term business transactions neither the customer nor the supplier can be quite sure at the start what form the final deliverable will take. The parties would normally agree an initial specification, but they must be enlightened enough to realize the possible need to vary the specification during the supplier's process. The examples outlined here are all within the direct experience of the authors.

- A reason for changing the specification in course of the transaction may be that the initial specification of a long-term project is too conservative, and external circumstances – and the customer's requirements – change while the supply process is underway.
- Another scenario is an over-ambitious specification for a long term project, seeking to exploit developing technology, the contracting parties anticipating the emergence of new materials and devices. If the expected technology development does not take place or is only partially realized, the project fails, unless the specification is derated.
- The specification stated in the order might have to vary if the law regulating the deliverable changes during the supply process. An example would be transfer from British to European standards, or emergence of new standards.
- Perhaps the most interesting is the case, already quoted, when the specification is correct: neither too conservative nor too futuristic, being a valid reflection of needs at the time of delivery. However, the newly procured system is so powerful that its very introduction modifies the environment substantially, rendering the newly developed deliverable prematurely obsolete. In such a case the parties must attempt to model the anticipated usage, attempt to estimate from the model the effect of the prospective system, and devise the specification accordingly.

Modelling such dynamic business transactions is difficult, since an elaborate interaction between customer and supplier continues throughout the supply process. In the software industry various 'life-cycle models' have been developed. P/p modelling is helpful, enabling the problem solver to plan for contingencies, keep track of events, and preserve continuing understanding between the parties concerned.

Business transaction with service as deliverable

As we have seen, the subject of the business transaction can be a service rather than an item of goods. The supplier might perform the service on a single occasion, or repeatedly over an extended period. Compared with the P/p graph of figure 14.3, in some cases the transaction might be almost reversed, as shown on the example of figure 14.6.

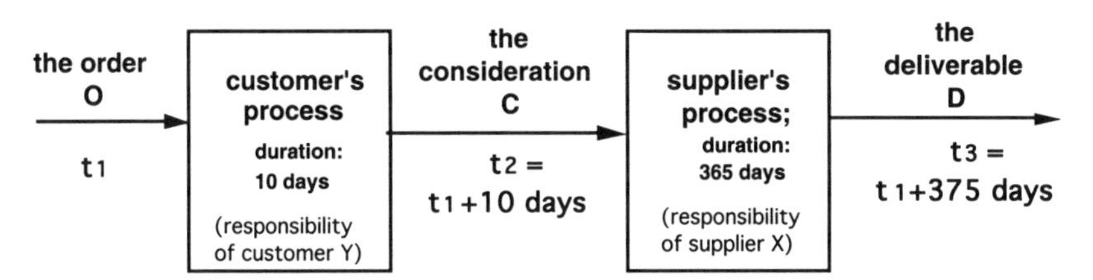

Figure 14.6: Product/process model of a simple business transaction for a one-year service (b-type key)

Here an industrial customer takes out a one-year contract for the maintenance of some kind of plant. The ‘consideration’ – the cost of the service – is payable in advance of services rendered, within 10 days of the date of order. On receipt of the payment the supplier undertakes to provide emergency service on demand, together with quarterly preventive maintenance, for the period of a calendar year. During the ‘supplier's process’ part-deliverables are made in the form of services rendered, and the two parties interact. To represent the interaction process, one needs a more detailed model of the second process box of the figure. Over-all responsibility stays with the supplier throughout, since he/she has accepted the payment for the service, and will only have discharged this responsibility at the closing date of the service period.

Business transactions involving subcontractors

Frequently part or all of the business transaction involves third parties: participants *other* than those named in the contract. The basic transaction of figure 14.1 still applies, since it shows the supplier's and customer's processes as 'black boxes', revealing no detail about the actions which the supplier and customer must carry out to meet their obligations. The figure does not give details of the additional business transactions into which the parties may enter: this is their respective private concern.

Example 14.10

Supplier X engages a haulage contractor Z to collect the deliverable and transfer it to the premises of customer Y (figure 14.7). This introduces the third party Z into a business transaction between X and Y, such as that of figure 14.3. The transportation process will change the attributes of the deliverable (time has passed and deliverable D' is a new product, not identical to D), even if the only noticeable change is in the geographical location of the deliverable. But should the goods be damaged in transit, should they be lost or delayed, who is responsible: X or Z?

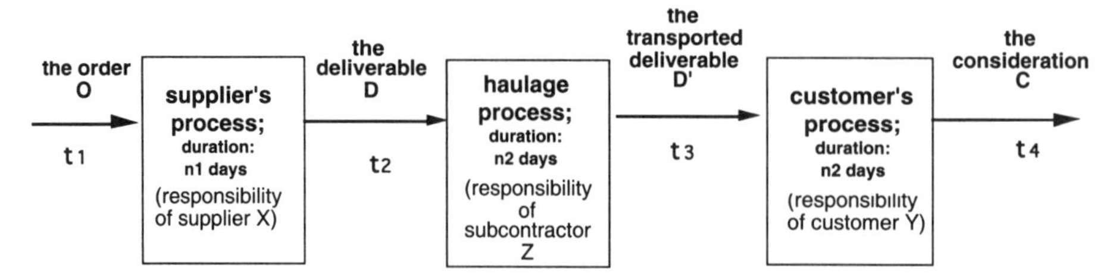

Figure 14.7: Example of a business transaction involving a third party (b-type key)

Figure 14.7 is an unsatisfactory representation of a business transaction. The notion of 'contract' postulates that all business transactions take place between *two* parties, not three. If X decides to engage Z as a subcontractor then X remains in complete charge of the transaction with Y, and it is entirely X's responsibility to assure that Y receives the deliverable in fit state and in good time. There is a separate business transaction between X and Z, governed by a contract between these two parties, but this is not Y's concern. The subcontractual arrangement between X and Z does not feature in figure 14.3, but would be 'hidden' inside the supply process p_S. One may represent this by another P/p graph that shows the business transaction between X and Z *nesting* within the supplier's process (figure 14.8).

Quite different is the case when the customer sends the haulage firm to collect the deliverable. Now the involvement of Z is on Y's instigation, hence Z is the subcontractor of Y. The contract between Y and Z is none of X's business: the supplier's responsibility concludes when X transfers the goods to Z, but Z is not an autonomous participant in the transaction, merely a representative of Y. The business transaction between Z and Y is now nested within the customer's process as in figure 14.9, and would not appear in the over-all graph of the transaction in figure 14.3.

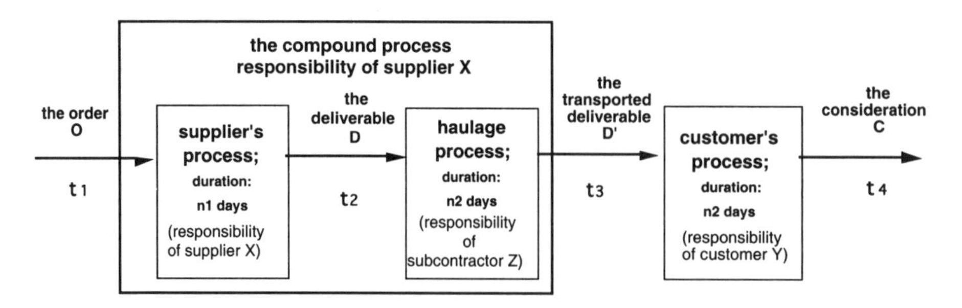

Figure 14.8: Third party under subcontract to the supplier (b-type key)

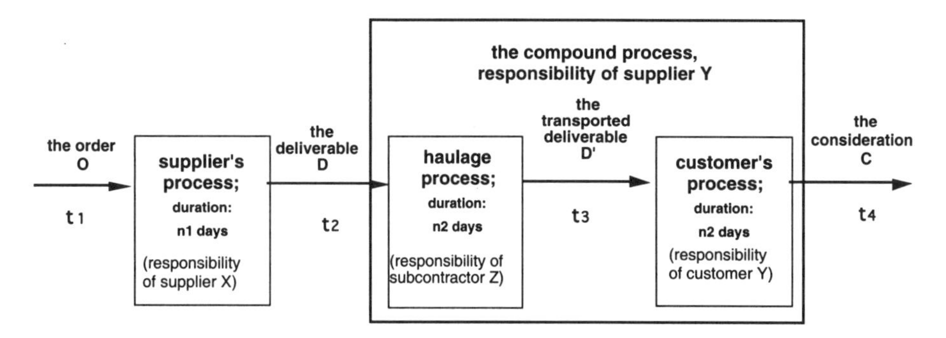

Figure 14.9: Third party under subcontract to the customer (b-type key)

Internal 'subcontractor'

Consider again the simple transaction of figure 14.3 involving only X and Y, neither party employing a subcontractor. The supplier – the individual X, who may be the owner or the Chief Executive of the company – is personally responsible for the business transaction, but would seldom carry out all of the tasks of the supply process. Instead, X would engage one or more *employees* to perform the various detailed jobs. X might instigate the formation of a *project team*, or might divide the supply task, allocating subtasks to the various divisions, departments, groups and individuals of the company. Thus, supplier X delegates responsibility for parts of the supply task within the organization, amounting to the engagement of *internal subcontractors*. The contract principle still applies: from the viewpoint of customer Y, supplier X personally is in complete charge, carrying all the responsibility for the supplier's side of the transaction, and the model of figure 14.3 is valid. However, the supply process p_S of figure 14.3 is *internally structured* as a (usually multilevel) hierarchy of business transactions between a whole network of internal 'customers' and 'suppliers' in X's employ. Should anything go wrong, X cannot hide behind his/her own subordinates who carried out the detailed task.

Note that the notion of business transaction is valid for the case when the supplier is a University, a local authority or a government department, and the customer is a member of the taxpaying public. The notion of contract makes it explicit that the Vice Chancellor, the Chairman of the local Council, or the Minister is personally responsible for the quality of the deliverable, usually a service to members of the public. If the person in charge claims ignorance of the detail, this is an indication of managerial incompetence.

Procurement and marketing

Many business transactions between contracting parties come about after negotiations that involve a 'broker': an intermediary who helps to establish the transaction and may be an external or internal subcontractor of either party.

When the broker is the supplier's subcontractor, his/her role may be to market and distribute the deliverable, making its desirable characteristics widely known, and negotiate with the customer to achieve favourable contractual terms on the supplier's behalf. This may be a task for a branch of the parent company, or a marketing consultant.

When the broker is the customer's agent, the role is to negotiate with the supplier, spot any weakness in the specification of the deliverable, identify any risk or uncertainty that might threaten the supplier's process, and negotiate favourable terms for the customer. Large organizations, such as the Ministry of Defense or a big multinational company, might maintain a Procurement Executive to perform this intermediary function. The relationship between the operational department and the Procurement Executive of the organization is not always harmonious, the former resenting the contribution of the latter, viewing it as unnecessary disruption of direct line of communication with the supplier. Our experience has shown the value of P/p modelling in making explicit the role of each of the three parties, promoting mutual respect and cooperation.

14.5 Summary

Here are the key ideas of this chapter:

- In the work environment two parties – the supplier and the customer – interact through *business transactions*, governed by *contracts*. The four elements of a business transaction are the *customer*, the *supplier*, the *deliverable*, and the *consideration*. The supplier is personally responsible for the deliverable; the customer is personally responsible for the consideration.
- The contract between customer and supplier may be *external*, where the parties represent two distinct organizations, or it may be *internal*, the parties being managed groups or individuals internal to a given organization. Under the contract, the relationship between customer and supplier is symmetrical.
- To facilitate test of *conformance*, the contract should use *measures* for expressing the key features of the deliverable and the consideration, and for identifying the contracting parties uniquely.
- The notion of *quality* includes conformance, but goes far beyond it, extending to personal and professional ethics. These, as well as good business sense, dictate that business transactions should satisfy the long-term interests of *both parties*, should meet legal and statutory requirements, should respect the *environment* and be consistent with the needs of the *community*.
- P/p models are the tools for representing contracts and business transactions, assist in defining the terms of the contract, clarifying the processes of the business transaction, preventing misunderstanding between the parties, and assuring quality.

14.6 Footnotes

1 'Compensation' is used in civil law to mean recompense or counterbalance.

2 Traceability is one of the requirements of the quality standard, which defines:

traceability
ability to trace the history, application or location of that which is under consideration

ISO/FDIS 9000:2000

Instead, we propose:

traceability
attribute of the sequence of representations of a referent over its life history that it is possible to reconstruct the value of its selected key attributes at any time instant in the past

Our working definition

Glossary

Introduction

This book adopts definitions from general purpose dictionaries or from standards, wherever possible, and offers 'our own working definitions' where external sources do not prove adequate definitional foundations. To make the definitions adopted easily identifiable, they are shown in the text in frames. In the book we quote other definitions as examples, usually with explanations as to why they are inappropriate for our purposes. The Glossary contains only those definitions that form the definitional foundations of the book.

The Glossary presents the key ideas of the systems methodology in a nutshell. It condenses the key concepts of the book into a few pages of structured text, stripping out explanations, examples, notational details and illustrations, showing only the skeleton of the ideas. Its very terseness helps to articulate the methodology as currently formulated, and to identify room for further development.

The format of the Glossary is a table comprising an alphabetically ordered list that also indicates the source of the definitions and their location in the text. It incorporates definitions of the general concepts and systems concepts presented in Part 1 as foundations of the systems methodology, and refers to formal definitions of some of these concepts, presented in Part 2. It also includes some definitions arising from Part 3 for notions of practical interest. These are offered as examples for prospective users of the methodology who will need to define concepts arising from various application domains.

Each definition in the Glossary Table has a unique alphanumeric label.

- The first character of the label indicates the 'level' of the definition. Level 1 stipulates definitions using only words with generally agreed (Level 0) meanings that could be found in general purpose dictionaries. Level 2 definitions use general terms and terms at Level 1. The highest level term in a definition at Level 5 is Level 4, etc. Definitions at Level 2 or above indicate in **bold** the use of terms defined in the Glossary.
- The second character of the label is a randomly chosen lower case letter.

In the interest of clarity and ease of usage, the number of glossary definitions is kept to a minimum. An attempt is also made to word definitions concisely. However, in some instances the definitions include some redundancy to soften the wording and aid understanding. For example, the definition of 'P/p model' talks of 'attribute value' whereas strictly speaking 'value' would suffice, since its definition refers to 'attribute'; similarly, instead of referring to 'black box' and 'structure', the definition of 'constructivity' reads better when one uses the synonyms 'structural representation' and 'black box representation'.

Glossary Table

Label	Term	Definition	Source	Text ref
3a	attribute	a characteristic of the **referent**	Our def	3.5
6a	a-type network	a **network** with arcs **representing** actions and nodes **representing** passive **entities**	Our def	4.5
2j	bipartite graph	a **graph** whose vertex set can be partitioned into two sets in such a way that each edge joins a vertex of the first set to the vertex of the second set	Atten-borough	10.11
4k	bipartite tree	a **tree** whose vertex set can be partitioned into two sets in such a way that each arc joins a vertex of the first set to the vertex of the second set	Our def	10.11
6b	black box (or black box re-presentation)	**representation** of the **referent** as a set of **interrelated values**	Our def	4.3 [1]
2a	boundary	that which serves to indicate the limits of an **entity**	based on Shorter OD	3.2
6c	b-type network	a **network** with nodes representing actions and arcs representing passive **entities**	Our def	4.5
11b	business transaction	a **process** involving a **customer** and a **supplier** in the interchange of a **deliverable** against a **consideration**	Our def	14.1
7a	cactus	nodal element of a **b-type network**, having two or more **inputs** and/or two or more **outputs**	Our def	5.1
10j	catastrophic interrupt	a **product** that halts a **process** for an indeterminate **time** period although it had been planned as atomic	Our def	12.5
10a	collection gate	**gate** which assembles a set of **products** into a **product cluster**, in accord with a rule	Our def	5.1
2g	conformity	fulfillment of **requirement**	ISO/FDIS 9000:2000	14.3
10m	consideration	**product** passing from **customer** to **supplier**	Our def	14.1
7f	constructivity	the **attribute** of a **structural representation** that its **interrelations** are **well defined**, its atomic components are characterized as **black boxes**, and it is possible to derive from it the **black box representation** of the **referent**	Our def	4.4
12b	contract	an information **product** representing a formal agreement between **supplier** and **customer** regarding a **business transaction**	Our def	14.2
11c	customer	organization or person that requires a **product** and can provide another **product** as **consideration**	Our def	14.1
1a	definition [2]	precise statement of the essential nature of a thing	Shorter OD	3.4
10k	deliverable	**product** passing from **supplier** to **customer**	Our def	14.1

4a	descriptive representation	**representation** of the **referent** at some specific **time** of the present or the past	Our def	3.8
1b	diagram	a figure composed of lines, serving to illustrate a statement, or to aid in a demonstration	Shorter OD	3.9
2n	directed graph	a **graph** where all edges are replaced by arcs (edges carrying an arrow)	Atten-borough	3.9
10b	distribution gate	**gate** which divides a **product cluster** into a set of **products**, in accord with a rule	Our def	5.1
6h	efficiency (economic)	the ratio of the monetary **value** of the **output** to the monetary **value** of the **input**	Our def	8.5
6j	efficiency (physical)	the ratio of the **value** of **output** energy created in the required form to the **value** of the total amount of energy **input** used	Our def	8.5
1d	entity	that which can be individually defined or considered	ISO 8402: 1994	3.1
8q	formal model (often shortened to 'model')	**black box** with all **attributes** given as **measures,** or a **constructively** defined **structure**	Our def	4.5
7b	framework	**b-type network** where active and passive **entities** are characterized by **well defined attributes**	Our def	4.5
5e	gate	**modelling** aid, imaginary active **entity** operating instantaneously and absorbing no resources	Our def	5.2 [3]
5k	generalized bipartite tree	**bipartite tree** in which (directed) arcs are replaced by (undirected) edges, two kinds of arcs alternating along each path between root and leaf	Our def	10.1
1e	graph	a finite set of nodes (or vertices) and a finite set of edges which connect pairs of nodes; the set of nodes must contain at least one element	Atten-borough	3.9
9x	graph model	**framework** where all active and passive **entities** are characterized by their **formal model**	Our def	4.5
3p	input	passive **entity** representing the effect of the environment on the **referent**	Our def	4.5
3b	interested party	person or group having an interest in the success of a **project**	based on ISO/FDIS 9000:2000	2.1
2k	interrelation	a way of grouping two or more **entities** in accord with some concept	Our def	4.2
1f	language	words and methods of combining them for the expression of thought	Shorter OD	3.9
7c	measure	symbol of a symbol system designating the **value** of an **attribute** of a **referent**, together with the formal characterization of the **variable** and scale	Our def	8.1 [4]
10n	measurement	the **process** of assigning a **measure** to a **well defined attribute** of the **referent**	Our def	8.1
1g	media	a generic term, mostly used to indicate means of transmission of information or entertainment	Fontana	3.9

1h	methodology	definition of the aims, concepts, methods, principles of reasoning and domain of discourse of some discipline, and the relationships between its subdisciplines	based on Fontana	4.11
–	model (see formal model)	-	-	-
4c	model (popular usage only)	a purposefully simplified **representation** of the **referent** which preserves its selected characteristics	Our def	4.5
4d	modelling	activity of creating a purposefully simplified **representation** of the **referent**	Our def	3.10
5a	network	**structure** of a **referent** or of a class of **referents** as a labelled, connected, **directed graph** with one or more **inputs** and one or more **outputs**, such that there is at least one path from each **input** to at least one of the **outputs**, and each **output** is reachable from at least one of the **inputs**	Our def	4.5
3q	output	passive **entity** representing the effect of the **referent** on the environment	Our def	4.5
1m	paradigm	a set of scientific and metaphysical beliefs that make up the basis on which scientific theories can be tested, evaluated, and if necessary revised	based on Camb. Dict of Philosophy	1.7
11a	P/p framework	**P/p network** representing a class of **referents** where classes of **products** and **processes** given as **black boxes** are characterized by **well defined attributes**, their **variable** type and bounds, classes of **products** and **processes** given as **structures** are **constructively** defined, classes of **product clusters** are given as sets of **product** classes, and **gates** are characterized by their type and rule	Our def	5.3
13a	P/p graph	collective term designating **P/p networks, P/p frameworks** and **P/p models**	Our def	5.3
10q	P/p methodology	definition of the aims, concepts, methods, principles of reasoning and domain of discourse of **products** and **processes** as **systems**, and the relationships between its subdisciplines of systems theory, communications, **modelling**, **measurement** and **quality** management.	Our def.	4.12
12a	P/p model	**P/p framework** representing an individual **referent**, where **products** and **processes** are characterized by their attribute **values**	Our def	5.3
10e	P/p network	acyclic **b-type network** where each arc is a place-holder for a **product** or a **product cluster** and each node is a placeholder for a **process** or a **gate**	Our def	5.3
5b	predictive representation	**representation** of the **referent** at some specific **time** in the future, deduced from the **descriptive representation** with the aid of some theory, or else **representation** of a planned **referent** at a specific **time** when it is eventually realized	Our def	3.8

6e	prescriptive representation	the required attribute **values** of a **referent**, or the bounds within which the attribute **values** must lie at a specified **time** instant, or over a specified **time** period	Our def	3.8
1j	problem	an unsatisfactory situation	Our def	2.1
10c	problem specification	**specification** whose **measures** characterize the shortfall between (1) the **formal model** of the **prescribed, predicted** or desired **referent** at a specific **time** instant of the present or the past, and (2) the **descriptive model** of the same **referent**: its *actual* characteristics at the same **time** instant	Our def	6.2
9c	process	**representation** of an active **referent** as a set of **interrelated attributes**, transforming an input **product** into an output **product** over a **time** period. NOTE: The attributes characterizing a process must include duration, domain, transfer function, status and for man-made systems owner and cost. The interrelations include coattribute and time stamp.	Our def	4.10 [5]
8b	product	**representation** of a passive **referent** by an **attribute** set containing no **time** duration **attribute** (or a **time** duration **attribute** whose **value** is zero), and an **interrelation** set that includes (1) the **measure** of the real **time** instant at which all **attributes** are valid, and (2) the coattribute **interrelation** asserting that all **attributes** characterize the same **referent**	Our def	4.9 [6]
9d	product cluster	a set of two or more **products** with a common **time** stamp	Our def	5.1 [7]
2c	project	planned, coordinated, controlled activity with its own budget and other resources, whose object is to solve the **problem**	based on ISO/FDIS 9000: 2000	2.1
2d	prototype	an exemplar of the solution of a **problem**	Our def	6.9
4j	quality	degree to which the characteristics of a **system** to fulfil **requirements** of **interested parties**	based on ISO 9000: 2000	6.6
2e	referent	the **entity** of interest	Our def.	3.1
3d	representation	expression of ideas about the **referent**	Our def	3.8
1k	requirement	need or expectation that is stated, customarily implied, or obligatory	ISO/FDIS 9000:2000	6.1
10d	requirement specification (direct strategy)	**specification** prescribing the desired characteristics of the problematical **referent**	Our def	6.4
10f	requirement specification (indirect strategy)	**specification** of a mechanism for bringing about the desired characteristics of the problematical **referent**	Our def	6.4

10g	scheduled interrupt	a **product** occurring at a planned **time** instant to halt a **process** for a set **time** period because this is managerially expedient	Our def	12.5
9a	specification	a **formal model** of the **referent**, characterizing its relevant **attributes** by their **measures**	Our def	6.2
4f	structure (or structural re-presentation)	**representation** of the **referent** as a set of **interrelated** components, each component being represented by a unique label	Our def	4.4 [8]
9h	supplier	organization or person that has a **product** to offer and expects a **product** in compensation	Our def	14.1
11e	supplier's specification	a **product** which is the **prescriptive representation** of the **entity** to be developed by the **supplier**, incorporating all of the **attributes** given in the **requirement specification**, and **attributes** representing the **supplier**'s own **requirements**	Our def	6.5
3h	system	a set of **interrelated entities**	Our def	4.7
2m	time	a characteristic common to all **entities** in the real world, either as position ('real time'), or as distance (time duration)	Our def	3.7
6g	traceability	**attribute** of the sequence of **representations** of a **referent** over its life history that it is possible to reconstruct the **value** of its selected key **attributes** at any **time** instant in its past	Our def	14.6 [9]
3k	tree	a **directed graph** without cycles which has exactly one node called the 'root' with no incoming arc, (or no outgoing arc), every other node has exactly one incoming (outgoing) arc, and every node other than the root is on a path from (to) the root	Stanat	4.9
6f	universal bipartite tree	single level **generalized bipartite tree** with finite number of leaf nodes	Our def	10.5
10h	unscheduled interrupt	an unplanned but foreseeable **product** that halts a **process** for an indeterminate **time** period	Our def	12.5
5c	value	the extent, amount or instance of a **well defined attribute** of an individual **referent** NOTE: value may be qualitative or quantitative	Our def	3.5
10r	validation	convincing demonstration under defined operating conditions of the **conformity** of the **specification** against the **requirements**, or the implementation against the design, or the implementation against the **requirements**	Our def	6.1
6d	variable	alphanumeric symbol designating a **well defined attribute** of a class of **referents**, indicating the domain and dimension of possible **values**	Our def	8.1
10s	verification	formal proof of internal consistency of the **specification** or the design of the **referent**, or of the **conformity** of the design to the **specification**	Our def	6.1

4g	well defined attribute	definition of an **attribute** that is meaningful, grounded, and free of circularity	Our def	3.5
3c	well defined interrelation	an **interrelation** which is meaningful, grounded and free of circularity	Our def	4.2

Assuring the quality of the Glossary

When defining a term in the text at Level 2 or higher, care is taken only to use general terms, or terms which have already been defined. The Glossary Table aids testing that this is so. The Glossary Table helps in checking that definitions are meaningful and informative, in detecting ambiguity, vagueness or other weaknesses, and in identifying opportunities for improving the clarity of the definitions.

Quality assurance of definitions is further aided by preparing a full range of *dependency graphs:* bipartite graphs representing the interrelations between the term under definition and the terms used in the definition:

- in the absence of *circularity,* the graph of each definition should unfold into a tree,
- in the absence of *undefined terms,* each term should be defined only by use of lower level terms than itself, and
- each definition must be *traceable* to Level 1 terms.

As a quality check, we have drawn up the dependency graph of each of the terms defined in the Glossary at Level 2 and above, although it would be inappropriate to include them all here.

Graphical representation of definitions is a powerful aid to understanding and assimilating concepts, their interrelations and implications. We urge the reader to construct the dependency graph of some of the important definitions in the text as an exercise, and adopt the habit of using such graphs when constructing his/her own definitions in practice.

Dependency graphs – Glossary Example 1

Graph 1 is the representation of the definition of 'P/p graph': at Level 13 one of the highest-level definition in the Glossary. We track this definition to its Level 1 foundations, using it to demonstrate the method of construction of dependency graphs.

For this example we search the graph 'depth first'. Other search procedures are equally acceptable. The procedure is as follows:

1. Draw up the graph of the term under definition; this term is called the 'definiand' (Graph 1).
2. Select the node corresponding to the highest level definition used. In case of a tie, select *one* of the highest level definitions at random.
3. Represent the selected definition in Graph 2.
4. Select the highest level term in the graph just drawn, etc., and proceed in this way until reaching the bottom level: the term whose definition uses only Level 1 definitions. This marks the end of the first search through the graph.

In this example 12 graphs are needed to reach the bottom of the depth-first search for the first time, and the published part of the example finishes here. To construct the complete definition of the term 'P/p graph', the search continues:

5 Returning to Graph 1, identify the term at the highest level definition whose graph has not yet been drawn. If no such term exists (as in case of our example) then search Graph 2, etc.

6 Draw up the graph of the highest level term found (in this example the term is 'process' in Graph 2, yielding Graph 13, not included here).

7 Search the graph depth-first, until reaching the bottom level.

8 Repeat the process until all graphs are completely searched.

In this example the search leads to the construction of graphs for 27 terms of the Glossary Table. The terms involved, and the serial number of their graphs, is listed in the Table of dependency graphs below.

Serial No of dependency graph	Term
G1	P/p graph
G2	P/p model
G3	P/p framework
G4	P/p network
G5	product cluster
G6	product
G7	measure
G8	variable
G9	value
G10	well defined attribute
G11	attribute
G12	referent
G13	process
G14	representation
G15	interrelation
G16	time
G17	constructivity
G18	black box
G19	structure
G20	gate
G21	modelling
G22	b-type network
G23	network
G24	input
G25	output
G26	directed graph
G27	well defined interrelation

Table of dependency graphs of Glossary Example 1

Examining the table of dependency graphs, one would look for the absence of expected terms that would point to vagueness or *incompleteness* of some of the definitions. The presence of inappropriate terms would show at best that some of the definitions are redundant, and at worst that they are ambiguous or erroneous. Pointing to only one example, it would be clearly wrong for the definition of 'P/p graph' not to build on the concept of 'structure', and it is reassuring to find 'structure' in the table of dependency graphs.

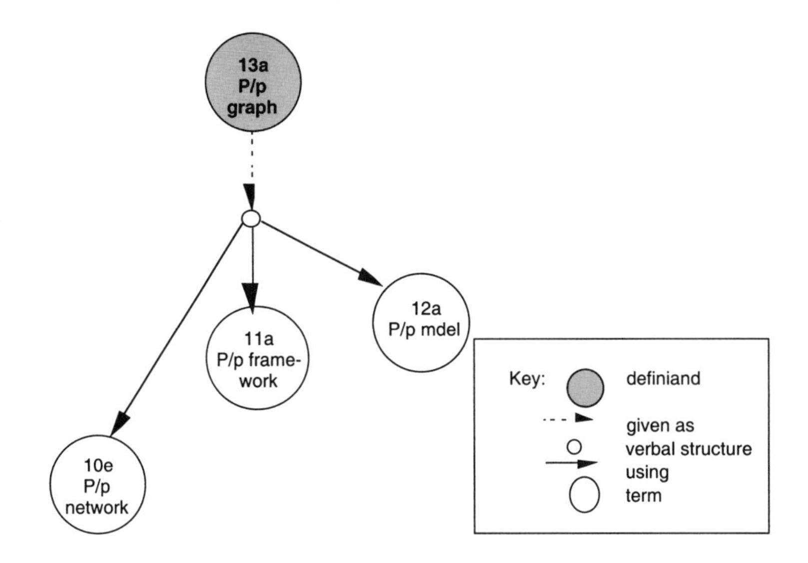

Graph 1 (Key applies to all dependency graphs)

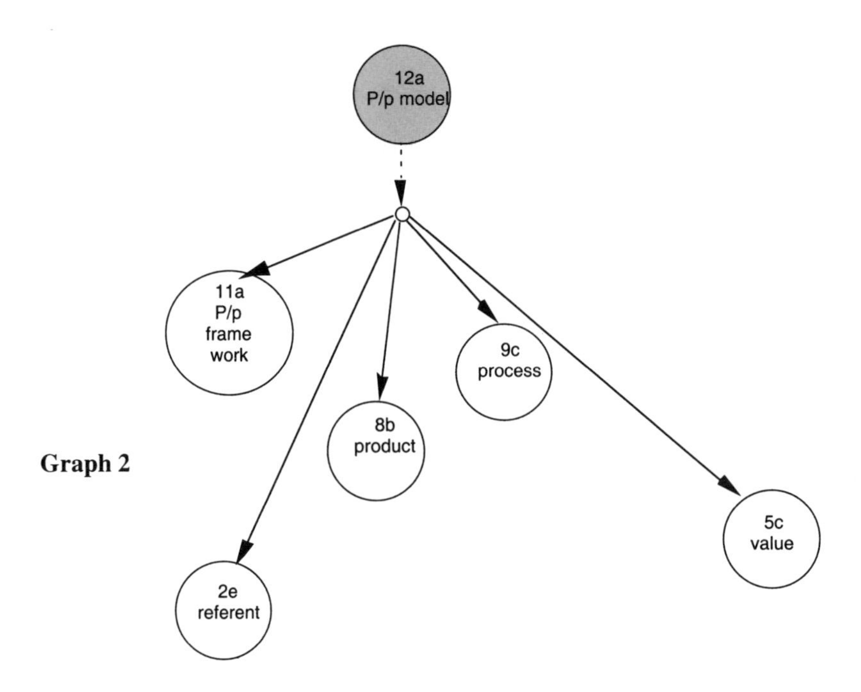

Graph 2

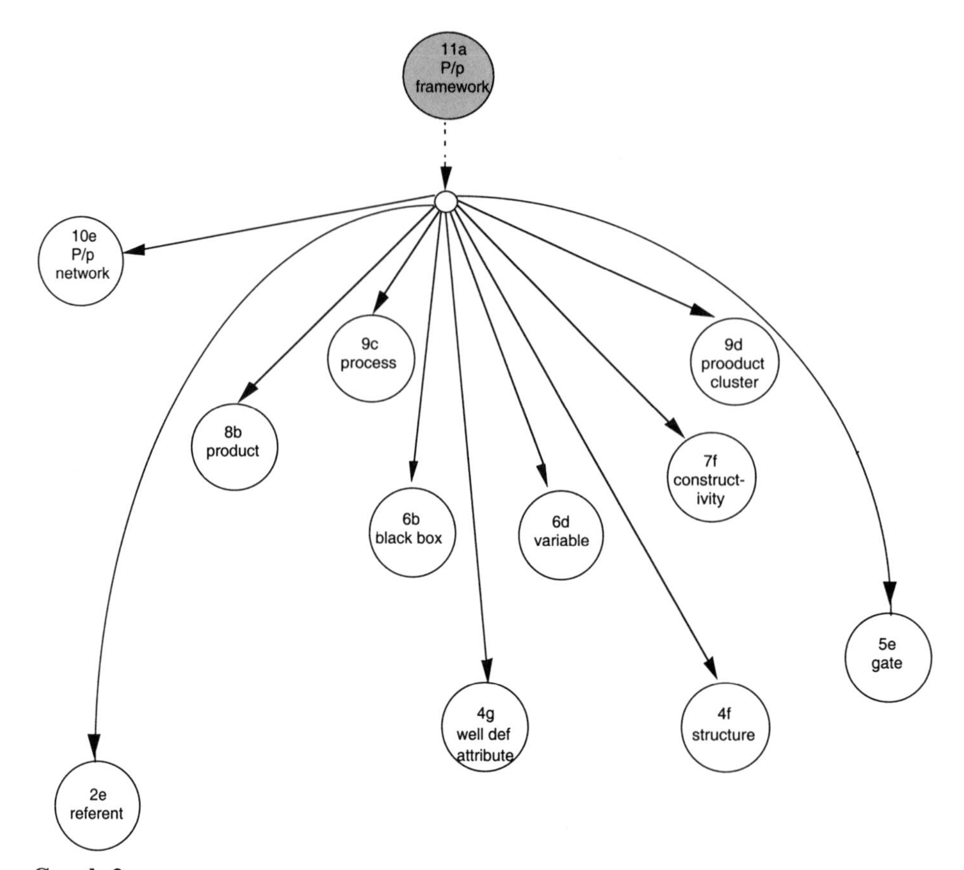

Graph 3

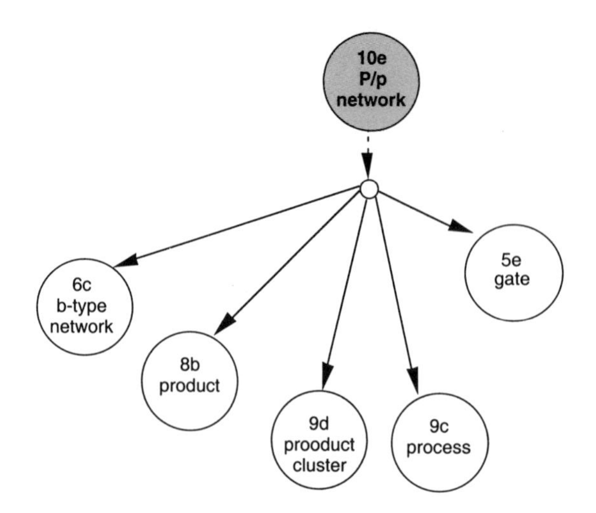

Graph 4

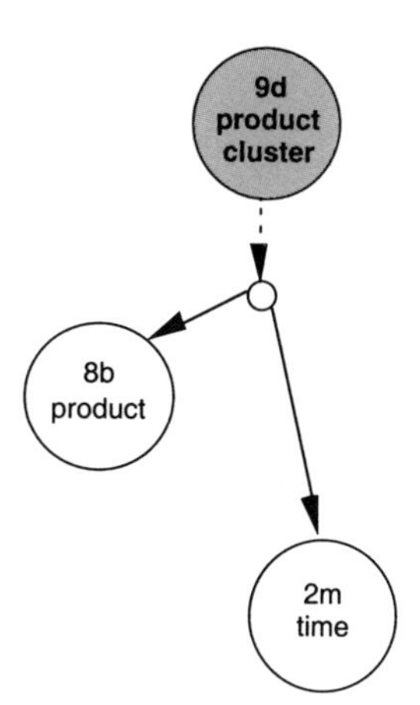

Graph 5

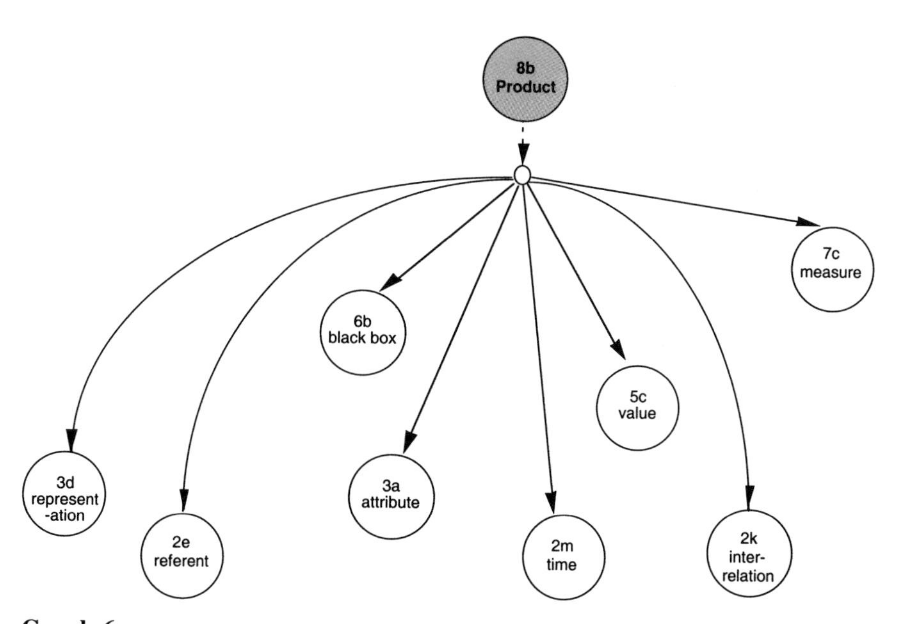

Graph 6

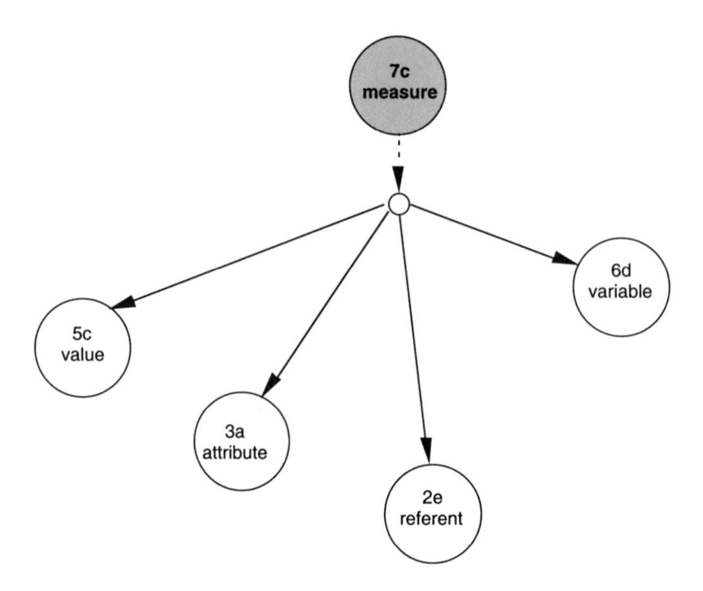

Graph 7

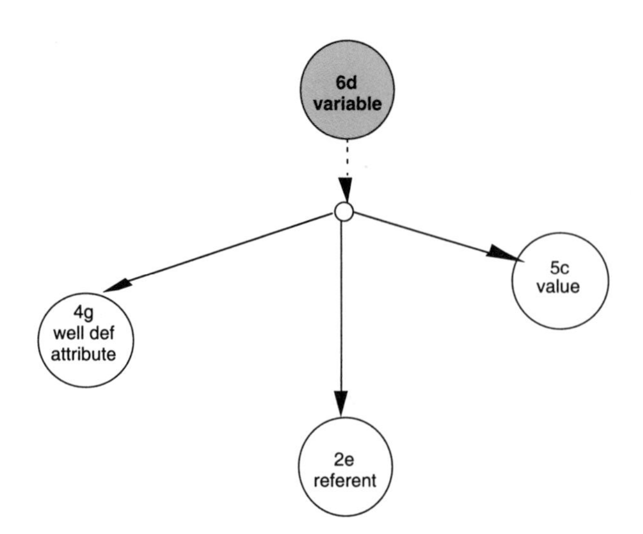

Graph 8

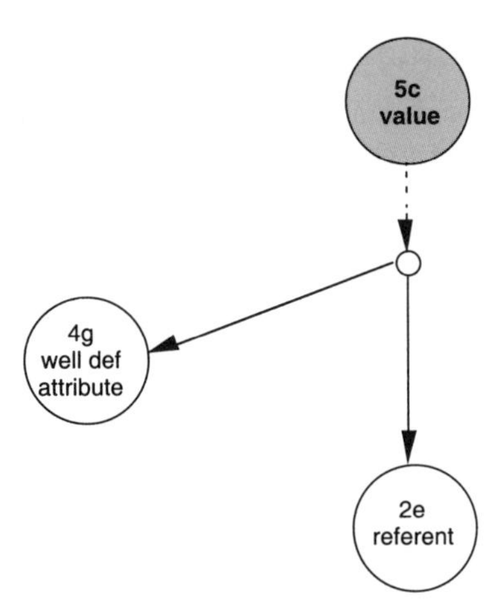

Graph 9

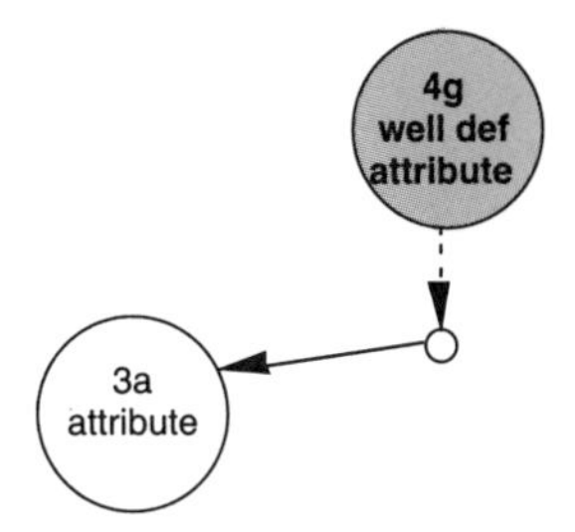

Graph 10

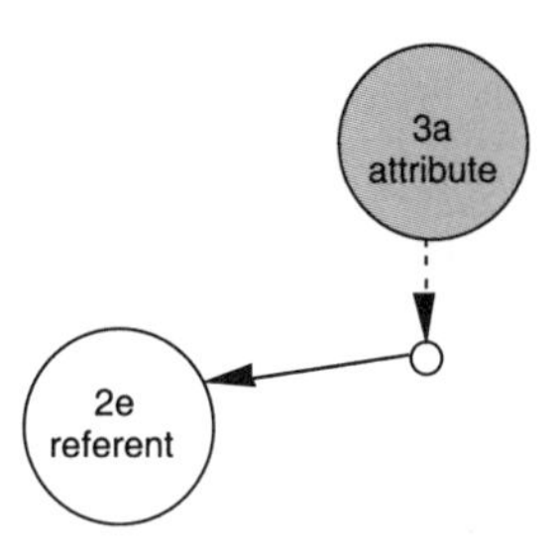

Graph 11

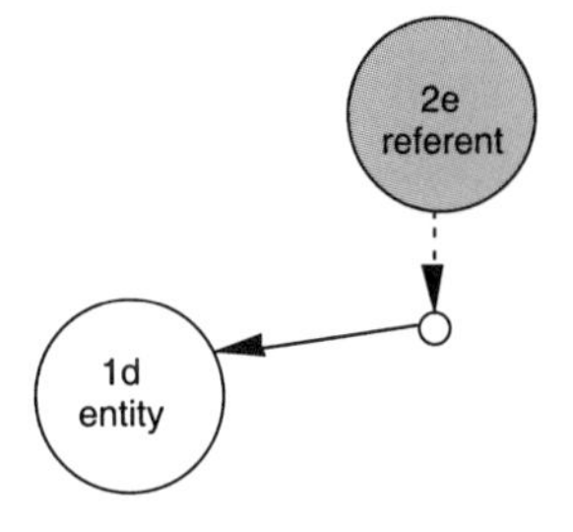

Graph 12

Some comments on dependency graphs

Compiling the dependency graphs is a tedious and error prone business, obviously more suited to the computer than to the human processor. However, one gains valuable insight doing it by hand.

It may also be thought clumsy to have 27 graphs in support of a single definition. There is nothing to prevent merging all of these graphs into a single graph by substitution, except that the resulting graph might turn out to be an unfathomable cobweb of arcs. A disciplined approach to reducing the number of graphs without obscuring them might be to merge those without any branching. In the Glossary example 1, graphs 10, 11 and 12 could be so combined.

The definitions of the Glossary have common foundations, hence the graphs compiled in course of Glossary example 1 turn out to be useful in graphical representation of other definitions in the Glossary. As an example, Graph 28 represents the Level 8 definition of 'formal model'. Checking the table of dependency graphs of Glossary Example 1 shows that all the constituent terms of this graph have already been drawn up when working on the definition of 'P/p graph'.

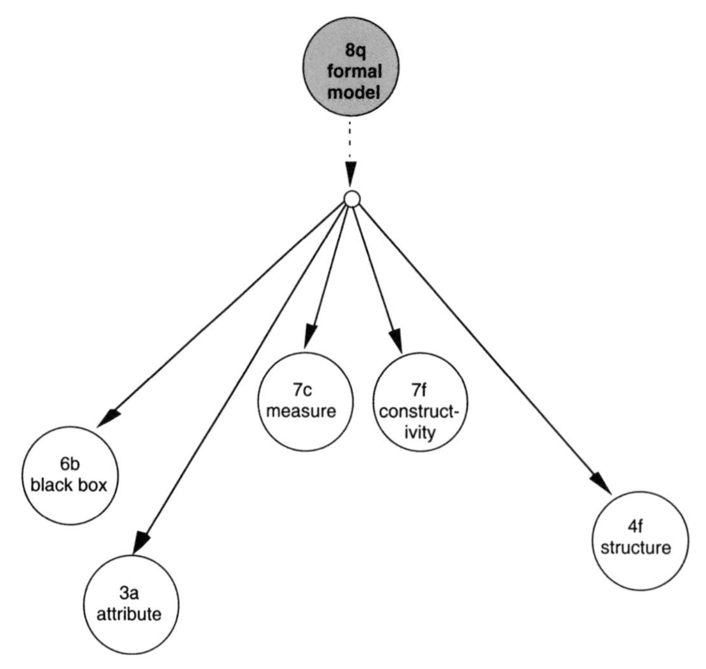

Graph 28

Footnotes and References

1 See also 9.5.

2 BS-EN ISO 9000:2000 uses the term 'inherent characteristic' instead of SOD's term of 'essential nature'.

3 See also 11.4.

4 For simplified definition see 3.6

5 See also 11.3

6 See also 11.2

7 See also 11.2.

8 See also 10.7

9 See section 9.2 for the ISO definition of 'traceability – metrology'.

Appendix: Notes to lecturers

We offer here some guidelines for introducing a 'P/p methodology stream' into an existing undergraduate course. Since systems are for all (!), the guidelines might apply to a great variety of programmes, among them computing and information technology, business studies and accountancy, engineering and management, social science and medicine. The P/p methodology will enhance any of the *existing* courses in these subjects, integrating the course elements into a coherent whole, and providing a framework for self-study and continuing professional development of the graduate.

The P/p methodology might also stimulate the development of completely *new* undergraduate programmes, offering concepts and methods which are useful in their own right, and integrating the various subjects of the course into a coherent whole. The methodology might provide, for example, the backbone of courses which seek to integrate engineering and management, hardware and software engineering, information technology and social science. However, these Notes concentrate on the case where the 'P/p methodology stream' is to form part of an existing course.

All undergraduate courses are overcrowded, suffering from shortage of time: the dilemma popularly referred to as 'having to fit a quart into a pint pot'. Time pressure is particularly severe in courses where the subject is fast developing, and, to include new material, course designers must curtail valuable parts of the established curriculum. With this in mind, these guidelines restrict the 'P/p methodology stream' to at most 1 module in any semester.

Assumptions regarding the curriculum

The design of undergraduate programmes varies widely from subject to subject, from country to country, from one university to another. In preparing these guidelines, we make some general assumptions about the characteristics of the existing curriculum.

- Undergraduate courses might be of 3-year or 4-year duration.
- Years divide into 2 Semesters of 11 – 12 weeks' duration.
- Undergraduate courses are modular, each module comprising 30 to 40 contact hours and over 80 total hours of study.
- The curriculum of existing undergraduate courses might comprise four streams:

  (i) *foundation* subjects, such as mathematics, science, communications,

(ii) *specialist focus* subjects at the centre of the course, usually taught by the 'home' department,

(iii) *other specialist* subjects of relevance, including elective subjects, often contributed by other departments or other faculties,

(iv) *general* subjects of interest, such as quality, safety, finance, management, environmental and social considerations. P/p methodology would form a fifth stream in such a course.

- The 3-year curriculum includes an Individual Project and the 4-year curriculum also includes a Group Project.
- Teaching of the P/p methodology starts in Semester 1, and occupies one module in the first 4 semesters. Thereafter the P/p methodology is incorporated into the Individual Project and the Group Project.

Some further assumptions

The curriculum is to be:

- revised year by year, in accord with the principles of continuous quality improvement,
- supported by a programme of staff development and curriculum development in all areas, including the P/p methodology stream,
- complemented by a strategy of research activity and external / internal collaboration in all areas, including the P/p methodology and its applications.

Developing a teaching programme

Table A1 shows, semester-by-semester, the design of a possible P/p methodology stream in a vocationally oriented undergraduate course.

Initially the P/p methodology stream would be taught by a 'project champion', with the essential support of the Head of Department, but – typically – without much interest shown by the rest of the academic staff.

Progress towards an integrated curriculum could well start by lecturers of the general stream seeking to stimulate the interest of the class, recognizing the P/p methodology as a means of linking their subject to the rest of the curriculum.

Continued progress towards integration might be achieved through *research* into the application or the development of the P/p methodology. Most projects would require contributions from specialist experts of the teaching team who, in course of the project, would observe the methodology at work, would use it in their part of the research project, and would then naturally transfer it to their teaching.

	Aim	Subject matter	Reference in "Systems for all!"	Background material	Learning methods	Assess-ment
Semester 1	acquire concepts; use them in familiar situations; gain awareness of use in the subject of the course	Measure-ment Definitions Language and communica-tion Representa-tion and modelling	Ch 8, Ch 3	Examples of concept formation, definition and measuremen t in literary texts, general texts course-specific texts and standards	Lectures, tutorials, exercises, discussions, debates Link to practical work of the course	Course-work & Exam
Semester 2	acquire concepts; use in familiar situations	Systems Black box Structure	Ch7 Section 4.3, 4.4, 4.6 Ch 9, Ch 10	'Good' systems texts	Lectures, tutorials, exercises, discussions, debates Link to practical work of the course	Course-work & Exam
Semester 3	acquire concepts and use them in the domain of the course	Products and processes Networks P/p modelling	Section 4.5, 4.8, 4.9, 4.10, Ch 5, Ch 11	'Good' systems texts Cautionary tales Talkative systems texts	Lectures, tutorials, discussions, debates Small project	Course-work & Exam
Semester 4	acquire concepts, and start gaining skills of system integration	Problem solving	Ch 2, Ch 6, Section 4.11,	Systems philosophy, Cautionary tales and talkative 'systems' texts	Reading, Case study	Course-work & Exam
Semester 5, Semester 6	use systems methodology in project work	P/p methodology in practice	All	Good and talkative texts on hard and soft systems	Individual project	Part of project assess-ment
Semester 7, Semester 8 (4-year courses)	transfer concepts and methods to course subjects; acquire skills of P/p methodology	P/p methodology / knowedge integration	Ch 1, Part 3	Books on specialist and supporting subjects of the course	Exercises Group project Students' own seminar presenta-tions	Course-work

Table A1: Possible P/p methodology stream in the undergraduate curriculum

The success of the teaching programme hinges on an effective *staff development* policy. Introduction of a P/p methodology stream assumes the firm backing of the Head of Department, requires a competent 'project champion' familiar with the methodology and its applications, and the project champion needs the support of one or more colleagues. Through internal seminars, conferences and collaborative research the staff development programme would build up the competence and confidence of the rest of the staff of the home department. An open door policy would offer encouragement and opportunities for staff of other departments and external collaborators to join in. Through research, development, consultancy and publications the staff development programme would gather momentum, the integrated programme would become established and would improve continually.

Below we introduce an example taken from the field of engineering in which integration of four specialist components of an undergraduate course is achieved by using P/p methodology. Engineering is only one of the fields where interdisciplinary education is required, and the P/p methodology is applicable to any integrated course, undergraduate or postgraduate, including those containing both hard and soft sciences. We cite a few examples:

- computing, communications, marketing and management science;
- business studies, human relations, law and environmental science;
- management science, software engineering, business studies and contract law.

Building up the 'Integrated Engineering' Curriculum of an Engineering Department – an example

A University Department might currently offer a multidisciplinary course whose specialist subjects are Electrical/Electronic Engineering, Computing and Information Technology, Manufacturing Engineering and Mechanical Engineering. Such a course, or a similarly constructed course, may be entitled 'Mechatronics', 'Systems Engineering', or, in our example, 'Integrated Engineering'. Integration is weak, since it can only be achieved incidentally through such means as case studies, project work, etc. (Figure A1).

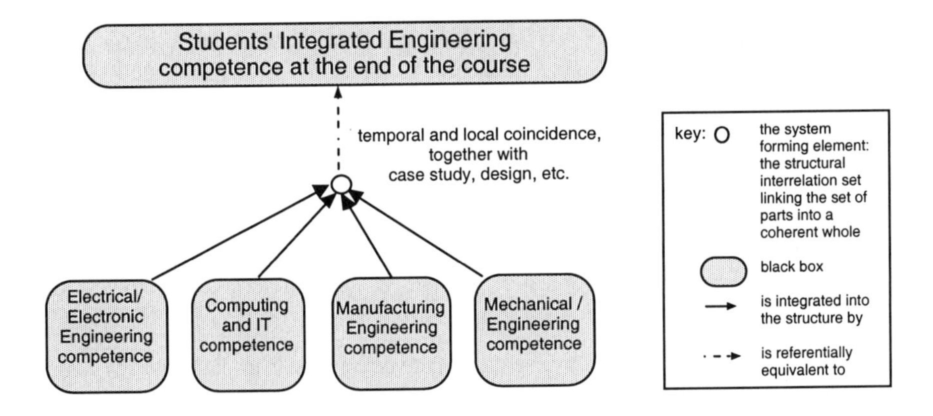

Figure A1: The present version of an Integrated Engineering Course – the 'P/p methodology' component is missing

Semesters 1 to 4

Figure A2 shows the modified curriculum, with a 'P/p methodology' stream taught in the first four semester of the course. At the end of this period students will have become acquainted with the P/p methodology, but will have very limited experience with its application. The P/p methodology will have added yet another domain of competence to the rest. The structure forming interrelations between the course components is still weak. However, integration will already begin: since the P/p methodology is based on systems, the lecturer in charge can offer examples which link two or more of the specialist subjects of the course.

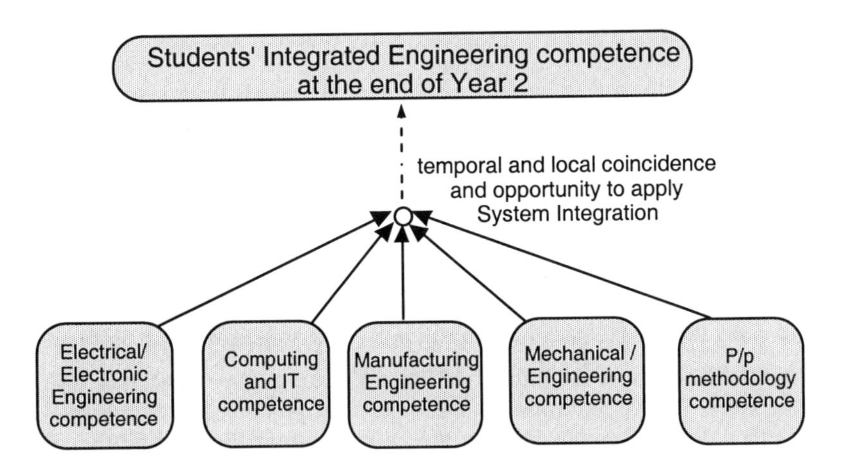

Figure A2: The first two years of the Integrated Engineering Course – the 'P/p methodology' component is now present, but the system forming element is weak (key as for figure A1)

Semesters 5 and 6 of the BEng, and Semesters 5 to 8 of the MEng course

Project work – a key element of engineering courses – offers scope for students to demonstrate their competence to apply the material learned in the course. Here the P/p methodology skills are put into practice in managing the project and integrating the specialist components of the task. All students carry out an Individual Project in Semesters 5 and 6. In addition, MEng students participate in a Group Project in Semesters 7 and 8, and undertake a small project of investigation or research.

As figure A3 illustrates, by the end of the course the P/p methodology is no longer a free-standing component of the course but a structure-forming element, yielding the Integrated Engineering competence as a unified whole.

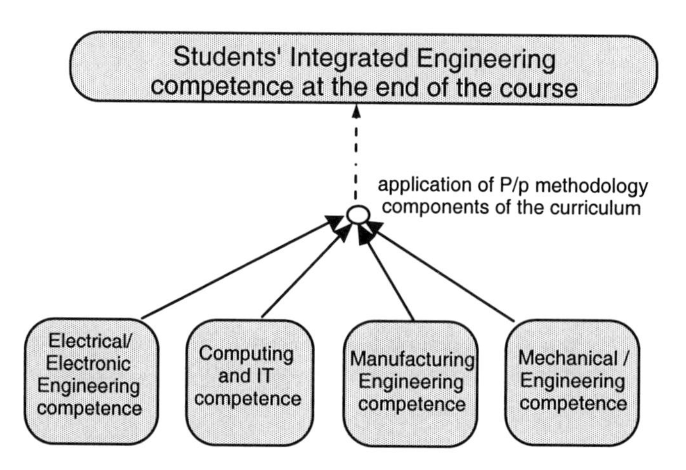

Figure A3: The full Integrated Engineering course, with the 'P/p methodology' component applied in practice (key as for figure A1)

INDIVIDUAL PROJECT FOR THE BENG STUDENT

While the P/p methodology might be put to good use in any part of the course, in the BEng course the Individual Project offers the only opportunity for the student of using the P/p methodology in solving a sizeable engineering problem.

In the BEng course the Individual Project would be an engineering task using *one or more of the constituent specialist disciplines* of the course. The P/p methodology is employed from the initial stage of formulating the specification throughout design and implementation to the concluding stage of validating the solution, and also in planning, organizing and documenting the work.

INDIVIDUAL PROJECT FOR THE MENG STUDENT

For the high fliers of the MEng course the Individual Project must offer scope for tackling an even more challenging task than that for BEng. The MEng project requires the use of *one or more of the specialist disciplines* of the course, together with *any other discipline*, integration being achieved by use of P/p methodology. Here also, the methodology is to be used from specification throughout all phases of design and implementation to validation of the solution, and also in managing the Individual Project and documenting the work.

THE GROUP PROJECT

The Group Project is an essential feature of MEng courses. In the Group Project the P/p methodology is used in specifying the project as a whole, devolving the complete task into a set of related specifications of individual tasks for each member of the group, managing and documenting the subtask of each individual, managing the work of the group, integrating the solutions of subtasks into a complete solution, validating the complete solution, and documenting the project as a whole.

INVESTIGATION / RESEARCH TASK OF THE MENG CURRICULUM

The MEng graduate is the future Chartered Engineer, characterized by his/her competence to manage "innovation, creativity and change" (Engineering Council: Standards and Routes to Registration, 1997). To prepare students for such a role, in the final semesters of the MEng course students should be offered the opportunity to appraise and deliberately test the limitations of the disciplines learned in the course. As examples of this kind of activity, students might:

- revisit a difficult part of one of the specialist subjects of the course, seeking deeper insights through the use of P/p methodology,
- attempt to establish common ground between related aspects of distinct specialist subjects,
- challenge the P/p methodology itself through attempting 'soft systems' tasks.

Research

As in other areas of the curriculum, the competent Engineering Department must establish subject authority in P/p methodology by research, consultancy and educational innovation, and demonstrate achievement through publication of the results and educational experiences of the staff. Research projects could be application-driven, they might be directed at developing the P/p methodology itself, or might demonstrate educational innovation.

Research can be carried out in several fields, for example:

- reviewing systems methodologies, developing an evaluation and applying it to conduct a comparative analysis of systems methodologies,

- developing computer aids for implementing the P/p methodology,
- identifying limitations of the P/p methodology and developing the methodology to overcome some limitation,
- applying the P/p methodology to complex projects and to other undertakings requiring interdisciplinary cooperation in engineering and related fields, such as strategic planning or quality management,
- archeology: analyzing problems which have arisen, or may yet arise, in projects of public interest,
- extending metrology into areas not covered in ISO as currently constituted,
- broadening the syllabus to incorporate other branches of engineering, or to combine engineering with other disciplines within the same, coherent curriculum,
- exporting the teaching of the P/p methodology, acting as advisors to other institutions seeking to mount 'Integrated' courses.

References

EXAMPLES OF CAUTIONARY TALES:

Robert Glass: Software runaways. Prentice Hall, 1998
Charles Perrow: Living with high risk technologies. Princetown Paperbacks, 1999
Reports of the National Audit Office
Leveson: Safeware, system safety and computers. Addison Wesley 1995
Collins: Crash (with year 2000 update). Simon & Schuster, 1998

EXAMPLES OF 'GOOD' (BUT NOT EASILY READABLE) SYSTEMS TEXTS:

Umpleby and Sadovski: A science of conceptual structures. Hemisphere, 1991
Sowa: Conceptual structures. Addison-Wesley, 1983
Blauberg, Sadovski, Yudin: Systems theory. Progress, 1977

EXAMPLES OF 'TALKATIVE' SYSTEMS TEXTS

Emery: Systems thinking. Penguin, 1970
Espejo, Harnden: The viable system model. John Wiley, 1989
Stafford Beer: Diagnosing the system. John Wiley, 1985

EXAMPLES OF SOME OTHER TEXTS OF INTEREST

Bunge: Scientific research. Springer Verlag, 1967
Kyburg: Theory and measurement. Cambridge Univ Press, 1984
Roberts: Measurement theory. Addison Wesley, 1979
Fenton and Hill: Systems construction and analysis. McGraw Hill, 1993 (mathematics)

Bruner et al: Portable MBA. John Wiley, 1998
Martin and Clure: Diagrammatic techniques for analysts and programmers. Prentice Hall, 1985
Stevens et al: Systems engineering – coping with complexity. Prentice Hall, 1998

Index